Volume 9

GEAR

INDUCTANCE

The ILLUSTRATED
SCIENCE *and*
INVENTION
ENCYCLOPEDIA

International Edition

H. S. STUTTMAN CO., INC. *publishers*   New York, N.Y. 10016

how it works

Published by H. S. STUTTMAN CO., Inc.
New York, N.Y. 10016
© Marshall Cavendish Limited 1974, 1976, 1977

GEAR

Gears are toothed wheels used to transmit power between components of a machine. Cars, clocks, machine tools, adding machines, cameras, and many other devices essential to our modern way of life contain various kinds of gears. The invention of the toothed wheel is second in technological importance only to that of the wheel itself.

The most important single use of gears is to transmit motion from a power source, such as an INTERNAL COMBUSTION ENGINE or an ELECTRIC MOTOR, to a shaft which can do useful work, such as the propeller shaft in a car or the spindle of a machine tool. The power must be transmitted at a usable speed. When two gears are running together the larger one is called the gear and the smaller is called a *pinion*. If the pinion drives the gear, the unit is a *speed reducer*; if the gear drives the pinion, it is a *speed increaser*. Gears are more often used as speed reducers than the opposite, because the speed of an electric motor, for example, is normally much too high to be used by a machine without reduction.

The second major function of gears is to provide a usable range of *gear ratios* in a machine: three or four forward gears in a CAR, for example, or a wide range of cutting speeds in a LATHE. The gear ratio is the ratio of the number of teeth on one gear to the number of teeth on the other, and determines the amount of speed reduction or increase which takes place. For example, if a pinion has twenty teeth and the gear has sixty, the ratio is 1:3, and the gear will make one revolution for every three of the pinion. Since the teeth on a pinion each do more work than the teeth on the gear, the pinion is sometimes made of harder material in order to equalize the wear.

When one gear drives another, they turn in opposite directions (unless one of them is an internally-toothed gear). If it is required that they turn in the same direction, a third gear called an *idler* gear is interposed between them. Idler gears are sometimes used in GEARBOX [transmission] designs to provide the reverse gear.

Configuration

If two gears running together are imagined to be two smooth wheels whose surfaces are touching, the diameter of each wheel is the *pitch diameter* or the *pitch circle* of the gear. The part of the gear tooth that extends beyond the pitch circle is called the *addendum*; the *dedendum* is the part of the tooth inside the circle. The *root circle* is the diameter of the gear measured at the base of the tooth. The *pitch* is the distance between a point on a tooth and the corresponding point on the next tooth, measured on the pitch circle. This is known as *circular pitch*. To facilitate calculations, the *diametral pitch* is more commonly used, this being the number of teeth per inch of diameter, measured on the pitch circle.

Backlash is the play between two meshing gears, and can be more specifically defined as the difference between the distance between two teeth and the width of the engaging tooth. Backlash between two gears can be altered by changing the centre distance between them; the correct amount of backlash is designed into a gear system, which means that the distance between the centres must be within tolerance. Incorrect backlash will cause noisy operation, loss of efficiency and excessive wear. In particular, too little backlash may cause generation of heat. In general, the important considerations in determining proper backlash are the operating speed and the space required for a film of lubricant; slowly moving gears need less backlash. Minimum backlash designs are expensive to manufacture and install properly; they are therefore only attempted where timing or accuracy is important, as in certain instruments.

There are several different types of gear systems, which can be described in the following categories: *spur gears*, *bevel gears*, *helical* gears and *worm* gears.

Spur gears

Spur gears are the most common type. They have straight teeth and are used to transmit power between two parallel shafts or shafts in the same axis. Their efficiency can be more than 95%.

The sides of the teeth, in profile, describe an *involute* curve. (If a piece of string is wrapped around a cylinder, a point on the piece of string will describe an involute curve as the string is held tautly and unwound.) The sides of the teeth must be curved; otherwise the operation of the gears would be noisy, wear would be excessive, and a great deal of vibration would be generated. The involute curve has been found to be best because when an involutely curved tooth surface transmits power to an involutely curved mating tooth, as much of the power is transmitted as possible even if the centre distance between the shafts varies slightly. The point on the side of the tooth which is also a point on the pitch diameter of the gear is the point at which the power is transmitted most efficiently. The exact curve of the tooth surface is computed from the *base circle* of the gear. The base circle is just below the pitch circle and is the point at which the involute curve from the top of the tooth ends. The tooth terminates in a straight radial flank to the root.

An arrangement of spur gears in which one or more small *planet* gears travel around the outside of a sun gear, while at the same time running around the inside of an enclosing *annulus* gear, is called a planetary or EPICYCLIC system. (An annulus is an internal spur gear; that is, it has teeth on the inside of it instead of the outside.) An epicyclic arrangement allows more than one gear ratio to be selected without moving

Below: cutting a spur gear. A medium viscosity cutting oil is used. The oil keeps the tool and the work cool, lubricates the contacting surfaces, and flushes away the chips or 'swarf'. Cutting oils contain additives according to the metal cutting job to be done.

ESSO

gears in and out of mesh, by locking various components or combinations of components of the system. It is used in bicycle gears, AUTOMATIC TRANSMISSIONS and other applications.

A flat piece of material, oblong in cross section, with involute teeth cut on one side of it is called a *rack*. A *rack and pinion* gear system, in which a spur gear runs back and forth on a rack, is used in the steering mechanism of some cars, in hydraulic DOOR CLOSERS, and for reciprocating motion of tables or workheads of machines.

Bevel gears   Bevel gears are shaped like sections of cones. They are used to transmit power between shafts whose axes intersect. The teeth on an ordinary bevel gear are straight but tapered in length and depth; if extended in length, they would meet at a point ahead of the gear on the axis of the shaft called the *pitch cone apex*.

Hypoid bevel gears have teeth which are straight, but cut on

Left: an engineer checks teeth on a double helical pinion for a marine diesel gearbox. At left foreground and at rear are case-hardened main wheels.

Left: 1. A section of spur gear teeth. The curve of the side of the tooth is an involute curve. 2. Spur gear teeth in diagram. 3. Worm and gear. The ratio shown here is 18:1. If the worm speed were 360 rpm, the speed reduction would be to 20 rpm for the gear. Such a speed reduction might be used to drive a conveyer. 4. Spur gears in mesh. 5. Helical gears meshing. They will generate an axial thrust. 6. Bevel gears connect shafts whose axes intersect.

VICKERS LTD

OSBORNE / MARKS

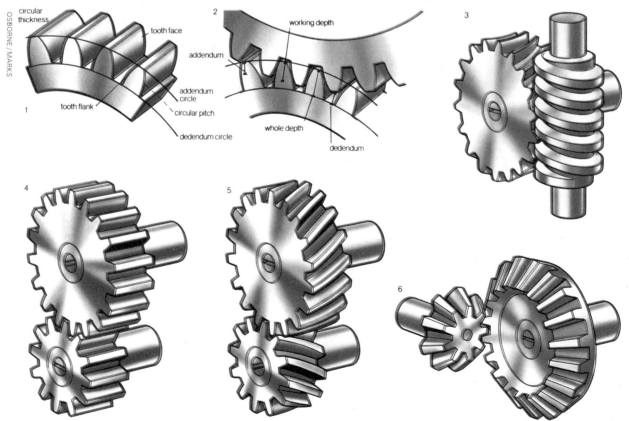

the face of the gear at an angle to the axis of the shaft. They can be used to transmit power between two shafts whose axes cross each other, but not in the same plane.

Helical gears
Gears which are shaped like sections of cones, such as bevel gears, or like sections of cylinders, such as spur gears, can have spiral teeth on them, enabling them to be designed to transmit power between shafts at any angle to each other, according to the spiral of the teeth. They are called helical gears. The curved teeth enter the mating teeth while the previously meshing teeth are still in contact; this means that some sliding of the teeth against each other takes place, and that power is transmitted with relative smoothness and silence. Helical gears, like hypoid bevel gears, can be used to transmit power between shafts which are not in the same plane; their combination of running characteristics and design possibilities makes them ideal for pinion and crown gears in the DIFFERENTIAL of a car. Such a differential runs smoothly and quietly, and enables the propeller shaft of the car to be in a lower plane than the rear axles, making it possible to lower the centre of gravity of the car.

When helical gears are used to transmit power between two parallel shafts, they generate a sideways thrust which may be objectionable. To overcome this, two sets of helical gears can be used, with the thrust in opposite directions, cancelling each other out. For this application, the gears are sometimes machined out of one piece of metal with helical teeth meeting in the centre of the face and spiralling outward from each other; these are called *herringbone* or *double-helical* gears.

Worm gears
When a pair of gears having helical teeth is used to transmit power between two shafts whose axes intersect, but not in the same plane, very high gear ratios are possible. In such a case, the gear ratio is commonly as high as $1:100$; the pinion may have multiple threads, or only one thread, which will curve all the way around it and resemble a screw thread. Such a pinion is called a worm. The speed reduction of a worm and gear unit is very great, and is used between an electric motor and a slowly moving CONVEYER, for example.

In such a unit, a great deal of sliding takes place between the teeth, and the efficiency of it is not high. Sometimes the gear is made to partially envelop the pinion in the area where the teeth mesh, in order to increase the load-carrying capacity. Normally, the gear cannot drive the worm, the spiral of the worm teeth being too much greater than that of the gear teeth; if the unit is designed so that the gear can drive the worm, it is more than 50% efficient, and can be used as a speed increaser. Such a unit can be used to drive a SUPERCHARGER, for example.

Non-metallic gears
Where quiet operation at high speeds is desired, and if the operating load or torque is not too high, one or both gears may be made out of plastic or a fibrous composition material. The timing gear in a car, which drives the camshaft from the crankshaft by means of a chain, is frequently non-metallic. The speed of the timing gear is high; while the timing is important, the load carried is relatively small.

Gear cutting
The machines used for cutting gear teeth comprise three general types. For cutting spur gears, a cutter blade conforms to the size of the space between the teeth. The second type generates the teeth either by a pinion shaped cutter which rotates in unison with the blank and by reciprocation cuts the teeth, or alternatively uses a cutter which is a section of a rack and planes the teeth as it moves across the face. The third type is a *hob*, which is a worm with gashed and relieved threads to give a cutting action.

GEARBOX

A gearbox is a set of GEARS with a shifting lever which provides a selection of gear ratios between two components of a machine, such as a machine tool or an automobile.

The most familiar application of the gearbox is in the CAR. The gearbox, or *transmission*, is located in the drive train between the engine and the drive wheels, and is a necessary part of the car because an INTERNAL COMBUSTION ENGINE does not have much power at low speeds. In order to move the car from a standing start, the gear ratio between the engine and the driving wheels must be such that the crankshaft of the engine is turning over at a relatively high speed. A simple three-speed gearbox allows the crankshaft to turn at roughly four, eight or twelve times for each revolution of the wheels, depending on the gear selected.

A three-speed gearbox consists of a clutch shaft with a clutch gear on it which is turning when the CLUTCH is engaged; a *layshaft* [countershaft], which has several gears on it, one of which is always meshed with the clutch gear and is turned by it; and a *transmission* shaft, which transmits the power to the propeller shaft [drive shaft], and which has two gears on it, one larger than the other, splined so that they can slide on the shaft. Each of the two gears on the transmission shaft is fitted with a *shifting yoke*, a bracket for pushing it back and forth on the shaft. The shifting yokes are selected and shifted by the driver by means of the shifting lever, which pivots between the driver's compartment and the top of the gearbox case.

When the driver selects first gear, or low gear, the larger of the two gears on the transmission shaft is pushed along the shaft until it meshes with the smallest gear on the layshaft. Then the clutch is engaged, allowing power to be transmitted from the engine through the gearbox to the wheels. The gear ratio between the transmission shaft and the layshaft is $3:1$, and the effective ratio between the crankshaft and the wheels is about $12:1$ (because of further reduction gearing in the DIFFERENTIAL, another set of gears which transmits power between the propeller shaft and the drive wheels).

When the car is moving fast enough, about ten mile/h (16 km/h), the driver shifts to second gear, engaging the small transmission gear with the large layshaft gear. The gear ratio is now $2:1$ and the ratio between the crankshaft and the wheels about $8:1$. For cruising speed the driver shifts to third gear (high gear), forcing the smaller transmission gear axially (lengthwise) against the clutch gear. These have teeth on the sides of them which engage, and the gear ratio is now $1:1$; that is, the transmission shaft and the clutch shaft (hence the crankshaft) are turning at the same speed. The ratio between the crankshaft and the wheels is now about $4:1$. Thus the speed of the engine is always within the range of efficiency for the engine while the car moves from a standing start to speed.

The reverse gear is at the back end of the layshaft, and turns a small *idler* gear which meshes with the large transmission gear when the driver selects reverse. (When two gears mesh, they turn in, opposite directions; the inclusion of an idler gear between them means that they turn in the same direction, so that the car reverses its direction.)

In a gear system, speed reduction means an increase in *torque*. (Torque is a twisting force, such as the effort needed to loosen a tight cap on a jar.) Thus the gearbox, when first gear is selected, transmits less speed from the small layshaft gear to the large transmission gear (because when two gears turn together the larger gear turns slower), but transmits more torque from the crankshaft, to 'twist' the propeller shaft and overcome the inertia of the car to get it moving.

American cars with large engines have usually had three-speed gearboxes, but smaller European cars usually have four or five forward gears, because the usable range of speed of the engine is smaller. The gearbox on a large lorry may have sixteen forward gears or more, because of the torque required to get the great weight of a fully loaded lorry moving.

In the early days of motor cars, gearboxes were simple devices such as described above, and it took some muscle power and skill to shift the gears smoothly. The edges of the gear teeth were chamfered (rounded) so that they would mesh as smoothly as possible. Down-shifting was particularly complicated, requiring double-clutching (disengaging the clutch, revving the engine to a higher speed, and re-engaging the clutch after shifting gears).

As more and more people took up driving, it became necessary to make shifting easier, and gearbox design became more complicated. *Syncromesh* gears were designed, in which the gears are made to run at the correct speed before they mesh so that they can do so without grinding. One way of doing this is to provide conical sections on the sides of the gears which fit into one another; friction starts the gear turning before the teeth actually mesh. A *balking* provision is made in some designs to prevent the gears from meshing until they are running at speed. Some syncromesh gearboxes may have all the gears meshing all the time; power is not transmitted until a sliding 'dog' axially engages the appropriate gear. At first most gearboxes provided syncromesh only on the upper gears, but most models nowadays provide it on all gears.

Nowadays nearly all American cars, and many others as well, have AUTOMATIC TRANSMISSIONS, but some drivers like the feeling of control over the vehicle that they get from operating a manual gearbox. People who drive in competitions prefer manual gearboxes because skilful gear-changing can mean split-second advantages when negotiating hills and curves.

Below: a cutaway view of a British Ford gearbox designed for use with the V-4 engine. The shifting lever protrudes from the housing on the upper right. Synchromesh devices in this modern 4-speed box mean that the gears do not have to go out of mesh.

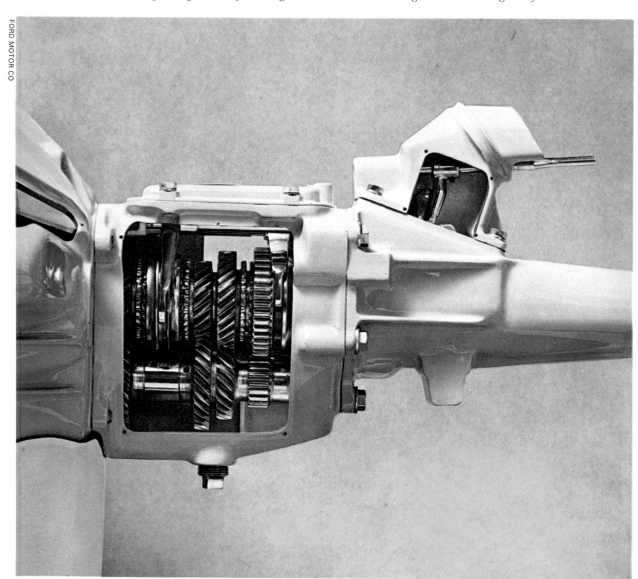

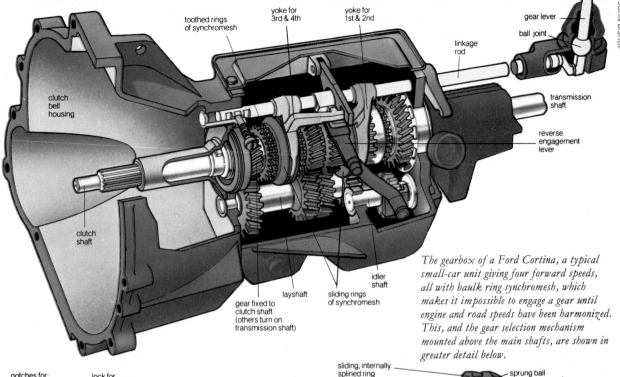

JOHN BISHOP

The gearbox of a Ford Cortina, a typical small-car unit giving four forward speeds, all with baulk ring synchromesh, which makes it impossible to engage a gear until engine and road speeds have been harmonized. This, and the gear selection mechanism mounted above the main shafts, are shown in greater detail below.

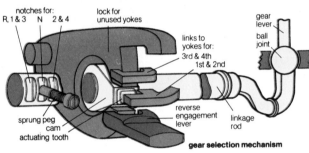

gear selection mechanism

synchromesh

The gear lever moves in two planes: fore and aft, which moves the linkage rod fore and aft in the other direction; and sideways, which twists the rod. Twisting makes the actuating tooth on the rod engage with one of three links, two to the sliding yokes for forward gears, one to the reverse idler gear. Unused links are held still by a locking bar moved up and down by a cam on the linkage rod.

All forward gears are permanently engaged, but freewheel until locked to the transmission shaft. They are locked gradually, for smoothness, by sliding a splined ring which first engages a clutch to synchronize gear and shaft, then moves on to bridge the two sets of teeth, providing a rigid drive. The baulk ring gives an intermediate semi-locked stage to prevent premature locking.

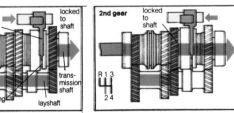
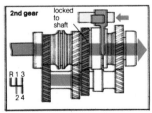
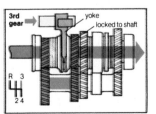
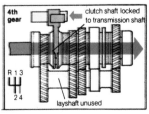
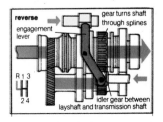

1st gear: the rear yoke is slid back to lock the rearmost gear to the transmission shaft. The gear on the clutch shaft turns the layshaft, driving the transmission shaft through the locked gear (line of power transmission shown in red).
2nd gear: the rear yoke is slid

forward to lock another gear to the shaft, and power is again taken from the layshaft.
3rd gear: this time the front yoke slides back to lock the adjacent gear to the shaft.
4th gear: the front yoke slides forward to lock clutch and transmission shafts together,

giving a direct drive while the layshaft simply freewheels.
Reverse: the engagement lever brings a small idler gear between layshaft and teeth cut on the rim of the rear synchro ring, so the transmission shaft turns backwards—but no part is played by the synchromesh.

GEIGER COUNTER

The Geiger counter is a device for detecting a charged particle. It was invented by H Geiger and E W Muller in 1928 and, though it has now generally been replaced by much more sophisticated detectors, it was a vital instrument in the early days of investigating the nature of the nucleus of the ATOM and the behaviour of the minute particles of which the atom is built.

Basic construction

In its usual form the counter consists of a glass tube about ¾ inch (2 cm) in diameter enclosing a metal cylinder, often of copper, about 4 inch (10 cm) long along the axis of which runs a thin metal wire, which may be of tungsten. The cylinder and wire are connected through the end wall of the glass tube to a source of electrical voltage. The tube is filled with a gas, usually argon, at a low pressure, equivalent to a pressure of a few centimetres of mercury. A voltage is set up between the cylinder (the negative electrode or cathode) and the wire (the positive electrode or anode) which is just a little less than that needed to create an electrical discharge between the two electrodes (see DISCHARGE TUBE). This voltage may be about 1000 volts.

Operating principles

When a charged particle with high energy flies through the glass tube it knocks *electrons* out of the atoms of the gas. These electrons, being negatively charged, make for the wire anode and the damaged atoms (which are positively charged argon IONS) make for the cathode.

Since there are 1000 volts between the wire and cylinder the electrons are affected by a high voltage gradient—rolling, as it were, down a very steep electrical hill. They pick up enough energy to knock further electrons out of atoms which in turn roll down the electrical hill picking up further energy and liberating further electrons. This is known as *electron avalanche*. At the same time the positive ions hit the cylinder with enough energy to release still more electrons. An avalanche of electrons therefore descends on the wire which can be detected as a pulse of electric current, indicating that a charged particle has passed through the tube.

Before a discharge, the Geiger counter is charged rather like a CAPACITOR, but when a discharge occurs both the stored charge and the corresponding voltage between the cylinder and wire is reduced. This 'kills' the discharge in the tube which would otherwise go on indefinitely—an important feature because while the discharge continues the device is insensitive to further charged particles arriving at the detector.

Another help towards stopping the avalanche is to put about 10% ethyl alcohol into the argon. Because of the way the atoms bump around, it tends to be the alcohol ions rather than the argon ions which reach the cylinder and there they prefer to break up rather than release more electrons. The alcohol vapour also smothers electron production within the gas mixture. It takes about a ten thousandth of a second to snuff out an avalanche and the voltage then builds up again so that the counter is ready to record another charged particle.

With the coming of electronic *amplifiers* the pulse of electric current could be made audible in a small loudspeaker. In this form it became famous as part of the equipment of uranium prospectors. It had the virtue of being very easy to operate and the clicks in its loudspeaker were simple evidence of the presence of high energy charged particles.

When a Geiger counter is switched on, irregular clicks will always be heard, originating in cosmic rays (very high energy

Above: prospecting for radioactive materials with a Geiger counter. Two electrodes are sealed within a glass tube containing argon gas at low pressure with external connections to a high voltage. A high energy particle ionizes some gas atoms and this creates a discharge.

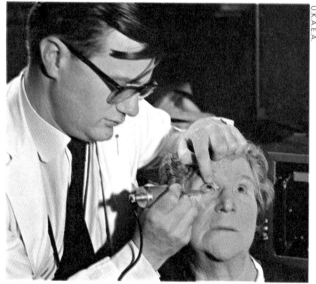

Above: this medical Geiger counter is detecting the amount of radioactive phosphorus that has collected in the eyes following its injection into the blood. The affected eye has a higher level.

Right: a Geiger-Müller tube. The thin wire anode is suspended along the central axis of a copper cathode. A high speed particle passing through the tube ionizes the air molecules. The free electrons are attracted towards the anode and, as they travel release further electrons, building up an 'avalanche'. The electrical pulse reaching the anode is transmitted to an amplifier.

particles which shower on to the earth from outer space) or in natural radioactivity (spontaneous emission of particles from some forms of chemical element which make up the natural environment). Uranium is a prolific source of natural radioactivity, disintegrating into other types of atom by emitting charged particles from its nucleus. It was the chatter of the loudspeaker of a Geiger counter detecting these emitted particles that brought a smile to the face of the prospector.

Limitations The Geiger counter has limitations in pinning down charged particles both as regards their position in space and their time of arrival. The counter can only say that a particle has passed through the volume enclosed by the glass tube. Nowadays scientists want to locate positions to an accuracy of a fraction of a millimetre if possible. The counter can say that a particle has arrived at a particular time to an accuracy of about a millionth of a second. This is usually adequate but the Geiger counter is then 'dead' and cannot detect other particles for a ten thousandth of a second while it recovers from the avalanche. Nowadays scientists want their detectors virtually continuously sensitive to the arrival of particles.

Another limitation is that it cannot give any information about what kind of charged particle has passed through it. This can be improved to a small extent by running the counter with a lower voltage between the cylinder and the wire. The full avalanche that is characteristic of the Geiger counter does not then occur. Instead the number of electrons which reach the wire depends on the number of electrons which the charged particle itself sets free in the tube. This helps to distinguish between particles. The size of the current pulse at the wire is then directly proportional to the liberated number of electrons and, when it is operated in this way, the counter is called a *proportional counter*. In the form of planes of thin, closely spaced wires, the proportional counter is still in vogue for studying particle behaviour at modern PARTICLE ACCELERATORS.

GENERATOR (see dynamo)
GEODESIC CONSTRUCTION (see frame construction)

Below: a portable radiation counter (Geiger counter) used mainly in laboratories and factories. It is battery operated and gives an audible indication as well as a visual display of the radiation count.

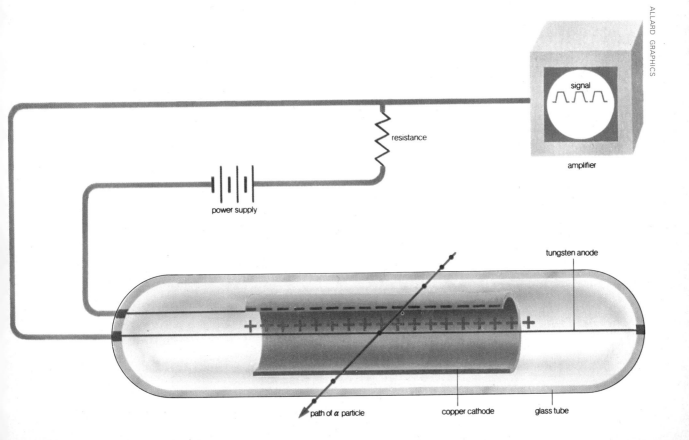

GEOLOGICAL TECHNIQUES

The purpose of geology is to discover and explain the structure and behaviour of the Earth's crust. The Earth is continuously in a state of change, a fact that has long been known from the observation of such violent earth movements as earthquakes and volcanic eruptions. Most movements, however, are imperceptibly slow, and until this century man was perplexed by the fact that whole mountain chains can be made of rocks raised from the floor of the sea, and contain remains of the shells of sea animals. It is now known that the life of a mountain chain, from its formation as sediment in the sea to its gradual wearing down by the forces of erosion, must be reckoned in terms of hundreds of millions of years.

Modern geology is based on a principle expounded in 1830 by Sir Charles Lyell, namely that the history of the Earth can be explained in terms of the natural processes now observed to be still in operation, such as the erosion of a mountain or the deposition of new sediments.

Rocks and minerals Examination of small specimens of rocks and the minerals they contain, either in the field or in the laboratory, is an essential technique of geology. Specimens may be collected in different ways: from an outcrop of rock with a geological hammer, from boreholes or from the seafloor with a device known as a *coring tube*, which works in a similar way to an apple corer. A vertical, hollow, weighted tube is dropped from a ship to the seafloor. The force of the impact rams the tube into the seabed and the corer is hauled back up to the ship with the rock sample inside it.

Identification of the constituent minerals in the sample of rock is the next problem; over 2000 minerals have been discovered. Some are recognizable by such visible features as colour, lustre (the way light reflects from the surface of the sample), cleavage (the way in which it splits) or crystal form. Simple tests may be made to determine the hardness of a mineral. Mineralogists have devised a scale of hardness from talc (1) to diamond (10); a mineral will scratch any other mineral lower on the scale.

The standard laboratory technique of examining rocks is to look at a *thin section* under a microscope. A slice of rock 30 microns (about a thousandth of an inch) thick is put under the microscope with light shining through the specimen from underneath. This arrangement allows the optical properties of the minerals to be studied, and also reveals the microscopic structure of the rock, which gives clues about its mode and place of origin. For instance, a rock composed of the shells of minute marine animals began as a characteristic sediment of the deep ocean.

Fossils If a sea animal dies and its bones or shell sink to the bottom of the sea and become covered by mud which is later turned by geological processes into rock, that rock will contain the remains of the animal as a fossil. Fossils may be formed in other ways: a fern leaf buried in a swamp may be preserved as an impression in coal, and rocks formed from intertidal mud flats often contain fossil traces of worm burrows and casts. The fact that animals and plants are continuously changing through the process of evolution has great significance for geologists.

There are two important facts about fossil species, the first of which is that once a species has died out, it never reappears in younger rock. The second is that no two species are identical, and therefore a new species is never exactly like an extinct one. These two facts have given rise to the principle that like fossil organisms indicate like geological ages for the rocks that contain them. This principle, coupled with dating methods

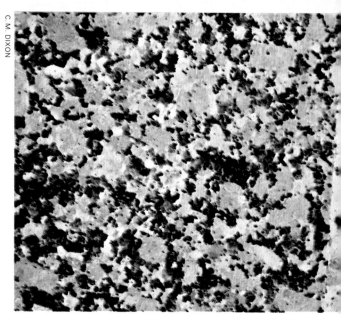

C. M. DIXON

Many rocks can be identified instantly. Above is a polished piece of red granite, an igneous rock, with its characteristic mottled look. By taking core samples of rocks, as seen below, the strata at various

ZEFA / PICTOR

depths can be determined. The coring tube and drilling rig are in the background. Thin sections can then be studied under a microscope: above is a sandstone magnified 125 times.

The shapes of rock outcrops are often a guide to their type. The hexagonal columns above indicate basalt, while the strata below are sedimentary sandstone and shale, tilted by earth movements.

such as the ARCHAEOLOGICAL TECHNIQUE of *radiocarbon dating*, has enabled geologists to establish a geological time scale, a chronological chart of the various events in the history of the Earth.

Economic geology

As well as contributing to our knowledge of the world in which we live, geology is of fundamental importance for its economic aspects. Most of the raw materials used by industry are taken from the crust of the Earth: fossil fuels such as coal and oil, ores, building stone and cement, and water. It is the task of the economic geologist to locate these natural resources.

His first task is to survey the geological structure of the area, that is, to find out what different rocks are present and how earth movements have influenced their relative position. The traditional technique of geological mapping involves detailed examination of the rocks outcropping at the surface and recovered from boreholes, but nowadays data gained by the methods of GEOPHYSICS play a large part. Aerial photographs are used for determining the overall structure of large tracts of unknown country. The photographs are taken in *stereoscopic pairs*, which when looked at through a STEREOSCOPE give the impression of relief which is itself largely dependent on the underlying geological structure.

Another method for finding the relief of unknown areas of land is to use sideways-looking radar equipment carried an aircraft. At sea, echo sounding devices using oblique echoes are used to determine the profile of the seabed, while coring and grabbing techniques yield information about its composition. Grabbing is similar to coring except that the grab is lowered as gently as possible to the ocean floor where it is tripped to close on impact. From a knowledge of the structure of an area, the geologist can predict how the rocks at the surface are continued underground.

Oil and gas are often found in association, and are known to be able to diffuse through porous rocks until they become trapped in certain rock structures. OIL EXPLORATION consists largely of the search for these favourable structures; once one has been found, it is tested for oil or gas by a test drilling.

All rocks are divided into blocks of different sizes by structures such as *joints* and *faults*, and it is along these structures that ores are generally found. Detailed structural mapping is needed to identify the structural setting where ore bodies may be found. Consideration of these structures is also important in the siting of major engineering works such as dams, bridges and tunnels. The engineering geologist must judge the geological feasibility of projects; for instance to predict whether or not a proposed dam or canal will hold water, or whether it will flow away along joints or through porous rock.

GEOPHYSICS

Geophysics is the science and study of the Earth's interior. As it is concerned with the whole planet, it incorporates many other fields of study, such as geology (the study of the Earth's crust), mineralogy and oceanography. As well as giving purely scientific information about the structure of the Earth, such as the formation of volcanoes and the existence of continental drift, the techniques of geophysics are used in the search for minerals, OIL EXPLORATION, and in civil engineering. With the advent of space exploration the same techniques are being used to study the interiors of the Moon and planets, which help to show the Earth fits in as a member of the solar system.

Seismology

The most important technique in geophysics is SEISMOLOGY. To study the interior of the Earth, geophysicists use sound waves of low frequency (below about 100 hertz), either in the form of explosions or as vibrations. These sound waves can travel through solid rock, and are reflected from different layers of rock to be picked up at the surface.

Such methods can only give information about the top few per cent of the Earth's interior. But much more intense seismic shocks are produced by earthquakes, and these natural waves can travel completely round the Earth in some cases. By studying the records obtained at widely separated stations, clues about the nature of the deep interior of the Earth are provided.

Once the approximate nature of subsurface rocks has been decided by seismic methods, better information can come from *well logging*. This consists of drilling boreholes, which may be as deep as 15,000 feet (4.5 km), through the rocks of interest. A sensitive microphone or *geophone* is lowered down the well and by firing seismic shots at the surface it is possible to find the velocity of sound in the various rock layers. In addition, such details as *radioactivity* and electrical conductivity of the rocks can be found.

Gravimeters

Different rocks have different densities, and a region of high density rocks will have a stronger gravitational pull than one of low density rocks. The effect of these *gravity anomalies* is very small, and is measured in units which are about one millionth of the overall pull of gravity. The small variations are measured on a *gravimeter*, which works on the same principle as a spring balance. A weight is attached to a very sensitive hair spring made of fine wire or quartz, and a pointer indicates the deflection of the weight caused by gravitational attraction. Despite its sensitivity, very robust gravimeters have been made, which are generally used in one of two ways. For a quick look at the gravity characteristics of an area, the device is flown in an aircraft over the area in a pattern of intersecting lines. This shows the general structure of a region a

Left: fossils appearing in sedimentary rocks—those formed from compressed sediments—are invaluable for dating rocks. Shown here are a crinoid (with a long stem) and coral colonies.

Right: a relief map of the Atlantic. It averages 16,000 feet (4900 metres) in depth, except for the central ridge which in places breaks the surface, such as at the Azores. This ridge is the source of upwelling material, which then spreads outwards. The Earth's magnetic field reversals are imprinted in strips, marked here in red with their age in millions of years. At the edge of the Caribbean, the seafloor dives below the plate which originated in the Pacific; this 'subduction zone' causes the Puerto Rico trench. The eastern seafloor, however, does not reach its subduction zone until the East African rift valley. Orange dots mark earthquake epicentres.

Seismic surveys are carried out by setting off small explosions, as shown above, or by using mechanical vibrators. The sound waves from these are reflected and refracted below ground, to be received back at the surface as a complicated series of echoes of varying delay and

intensity. The echoes are picked up by an array of geophones like the one in the right hand picture, spread out over the area of interest. The recording made can be analyzed by computer to yield data on the rock structures below ground.

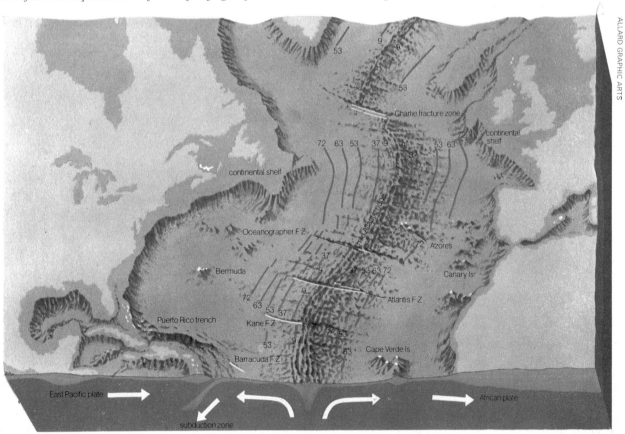

few hundred miles in size, and can yield valuable information about the mineral value of an area (such as the Arctic Slope of Alaska, whose oil potential has recently become apparent) as well as purely scientific details.

Alternatively, portable gravimeters may be taken, usually mounted in rucksack-style carriers, to many points in the area of interest. This technique can still be used at sea, but in a limited way. It allows a cheap (by comparison with seismic work) study of, say, a rock dome which may be full of oil or the zone of shattered rock under a possible meteorite crater. Recent advances in airborne gravimetry will probably make this approach outdated except where expense is a vital consideration.

Magnetic anomalies Just as regions of unusually high or low gravity are of interest, so *magnetic anomalies* are equally worth studying. The MAGNETOMETERS used have a compass-type needle which is held away from the north–south line by a fine spring. The tension in the spring gives a direct measure of the magnetic field strength. In more modern proton magnetometers, the magnetic field in a crystal bar alters the energy of the protons in it, which in turn affect nearby electrons and hence the electrical properties of the crystal.

Magnetometers, like gravimeters, can either be carried by hand in ground-based surveys or flown in aircraft where a quicker and not much less detailed picture is obtained. The magnetic anomaly method has the advantage that metal-bearing areas show up very strongly, such as the vast ore fields in the Australian outback.

From the GEOLOGICAL TECHNIQUE of taking *core samples* of near-surface rocks, more detailed magnetic studies can be carried out using more specialized magnetometers. These, for example, may spin the core sample and detect the small current induced in

coils by the oscillating magnetic field. When molten rock containing iron minerals solidifies to form a new stratum—after volcanic activity, for instance—it is affected by the Earth's magnetic field, so that the solid rock is weakly magnetized. In many core samples it is found that different layers of rock are magnetized in different directions. The upper layers will be magnetized in the same sense as the Earth's present field direction, but deeper layers may have reversed magnetism, with south and north poles interchanged. Deeper still, the magnetic rocks may have the same magnetism as surface rocks, and so on. This fossil magnetism or *palaeomagnetism* indicates that the Earth's magnetic field must have completely reversed direction several times over the period when the rocks were being laid down, each change lasting many hundred thousands of years. The causes of these reversals are still largely a mystery, but the fact of their existence can be used to trace geophysical changes in the Earth's crust.

Airborne surveys and, in particular, deep drilling at sea by research vessels, have shown that just as successive depths of core samples may have reversed magnetism, so on the sea bed adjacent strips of rock can show the same effect. These strips are parallel to the *ocean ridges* or submerged mountain chains which can be found in all the major seas. One such ridge, the mid-Atlantic ridge, rises above the ocean to form the volcanic island of Iceland; all the ridges are sites of volcanic activity.

Continental drift Geophysicists regard these strips of rock as convincing evidence for the existence of *continental drift*. It is easy to see on a map that Africa and South America can be fitted together if the intervening ocean is removed. Until recently, theories that the continents were once part of

one land mass which broke up, with the pieces drifting apart, were regarded as unlikely, if not downright absurd. Modern geophysics has changed this, and the new science of *plate tectonics* has been introduced to deal with the new concepts.

Geophysicists explain the palaeomagnetic reversals by saying that new portions of the Earth's crust are continually being brought up from the Earth's interior along these ocean ridges, and that as these move away from the ridges the seabed spreads wider. So instead of the older rocks being deeper, they are further away from the ocean ridges. The picture is complicated because as well as the continents drifting apart as the seafloor spreads, some have twisted out of alignment. The fossil magnetism of the rock strips shows just how much twisting of the continents has occurred.

To counterbalance the production of new seafloor at the ocean ridges, crust is also destroyed in the ocean deeps at the edges of some oceans, such as the West Pacific around Japan. There, the ocean crust dives under the thicker continental crust and is eventually consumed in the Earth's molten

Below left: a mud sampler just about to be lowered to the seabed. It is triggered automatically like a mousetrap when it hits the bottom, picking up a sample of surface sediment and rocks.

Below: a seabed corer, which rams itself into the seafloor by its momentum. The top end has fins like a bomb to keep it vertical, since cable is paid out faster than it drops. It will pick up traces of almost any rock, though it only cuts into softer ones.

Below right: this housing contains a proton magnetometer, for aerial surveys of magnetic anomalies.

interior. This powerful geophysical process is the cause of the earthquakes for which the region around Japan is notorious.

The crust of the Earth is now pictured as a series of relatively rigid flat blocks of rock, or *tectonic plates*, which float on a more fluid, plastic layer, the *mantle*. This model explains the mobility of the continents over many millions of years.

Other techniques Further evidence for the theories of seafloor spreading comes from studies of the heat flow from the Earth's interior, particularly below the oceans. Temperature measurements of the seafloor made from research vessels indicate that the heat flow near the ocean ridges is indeed higher than normal, suggesting that the theories are correct.

Geophysicists also use techniques which are more common in other sciences. The ARCHAEOLOGICAL TECHNIQUES of *thermoluminescence* and *radioisotope* dating reveal the ages of rocks. Thermoluminescence applies in the case of *igneous* materials—those which have once been molten but which have since solidified. By heating the sample, accumulated electrons caused by the decay of radioactive materials release energy in the form of light, which is detected to give a measure of the time which has elapsed since solidification.

In archaeology, the decay of an ISOTOPE of carbon is studied. Geological time scales, however, are far longer than those of archaeology and different isotopes are studied. In particular, the decay of potassium into argon and uranium into lead are useful. Using these and other techniques, the time scale on which such processes as continental drift take place can be worked out.

GEYSER (see heater)

GIN MANUFACTURE (see spirits, alcoholic)

GLASS

Glass is not a solid—it is a molten liquid of sand, usually with added limestone and sodium carbonate, which has been cooled to ordinary temperatures where it becomes very viscous and stiff, with all the normal properties of a solid. This condition is called *supercooling*: when most liquids freeze they become crystalline, the CRYSTAL size depending on the rate of cooling. Glass, however, is unusual in its properties.

The liquid nature of glass can be seen by looking at old windows, which tend to sag downwards. Old Roman flasks which have been found resting under stones are sometimes squashed flat rather than broken.

Glass can be made just from sand, which is crystalline silica or quartz, but the melting point is high (1700°C, 3092°F) and the result is still crystalline in nature. In this case, the material is known as a glass CERAMIC. The high melting point and crystalline nature make this unsuitable for normal sheet glass purposes. But adding about 10% of lime (calcium carbonate) and 15% of soda (sodium carbonate) produces a melting point of about 850°C (1560°F) and a much reduced tendency to crystallize (*devitrification*). There are usually other components, their quantity depending on the type of glass needed.

History   The first kind of glass made was *faience*, formed by melting the surface of sand grains together with soda or potash. This was used for making beads and small decorations at a very early date. In the second millennium BC the first true GLASS CONTAINERS appeared. The Romans had cast window glass, but it was not particularly clear and was just used to let the light in but keep the weather out. The glass was cast in a flat sheet, and perhaps rolled while it was still hot to make it thinner. Although a few churches had glass windows as

early as the seventh century, large sheets of transparent glass were not common until the seventeenth century.

Early processes involved either casting a sheet of glass, then rolling and polishing it, or blowing a globe of glass then spinning it on the end of a rod so that it flattened out into a disc, already fire-polished and smooth. Old glazing using this *crown* or *Normandy* glass requires small window frames, some of which contain the characteristic central 'bullseye' mark from the rod. Alternatively, in the *broad* glass process, the globe was swung so that it extended into a cylinder some five feet (1.5 metres) long by 18 inches (45 cm) in diameter. The ends were then removed, the cylinder was slit lengthwise and flattened in a kiln.

This method, and a mechanized development of it, were used until the early twentieth century when two important processes were developed, the Fourcault (1904) and Pittsburgh (1926). In these, a ribbon of glass is drawn vertically from the glass furnace up an *annealing* tower by powered asbestos rollers which grip the ribbon as soon as it has cooled enough, a few feet above the furnace. The annealing *lehr* or *leer* allows the glass to cool slowly at a chosen rate. This is necessary to prevent stresses caused by the surface cooling too rapidly. The glass is transparent with hard fire-polished surfaces but because of the process exhibits some distortion.

The float process   Since its introduction by the British firm of Pilkington in 1959 the float process has become the world's principal method of flat glass manufacture. Previously, any flat plate glass had to be cast, rolled and polished to remove the distortions.

The float process, unlike previous developments in flat glass manufacture, did not evolve from its predecessors. The

Below left: a German glass works in 1857. Stages in the making of sheet glass are shown, from the initial blowing of a globe to its drawing out into a cylinder. These are then cut and flattened out.

The sequence of pictures on this page shows the production of blown glass for decorative table use. The work is carried out by a team, with the apprentices carrying out the simpler tasks of gathering the glass, loading the furnace, and so on. Each item of glassware is passed from man to man until it reaches the master blower. An overall view of the works is seen in the top picture, with the furnace at top right and the master blower seated at lower left. A gatherer takes molten glass from a pot in the furnace and passes it to the first blower, who blows the first bubble and smooths the outside on a flat metal slab known as a marver (top right).

The shape of the glass is then moulded in a water cooled mould, shown at right, made of alder wood or graphite. By this time, the shape of the glass has been formed, and the glass is no longer red hot. It is then passed to the master blower, who adds a stem made from glass brought in the molten state from the furnace by a gatherer (lower left). The foot is then put on by the deputy master blower, who shapes it as the glass revolves, ending with a flat base.

The next stage is the annealing lehr, in which the glass is cooled at a carefully controlled rate, taking some four hours to do so. Finally, in the case of table glasses, the waste glass has to be cut off by jets of burning propane and a revolving table (lower right).

advance was based on completely new technology.

To make polished plate, molten glass from a furnace was originally rolled into a continuous ribbon. But because there was glass-to-roller contact, the surfaces were marked. These had to be ground and polished to produce the parallel surfaces which bring optical perfection to the finished product. But grinding and polishing incurred glass wastage amounting to 20% and involved high capital and operating costs.

In the float process, a continuous ribbon of glass up to 11 feet (3.3 m) wide moves out of the melting furnace and floats along the surface of a bath of molten tin. The ribbon is held in a chemically controlled atmosphere at a high enough temperature for a long enough time for the irregularities to melt out and for the surfaces to become flat and parallel. Because the surface of the molten tin is dead flat, the glass also becomes flat.

The ribbon is then cooled down while still advancing across the molten tin until the surfaces are hard enough for it to progress through the annealing lehr without the rollers marking the bottom surface. The glass produced has uniform thickness and bright fire polished surfaces without the need for grinding and polishing.

After seven years' work—and after 14 months of unsuccessful operations on a full scale plant which cost £100,000 [$250,000] a month—the float process was successfully making glass about 6 mm ($\frac{1}{4}$ inch) thick.

The natural forces within the float bath determined the glass thickness at about 6 mm—a fortunate phenomenon since 50% of the market for quality flat glass is for this thickness.

But the full potential of float could not have been realized without mastery of ribbon thickness. Just two years after float was announced, Pilkington could make a product half the thickness of the original float. The principle was to stretch the glass but in a gentle and controlled way so that none of the distortions arising in sheet glass processes could occur.

In the next three years thicker float was made. The spread of molten glass in the float bath is arrested and allowed to build up in thickness. The range of thicknesses now available commercially is 4 mm to 25 mm (1/6 to 1 inch) for the building trade, and glass down to 2.5 mm (1/10 inch) is manufactured for the motor trade.

Other types of glass

Patterned glass is made by using rollers with surface patterns after the glass has emerged from the furnace. Wired glass, with a criss-cross pattern of wire set inside it, is made by rolling a ribbon of half the required thickness, overlaying it with wire and adding a further ribbon of glass which fuses with the bottom one. To make the glass transparent, the surfaces must be ground and polished. The advantage of wired glass is that it holds together when broken by impact or heat.

Optical glass

Optical and ophthalmic glass is made in much the same way as other glasses with the important exceptions that the glass should be consistently homogeneous with no strain, striations or discoloration. Small differences in chemical composition or heat treatment can have considerable effects on the optical properties. Common glass usually contains iron oxides which discolour the glass. Sand used in the manufacture of optical glass is purer and the mix is suitably modified by the addition of various oxides of calcium, sodium, potassium, barium, or magnesium.

The batch is first melted, then the glass is refired by further raising the temperature. It is homogenized by being allowed to cool and then passed through a series of stirrers.

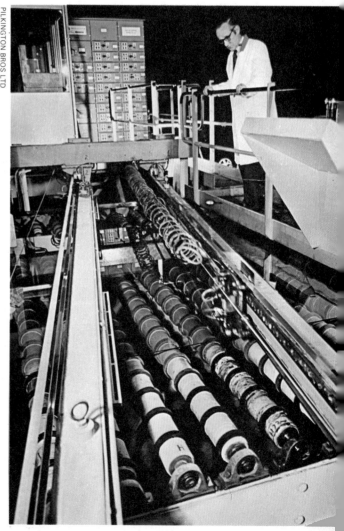

PILKINGTON BROS LTD

Sheet glass making by the float process. The raw materials—sand, soda ash, limestone, dolomite and crushed glass—are melted down and a stream of the molten glass spread on a bath of molten tin. At top left is the interior of the float bath. The next picture shows the ribbon of glass, still hot but not molten, passing into the annealing lehr where it cools down at a controlled rate.

After annealing, the glass passes under water jets (above) which stress the surface temporarily to help the cutting process farther along the line. Next, at lower left, the glass is scored by cross cutters so that it can be snapped off into stock sizes farther down the line. The cutting and storing are carried out automatically.

The float glass process is growing in importance, and produces high quality glass in large sheets with none of the imperfections often seen in window glass made using other processes. The picture at left shows the upward drawing of glass by one of these methods from a pool of molten glass. Only surface tension keeps it flat.

The optical properties of the glass are preserved by the critical melting, refining and stirring temperatures but the cooling rate is even more important, since this has an important role in determining the refractive index (light bending power) of the glass.

The cooling glass flows slowly down a delivery feeder and is sheared into globules or formed into sheet or slab for further processing. The globules are then moulded into lens blanks and passed into the annealing lehr.

Safety glass There are many uses for particularly strong glass which will not shatter easily, such as car windscreens [windshields] which must be able to withstand the impact of pebbles thrown up from the road. These materials are made from annealed glass which undergoes a further process of toughening or lamination. In the case of *toughened* or *tempered* glass, its temperature is uniformly raised until the glass is just beginning to become plastic. The glass is quickly lifted out of the furnace, bent where necessary between matching tools and then cooled uniformly all over by jets of cold air blown forcibly on to it. The surface then becomes very much stronger than normal, and both withstands shattering forces better and contains the glass if it does break.

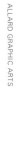

Laminated glass is made by sandwiching a layer of clear or tinted polyvinyl butyral between two pieces of annealed float glass. The sandwich is gently heated under vacuum which evacuates all air from the laminate, and is then heated to bonding temperature under pressure in an AUTOCLAVE. No adhesives are required. A number of layers may be used for increased strength.

Heat resistant glass If boiling water is poured into an ordinary table glass, the inner surface layer will heat and expand rapidly. Glass is a good insulator, so deeper layers will remain at room temperature. The resulting distortion may easily shatter the glass. In order to make glassware which will withstand oven temperatures, a certain amount of boric oxide (B_2O_3) and alumina is added. This reduces the expansion coefficient of the glass by a factor of three. Pure fused silica is particularly resistant to thermal expansion, and so is used for the production of high quality optics.

GLASS CONTAINERS

Glass has been used for making bottles and jars since its invention in the second millennium BC. Early vessels were built up on a clay or sand core, by dipping it in molten glass or by winding threads of hot glass around it. It was not until after 200 BC that the method of blowing glass vessels from a *gob* of molten glass on the end of a tube was introduced. This not only made better vessels, but was a much simpler and quicker process than the sand core method.

Early vessels were either free blown, resulting in a strong spherical shape, or blown into a mould, which gave the vessel an exact, repeatable shape and size and allowed designs to be impressed on it. Mould blowing forms the basis of the modern mechanical method of making glass containers, but for many centuries all glass was mouth blown, a craftsman's occupation which inevitably resulted in a slow rate of production.

It was only after 1882, when the glass industry in the north of England was paralyzed by a long strike, that mechanical methods came to be considered. The first machine was invented by a Yorkshireman named Ashley, and the design was greatly improved over the next 20 years. The fully automatic glass bottle machine was introduced by Michael Owens in the United States in 1903.

Raw materials The normal composition of glass used for mass-produced containers is silica (70–74%), calcium oxide (9–13%), sodium oxide (13–16%) and alumina (0.5–2.5%). There is a trend towards increasing the calcium, and

Above left: a laminated windscreen, which does not shatter and remains transparent if a stone hits it. Toughened glass, however, shatters all over if a stone hits it. Despite the larger pieces in the central area, vision is still difficult (lower picture).

Below: two glassmaking processes. On the left is the float glass method—not drawn to scale, as it is some 200 metres long. Such a production line can have a melting tank capacity of more than 2000 tons, and can operate continuously for several years without major repairs being necessary. On the right is the older sheet glass process, used mainly for window glass. The ribbon is started by lowering a metal 'bait' into the molten glass, then raising it.

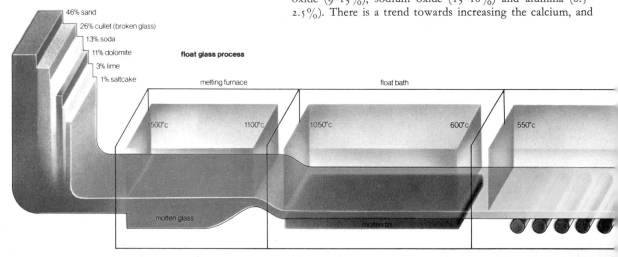

46% sand
26% cullet (broken glass)
13% soda
11% dolomite
3% lime
1% saltcake

float glass process

melting furnace

float bath

1500°c   1100°c   1050°c   600°c   550°c

molten glass

molten tin

reducing the sodium content, which not only reduces the price of the glass (calcium oxide is made from limestone and is extremely cheap) but also increases its strength, making it more suitable for modern thinwalled containers.

Glass naturally has a slight greenish tint from the presence of iron oxide in the raw materials, so clear glass is decolorized by adding small amounts of selenium and cobalt oxide. Coloured glass is frequently used, sometimes for decoration but often in containers for liquids such as wine or beer, which are affected by light. Green glass is made by adding varying amounts of iron, manganese, chromium and nickel oxides, depending on the shade required. An amber colour comes from a mixture of carbon, sulphur and iron. Blue is obtained by adding cobalt oxide or copper oxide; red from selenium and cadmium sulphide. Opal (milky) glass, which can be white or coloured, is made by the addition of fluorides or phosphates and alumina.

Glass furnaces are generally run for several months or years at a time, so most manufacturers cannot supply the entire range of colours.

Automatic manufacturing
Glass containers are manufactured around the clock to suit the continuous operation of the furnace. The furnace itself may hold from four to 100 tons of glass, and operates at temperatures up to 1590°C (2890°F).

The raw materials are weighed and mechanically mixed so that the minor constituents are evenly blended. They are then taken by a conveyer to be charged into the melting chamber of the furnace, where they fuse and mix into a homogeneous liquid mass.

From the melting chamber the glass, which flows as freely as water at this temperature, runs to the second zone of the furnace, the working chamber. This is a reservoir where finished glass is allowed to cool slightly, becoming slightly viscous and suitable for forming.

The furnace is generally mounted on a raised platform above the forming machines. Glass flows down through a long feeder channel in which it is brought to exactly the right temperature for forming into gobs. The weight of a gob, which must be constant to produce identical containers, depends on the viscosity of the glass and hence on its temperature.

A machine picks up the gobs and drops them into a passing line of rough moulds, where by pressing or compressed air blowing they are made into an intermediate shape called a *parison*, roughly the same shape as the intended container but smaller and thicker.

Another system uses suction to form parisons by drawing up molten glass from revolving pots and severing it with a blade.

Each parison is then transferred to a finishing mould and blown to its final shape. Moulds are generally made of cast iron, and are in several pieces so that they can be opened to let the container out. A plain jar mould has left and right halves and a separate bottom. Apart from the manufacturer's standard moulds, special moulds of unusual shapes are often made to a customer's specification: for example cosmetic jars.

The containers soon cool enough to stand on their own, and are released from their moulds and conveyed to the *annealing lehr*, a long heated tunnel where they are held at 600°C (1110°F) to remove stresses in the glass. Finally, they are inspected and faulty containers rejected; these are used as *cullet*—added to the raw materials when making a fresh batch of glass.

This process can make well over 200 containers a minute; other, semi-automatic processes are in use at smaller factories, using small pot furnaces holding less than a ton of glass, from which the glass is gathered by hand on an iron rod. There may be up to twelve pots per furnace, and each can hold a different colour if required.

Some high-quality bottles and glasses are still mouth blown.

Fully formed bottles being transferred from an automatic moulding machine on to a conveyer which takes them to the annealing lehr just visible in the background.

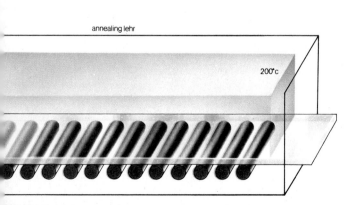
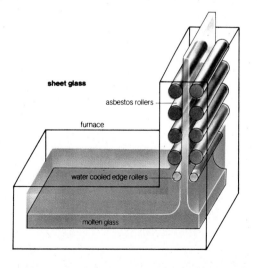

GLASS FIBRE

The earliest Egyptian glass vessels, used as containers for oils, unguents and perfumes, were built up from glass fibres spun laboriously by hand round lightly glazed cores of clay. After the development of the technique of glass blowing in the first century BC, glass fibres were used by glass blowers only to enhance their wares. In the early nineteenth century glass blowers would often spend idle moments making *friggers*, glass ornaments of sometimes a very extravagant nature to testify to their skills. One such frigger in the Pilkington glass museum is made to represent a glass fountain with birds which trail long, silky tails of coloured glass fibres.

At the turn of the century in Germany a commercial process was developed for the production of glass 'silk'. Deprived of access to supplies of asbestos during World War 1, the Germans pioneered the use of glass insulation material. The first commercial production of glass fibres in Britain began in 1928, but not until after World War 2 in the UK was there a need for efficient insulation material to satisfy the postwar building boom. The continuing development of glass fibre reinforcement materials has complemented and accelerated the use of plastics in twentieth century living.

Manufacture of glass fibres In the manufacture of glass fibres, alumina, boric acid and calcium oxide flux are added to the basic glassmaking mix of sand and soda ash. The batch is fed first into a continuous furnace where it becomes molten glass by the application of direct flame heating, and then into a fibre-drawing furnace, called a *bushing*. The glass fibres drawn from the bushing can be either continuous or discontinuous filaments, the latter being used in the manufacture of glass wool and glass tissue.

Glass wool is manufactured by the Crown process in which a relatively thick stream of glass is allowed to flow by gravity from a bushing into a rapidly rotating steel alloy dish which has many hundreds of fine apertures round its edge. Glass is thrown out through these apertures by centrifugal force to form filaments which are further extended into fine fibres by a high velocity blast of hot gas. After being sprayed with a suitable bonding agent, the fibres are drawn by suction on to a horizontally moving conveyer positioned below the rotating dish. The mat of fibres formed on the conveyer is carried to curing ovens which cure the bonding agent, then to trimmers and guillotines which shape the final product, which is normally either a flexible mat or a rigid board. The wool produced by the Crown process is of a very fine texture, the individual fibres having an average diameter of approximately 6.5 microns (0.0003 inch)—less than one tenth of the diameter of a human hair.

The manufacture of *glass tissue* differs from the Crown process in that in this process a number of small streams of molten glass are allowed to fall from bushings, but within an inch of the apertures they are caught by a blast of superheated steam. The high speed of the blast grasps each tiny glass stream and by a whipping action, visible only in high speed photographs, draws it out until it breaks away from the main stream and falls as a separate fibre into a *forming hood*. A binder is applied to the mat of fibres after they have fallen on to a collecting conveyer moving at relatively high speed. The resulting thin membrane, which is normally about 0.5 mm (0.002 inch) thick, can be either in plain form or reinforced with a continuous filament fibre.

In continuous filament manufacture, a continuous strand is produced, made up of a multitude of individual filaments.

PERMALI LTD/PHOTO: PAUL BRIERLEY

Molten glass is led from the furnace or 'tank' through a *fore-hearth* to a series of bushings, each of which contains several hundred very accurately dimensioned forming nozzles. With a constant head of molten glass maintained in the tank, fine filaments of glass are drawn mechanically downwards from the bushing nozzles at a speed of several thousand metres per minute, giving a filament diameter which may be as small as 5 microns (0.0002 inch), barely visible to the naked eye. The filaments from the bushing run to a common collecting point, where *size* (a protective and lubricating coating) is applied, and are subsequently brought together either as multiple or single strands on a high speed winder. The strands are then further processed to produce specially treated *rovings* (continuous strands of fibres suitable for twisting into yarns), woven glass cloth, or chopped strands and mats for the reinforcement of composites.

Uses of glass fibre products Although the main use of glass wool is in the insulation of domestic attics, glass fibre wool products are also used for heat and sound insulation of pipes, ducts, boilers and tanks in all types of domestic and industrial applications, and in road vehicles, railway locomotives, ships and aircraft. Glass tissue is used to reinforce the bituminous and coal tar protective coatings on buried oil, gas and water pipes. It also provides the reinforcing membranes of damp courses and roofing mats. Continuous filament glass fibres are used to reinforce thermosetting plastics and natural and synthetic rubbers. Special forms of glass fibre reinforcement are also available for use in inorganic matrices such as gypsum plaster, autoclave calcium silicate and cement.

The development of glass capable of resisting the alkaline conditions of Portland cement has led to the development of a completely new construction material, glass reinforced cement (GRC). This material can be sprayed into flat sheets or on to a variety of shaped moulds; the glass and cement can also be premixed and then spread with a trowel, cast, spun, pumped, extruded or injected. To give still further flexibility thin flat GRC sheets can, while still 'green' or uncured, be folded or pressed into a wide variety of complex shapes. GRC has the tensile strength of reinforced concrete and yet is ten times lighter. Its uses seem virtually limitless and applications already range from pipes and sewer linings to cladding panels for buildings, permanent shuttering, soil retaining walls and general street furniture such as bus shelters and benches. It is also used to make shells for low cost modular housing and for integral door and window frames.

Far left, top: a ship's hull made of glass fibre reinforced plastic. Ships of up to 600 tons can be made with hulls formed entirely from this material.

Far left, bottom: continuous filament glass fibres being wound on to a tube as reinforcement. Strands of glass fibres pass under a metal guide which gathers them into bands before winding.

Top left: an infantryman wearing a bullet-proof jacket made of a light, glass fibre-reinforced material.

Centre left: glass wool is laid between the joists of a domestic attic to prevent heat loss through the roof. The water tank is lagged with glass wool to prevent freezing in cold weather.

Left: the manufacture of a cab for a commercial vehicle. The cab is made from glass fibre-reinforced plastic formed in a mould.

GLIDER

A glider or *sailplane* is, in simple terms, an AIRCRAFT without an engine. Gliding as a sport originated just before World War 1 at the Wasserkuppe hill in the Rhön mountains, Germany. Before this date gliding had merely been an integral part of the efforts of man to fly.

In the early days of aviation the lack of suitable lightweight engines hampered the general advance and exploration of flying so most early aviators used primitive gliders to help them into the air. As a result, gliders have a much longer history than powered aircraft.

The first gliders were made by Sir George Cayley who, after a series of models, constructed at Brompton, near Scarborough, Yorkshire, gliders to carry a boy in 1849 and Cayley's coachman in 1853. Other gliders were made around the turn of the century by Otto LILIENTHAL in Germany, Percy PILCHER in England, and Wilbur and Orville WRIGHT in America, culminating in the first flight of a powered aircraft on 16 December 1903. From that date, apart from people learning to fly, gliding was mainly ignored until competitions were organized at the Wasserkuppe in 1920 and 1921.

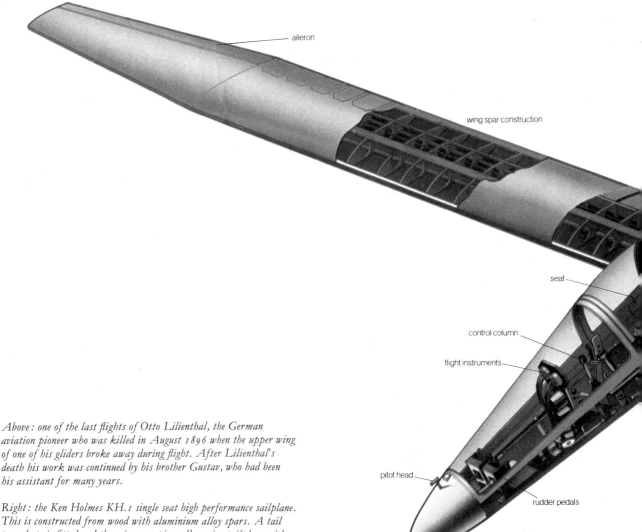

aileron

wing spar construction

seat

control column

flight instruments

pitot head

rudder pedals

Above: one of the last flights of Otto Lilienthal, the German aviation pioneer who was killed in August 1896 when the upper wing of one of his gliders broke away during flight. After Lilienthal's death his work was continued by his brother Gustav, who had been his assistant for many years.

Right: the Ken Holmes KH.1 single seat high performance sailplane. This is constructed from wood with aluminium alloy spars. A tail parachute is fitted and there is a one piece all moving tailplane with anti-balance tabs.

From these meetings the sport of gliding grew throughout Europe. It reached England in 1929, although a brief meeting had been held in Sussex in 1922. The first International Competition was held in Germany in 1937, but during World War 2 large transport gliders were built to carry up to 60 troops or small vehicles. After the war, sporting gliding spread throughout the world, and international competitions have been held on a regular basis in the various continents since the 1948 competition in Switzerland.

Launching   There are two basic methods of launching a glider into the air. The first is *winch launching*, in which a long steel cable is wound on to a powered drum and the glider is pulled into the air in a similar manner to the launching of a kite. The other launching method is using an aircraft to tow the glider up to any desired height. An earlier method, using an elastic rope to catapult the glider into the air from the top edge of a cliff or high hill, is now rarely used. Gliders may also be launched by towing them behind a car or truck.

Flying   Once in the air, a glider cannot maintain a steady horizontal flight path indefinitely, and the line of the flight path will slope downwards relative to the horizon. The angle be-

rudder

all-moving tailplane

small span drag flap

hinge on aluminium wing spar

retractable main wheel

tween the horizon and the flight path is known as the *gliding angle*, and the minimum value for each glider, known as *the best gliding angle*, is used to give a direct comparison as to the efficiency of each type of glider. Before the last war a high-performance glider had a best gliding angle of around 1:25. By 1955 gliders had improved, and the average gliding angle of 1:35 was being achieved. This was due to improved surface finishing and the use of laminar AEROFOILS, although the gliders were still made from the traditional wooden materials of spruce or pine with birch or gaboon plywood covering. Nowadays best gliding angles of 1:50 are being obtained but the constructional materials used are usually glass fibres with synthetic resins. These plastic materials give the very smooth surfaces necessary to suit the specialized aerofoils used on modern competition gliders in order to achieve best gliding angles at higher speeds than were previously possible.

Minimum 'sink' at high speeds is nowadays very important in a glider, as competitions usually consist of triangular courses around which the competitor has to fly as quickly as possible. After launching, usually by aero-towing, the pilot has to find a *thermal* or any other air that is rising upwards faster than the glider is sinking through it. Having thus climbed to a suitable height, the competitor sets off on the desired course as fast as possible, gradually losing height until another thermal is found, and so on until the course is completed. In addition to thermals, other types of rising air currents can be found when air is blowing up the face of a steep hill, or when waves are set up as air masses pass over mountainous countryside.

A glider is controlled in exactly the same manner as an aircraft, including the use of flaps when these are fitted. Most gliders are also fitted with air-brakes to limit the maximum speed and to assist landing the glider in small fields. Some gliders also have tail parachutes to act as air-brakes. Competition gliders carry a very comprehensive range of flying instruments, including an airspeed indicator, an altimeter and a *variometer* to show the vertical rise and sinking speeds. Oxygen equipment and radios are also carried, and jettisonable water ballast inside the wings to increase the speed, when weather conditions are good, and to achieve the best gliding angle.

Types of glider At an average gliding club today a visitor would find several different types of glider in use, and these would be either single or two seat machines. The two seat gliders are, usually, used for instructional flying, either showing students how to operate the controls of the glider or how to make circuits of the airfield to be able to land correctly. Gliders used for this type of flying may be quite old wooden machines, although new motorized gliders have recently been introduced into some clubs for this purpose. The engine is quite small but, by using powered gliders, a club can offer instructional flying at any time regardless of the weather. Other two seat gliders, of higher performance and built of light-alloy metal, are used to give lessons in advanced techniques of gliding.

Single seat gliders may be found in many different sizes and shapes. The modern glass fibre competition machines have wing spans of either 15 m (49.2 ft) to suit the Standard Class rules, or up to 23 m (75.5 ft) for the Open Class competitions. Many other older competition gliders, of wooden construction, are now used for practice and pleasure flying. Occasionally a pre-war vintage glider may be seen, but these rarely take to the air nowadays, except at special events and displays.

Above: a modern sports glider about to land. The parachute acts as an air brake to slow the glider and so enable it to land in restricted spaces such as small fields. Most sports gliders have removable wings so that they can be carried easily on small trailers.

Left: the Wasserkuppe hill in Germany where sports gliding originated shortly before World War 1. This picture was taken in 1925, and it shows a glider being towed back to the top of the hill after landing nearby. Gliding competitions were first held at the Wasserkuppe in the early 1920s, and soon became popular throughout Europe. Many international competitions are now held all over the world.

GODDARD, Robert (1882–1945)

Robert Goddard was a pioneer in the field of rocketry whose ideas and experiments paved the way for manned flights to the moon, but did not live long enough to see his work result in anything more useful than warfare.

He was born in Worcester, Massachusetts, obtained a PhD from Clark University there in 1911, and began teaching at Clark in 1914. By that time he had already worked out a theory of multistage rockets to escape the gravitational pull of the Earth, and had a detailed mathematical theory of rocket propulsion. Experimenting with solid-fuelled rockets, he proved that they would not only work in a vacuum but that they would work better that way. These experiments were financed mostly out of his own pocket, and were necessary because there was confusion between rocket theory and jet theory, which needs an atmosphere for the jet engine to push against.

During World War 1 Goddard developed military rockets of 1.5 to 7 lb (0.7 g to 7.7 kg) to be fired from hand-held launchers; these were being successfully tested when the war was over, and were the forerunners of the BAZOOKA of World War 2. In 1919, the Smithsonian Institution published Goddard's paper, *A Method of Reaching Extreme Altitudes*, which disguised rockets as a device for meteorological research, but on the last page proposed a rocket to be fired at the moon, with flashpowder payload so that astronomers would be able to see if the shot were successful. The Institution also provided funds for research.

In the early 1920s, Goddard gave up solid fuels in favour of liquid fuels, realizing that the rate of consumption of a liquid fuel could be controlled. He began to build high pressure steel motors with tapered nozzles for greater thrust, and fired his first liquid fuelled rocket on 16 March 1926, near Auburn, Massachusetts. It went 41 feet (12.5 m) high, landed 184 feet (28 m) away and averaged sixty miles per hour.

In 1930 Charles Lindbergh, the first man to fly the Atlantic solo, helped Goddard to get a grant from the Guggenheim foundation, and he was able to move to the desert in New Mexico to perform his experiments. Before World War 2 he had flown a rocket faster than the speed of sound and developed and tested a system of gyroscopic stabilization. He had received dozens of patents on the multistage idea, on pumps for propellents, regenerative cooling for engines, variable thrust engines, retrorockets for braking purposes, and many more. It is sometimes lamented that he did not receive more funds for research, but as it was pointed out after his death, he was probably happier conducting his experiments than he would have been overseeing others and defending his research to Congressional committees. Throughout World War 2 he worked on rocket motors and JATO (jet assisted take-off), and he died in 1945.

During the war the Nazis infringed his patents to build the V-2 rockets. In 1960 the United States government paid a million dollars (£416,000) to the Guggenheim foundation and Mrs Goddard for use of the patents in its own programme; in 1962 the National Aeronautics and Space Administration (NASA) dedicated the Goddard Space Flight Centre at Greenbelt, Maryland.

Below: Dr Robert Goddard with three assistants preparing a large pump-type rocket for testing on 31 January 1940. From about 1930 until America entered World War 2, the experiments were conducted in New Mexico. Then Goddard worked on war materials.

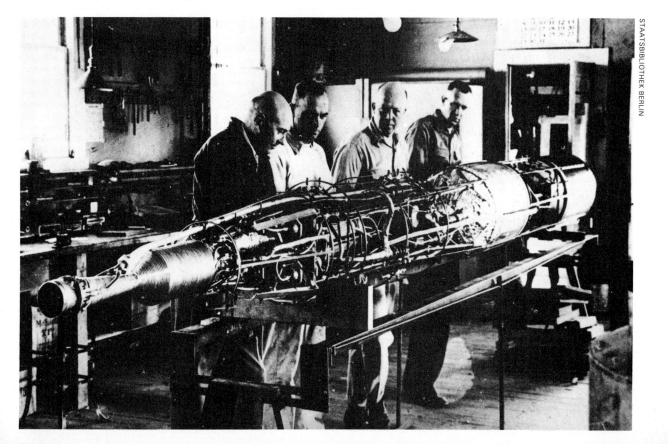

GOLD

The story of gold and the history of man have been interwoven over the whole of recorded time. The reason for the pre-eminent position of gold can be traced to one particular chemical property of the metal: it will not oxidize under any naturally occurring conditions. Consequently, it is found in its free state rather than combined with other elements, like most metals. It can be fire-refined, that is, melted and held at a temperature at which other less noble impurities will oxidize and float to the surface as dross which can be discarded. Also, it will keep perfectly bright and never tarnish, and its intrinsic freedom from very small oxide inclusions plays a large part in giving it its remarkably high malleability (ability to be shaped by hammering).

The fact that it is possible to obtain gold without advanced refining techniques meant that it was the earliest metal available to man. Its tarnish-free surface, attractive colour and very high density—one cubic foot (0.028 m³) of gold weighs over half a ton—as well as its rarity, make it highly prized.

Occurrence and extraction

Gold is widely distributed throughout the world, but only in a few localities is it present in sufficient quantities to make its recovery worthwhile. Some of the richer areas, such as California and Australia, have been pinpointed by the famous gold rushes of the 19th century, but the main producing region since the 1920s has been South Africa. Today South Africa is responsible for 60% of the total annual production of gold, while the USSR and North America each yield about 12%. There is even a very small gold mine in North Wales.

The primary source of gold, in common with minerals of other metals, is quartz veins which have penetrated older rocks. With time, however, the veins are eroded and their remains washed down to the sea by streams and rivers. The small particles of gold which can be found in sand or silt are known as alluvial or placer deposits. In the Rand field in South Africa the gold occurs in a quartz conglomerate rock thousands of feet underground. This gold at an earlier stage in its history has been an alluvial deposit in sand. Under the influence of pressure and heat at great depths the sand has formed a cement which binds together the quartz pebbles of the conglomerate.

Alluvial gold is simpler to win than vein or conglomerate gold. All that is required is a method of sifting through the silt and picking out the gold. Panning was the traditional technique of the prospector; a few pounds of silt were put in a pan and swilled away over the edge, leaving only the heavier gold particles behind. But since even in a fairly rich deposit there may be little more than 1 oz (28.3 g) of gold in every ton of silt or sand, commercial panning is now only of historical interest. Alluvial deposits are now worked on a much larger scale. They can be washed out of hillsides by powerful hydraulic jets similar to those used for mining china clay, although this method tends to add to the pollution of rivers and for this reason is currently forbidden in California. Alternatively, the deposits may be dredged up from the bottom of lakes. In fact it can be worthwhile to create a small artificial lake just to enable

Top right: gold, unlike most metals, is found in its free state, uncombined with other elements. This group of gold nuggets encased in quartz comes from Australia.

Right: part of the cyanidation process. A spiral classifier, consisting of a pair of Archimedean screws, separates coarse material from the fine gold-bearing slime before cyanidation.

a dredger to operate. The method is known as paddocking and it is possible by moving the bounds of the lake to cover large tracts of land and even dredge uphill.

Ore which has been mined from vein and conglomerate deposits must be crushed to release the gold. The amount of crushing required to liberate the gold depends on how finely it is disseminated through the rock. If it is present only as fine, dispersed particles, the crushed ore must be reduced to a very fine powder by stamp, rod or ball milling. The fine ore mixed with water is called a slime.

If the gold particles in alluvial deposits or crushed ore are sufficiently coarse (about 200 microns, 0.008 inch in diameter) they can be extracted by mechanical equipment such as rockers or strakes which in principle amount to little more than scaled up versions of the prospector's pan. A refinement of these techniques involves amalgamation. The gold is removed by washing the suitably crushed ore over slightly inclined copper plates coated with mercury. The gold alloys with the mercury to make an amalgam which is periodically scraped from the plates and distilled in an iron retort to recover the gold.

Where gold is present as very small particles in a slime (about 5 microns, 0.0002 inch in diameter) which neither settle quickly nor have a good chance of amalgamation during their passage over the mercury-coated plates, it can only be extracted by cyanidation. In this process, which was invented by MacArthur and Forrest in 1890, the slime is treated with a very dilute solution (about 0.05%) of sodium or potassium cyanide in the presence of air.

The solution reaction (Eloner's reaction) can be written:

$$2Au + 4NaCN + O + H_2O \longrightarrow 2NaAu(CN)_4 + 2NaOH$$

gold · sodium cyanide · oxygen (from air) · water · sodium cyanaurite · sodium hydroxide

Thus in solution, the gold can be separated from the rest of the slime by filtration.

The gold is recovered from solution by precipitation with zinc dust in the absence of oxygen. The solution is first held in a vacuum to remove the dissolved air. Next, finely powdered zinc is added to the stirred solution which leads to the precipitation of gold according to the reaction (here using potassium cyanide):

$$2KAu(CN)_2 + Zn \longrightarrow ZnK_2(CN)_4 + 2Au$$

potassium cyanaurite · zinc · potassium zinc cyanide · gold

This precipitate is collected in filters and heated in air to oxidize excess zinc, which can then be removed with other impurities as a slag.

Refining The purity of gold is referred to as its *fineness*. The totally pure metal is 1000 fine whereas an alloy containing say, 70% gold, is 700 fine, and so on. Gold extracted by the cyanide process normally assays 900 fine.

There are two important methods of further purification. In one, borax is put on top of the molten metal and chlorine gas bubbled through. Most of the base metals present as impurities are turned into chlorides which either come off as fumes or form a slag with the borax. The completion of the chlorination

Top left: after cyanidation, the slime is passed to clarifying tanks. The solids settle out and the dissolved gold is passed on to the next stage, treatment with powdered zinc.

Left: even after the gold is removed, the slime has value. This rotary filter is used in the recovery of uranium ore, which is present in quantities that make the process financially worthwhile.

ANGLO AMERICAN CORPORATION

Above: most gold is simply used as bullion and stored in bank vaults. Here, molten gold is being poured into ingot moulds on a casting wheel.

process is marked by the appearance of red-brown fumes of gold chloride. Chlorine purified gold is usually 995 fine, although the actual value depends particularly on the platinum content of the original melt, which is now removed. The base metal impurities such as silver are subsequently recovered by treatment of the slag.

Purification by the Wohlwill electrolytic process yields gold better than 999 fine. The gold is deposited by ELECTROLYSIS, using a technique comparable to that used for COPPER.

Applications 60% of all gold won from the earth is simply reinterred in bank vaults where it serves as currency.

Jewellery is perhaps the most familiar use of gold. The pure metal is far too soft for this application, however, and is rarely used. Careful alloying with silver, copper or other metals provides the necessary durability without adversely affecting appearance or corrosion resistance. The gold content of gold alloys is described in terms of carats rather than fineness, 24 carat being equivalent to 1000 fine.

Alloying with silver initially imparts a greenish tinge to the gold although as the silver content is increased beyond 25% the metal lightens in colour, becoming effectively white at about 70% silver. Gold alloyed nickel or palladium loses its yellow colour at comparatively low alloy contents. These alloys are known as 'white golds'. Gold-copper alloys, on the other hand, have a distinct red tinge. Gold used in jewellery is sometimes alloyed with both silver and copper in carefully balanced proportions so as to preserve as far as possible the true colour of pure gold.

Rolled gold is made by encasing a slab of base metal between gold sheets and rolling the composite down to the required thickness. ELECTROPLATING from a cyanide solution is the most ready way of obtaining a thin tarnish-resistant coating, and this technique is now developed to the stage where alloys of predetermined composition can be deposited.

Gold plating is also used as an internal coating for pipes and vessels which have to contain corrosive chemicals, and for jet engine parts. It is unattacked by acids with the exception of hot *aqua regia* (a mixture of 2 parts hydrochloric acid and 3 parts nitric acid).

The outstanding malleability of gold enables it to be beaten down into sheets of gold leaf no thicker than 0.1 micron (0.000004 inch). It is used for decoration and its applications range from park gates to lettering on books. Even thinner gold films, created by electrodeposition or by coating with a gold solution, are used as heating elements in aircraft windows, in the windows of buildings to reflect sunlight, and as heat shields in spacecraft.

Gold is used widely in electronics; its uses include long-life corrosion-resistant RELAY contacts and the tiny wires used to interconnect the elements of INTEGRATED CIRCUITS. In medicine, it is useful because it can be implanted in the body without corrosion or causing a physical reaction. Gold dental fillings are one of the oldest non-decorative uses, dating back to the last century; most industrial applications are far more recent.

Above left: float glass being inspected before it is put in a vacuum chamber where it will be coated with a fine layer of gold to make heat reflecting windows for buildings.

Left: in this integrated circuit array forming part of a guidance system for aerospace use, each chip is connected by 'spattered' gold conductor 'tracks' to solid gold links between the layers.

GOVERNORS

A governor is an automatic regulating system designed to control the rotational speed of a *prime mover* such as a diesel engine (propelling a ship, for example) or a steam turbine (driving an electrical alternator, for example).

Feedback In the early days of steam, a speed-governed engine was easily identified by the spinning fly-ball device which measured the speed as the displacement of its sleeve against a spring by the action of centrifugal force. Less obvious was the mechanical connection between the sleeve and the throttle valve of the engine. Such a simple governor worked with the aid of FEEDBACK; that is the system was adjusted continuously by using measurements of the quantity under control (in this case speed). The engineer could pre-load the sleeve spring to obtain the particular speed he wanted. Then an error from this desired speed, brought about by an unpredictable change of output load on the engine, would adjust the steam supply to the engine in order to return the speed to its proper value.

Hunting In 1868, James Clerk Maxwell gave the Royal Society a mathematical explanation of the undesirable 'dancing motion', nowadays referred to as *instability* or *hunting*, meaning a continuous oscillation of the speed of such governors. This heralded the development of the classical theory of automatic control, without the application of which these simple governors would have continued to behave in an erratic and unpredictable manner.

It was soon realized that, since the fly-ball device displaced the sleeve spring proportionately to the *square* of the speed (because of the nature of centrifugal force) instead of directly proportional to the speed itself, the sensitivity of the system was bound to change with the speed demanded of a particular system. So a system could be too sluggish at low speed and yet hunt at high speed. Fortunately in most applications, with the notable exceptions of engines used for road and rail transportation, the desired speed is not required to vary much if at all. It follows that, although it is now quite a simple matter to replace the mechanical fly-ball device with an electrical *tacho-generator*, capable of giving an output electric potential directly proportional to speed, many modern governors are still built around a device utilizing centrifugal force, although this is scarcely visually recognizable as such.

Load sensing The simple design of governor suffers from a further drawback known as *droop*; that is, a temporary or permanent change from the desired speed following a change in the output load imposed on the prime mover. An ideal governor, which does not suffer from droop, is called *isochronous* (meaning constant speed). One area where this matters particularly is in the generation of electrical power, where droop directly affects the frequency of the alternating supply. Governors for such systems may be fitted with a *load-sensing* device in which the load on the engine is measured and fed back as well as the speed. Such measurement of the load may be done by a coupling between the engine and the driven load or, where the load is an alternator, by measuring the electrical current in the machine. Inevitably this results in greater

G A ROBINSON

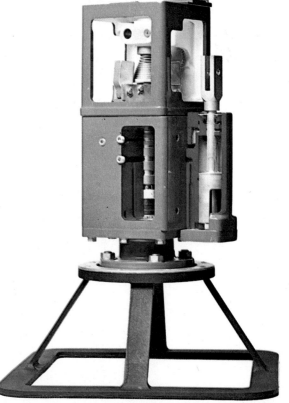

WOODWARD GOVERNOR CO / PHOTO: MICHAEL NEWTON

Top right: the traditional 'fly-ball' governor, devised by James Watt. As the balls spin, they fly outwards under centrifugal force, against the force of gravity. The outward motion moves a sleeve up the central shaft, directly altering the throttle setting. A modern governor (right) has square fly-balls acting against a spring rather than gravity. They operate a valve controlling oil pressure to a piston, which in turn varies the throttle or fuel setting.

complication and a more difficult design problem.

Without load sensing, a change of load will result in a buildup of droop taking a finite time. The control system can take corrective action only after the droop has occurred, and hence it is inevitable that the governor should suffer from *temporary* droop. Even after the transition following the load change, a small error in speed can remain; this is called *permanent* droop. Permanent droop can be avoided, without resorting to load sensing, by using a regulator which reacts to the rate of change of the speed error in addition to the error itself.

When load sensing is employed, the regulator can react at once to load change; that is it does not have to delay its action until droop has occurred. With careful design, temporary droop can be reduced significantly and, by the same token, permanent droop can be eliminated.

Other features of modern governors permit start-up and shut-down of prime movers without human intervention apart from pressing buttons. For example, a large and costly alternator set at a power station can be brought into service on the grid quite automatically and in an entirely safe and satisfactory manner, leaving the engineer to monitor the instrumentation and take appropriate action only should abnormal running conditions be revealed.

GRAMOPHONE (clockwork - see also record player

Below : a governor for an electrical generator. This has a motor on top to load the speeder spring, so that speed can be remotely controlled. This is a cutaway view : the unit is normally oil-filled.

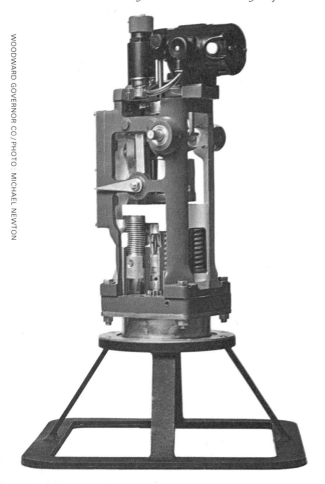

WOODWARD GOVERNOR CO / PHOTO: MICHAEL NEWTON

GRAPHIC DISPLAYS

The object of a computer *graphic display* or a *visual display unit* is to make the transfer of information between the COMPUTER and the user as easy and fast as possible. The majority of graphic displays are based on CATHODE RAY TUBE (crt) systems, but there are other computer graphic devices that are mainly electromechanical, such as plotters and PEN RECORDERS. About 60% of computer terminals sold at present are crt devices, and it is likely that in future most ON-LINE TERMINALS will be of this type.

There are two main categories of crt display: *alphanumeric,* which are by far the most common, and graphic displays. An alphanumeric display shows all the letters of the alphabet, all numbers and a limited number of other symbols. Graphic displays, on the other hand, can also show graphs, diagrams, lines, curves, circles and other geometrical shapes. Screen sizes, measured diagonally, range from about 7 inches (18 cm) on the smaller alphanumeric displays to about 21 inches (53 cm) on the larger graphic displays.

Alphanumeric displays Alphanumeric visual display units are electronic versions of the tele-typewriter form of input-output terminal, and have the advantages of higher writing speeds and noiseless operation. They do, however, have the disadvantage of not producing a printed record or 'hard copy', as they have no printing unit and all the information is displayed on the screen.

When the unit is used for the input of information to the computer, or to ask it a question, the operator 'types' it out on the keyboard, and it appears on the screen so that the operator can check it before pressing a key to enter it into the computer. If an enquiry has been made, the computer will process it and display the answer on the screen. Alphanumeric visual display units are used extensively in such areas as banking and airline seat reservation.

Graphic displays Graphic displays are able to display alphanumeric as well as graphic information, but they are normally used only in applications where diagrams are required. Operator communication can be by several means the most common being by a keyboard used in conjunction with a *light pen* or a *tracking ball*.

The high writing speed of the cathode ray tube enables drawings to be presented very quickly and complete with all the necessary annotations, and the tracker ball or light pen can be used to move all or part of the display picture across the screen in any direction. To enable the user to create new drawings, or to amend or erase parts of a drawing, a small cross (the *tracking cross*) or a spot is displayed on the screen, and moved around under the control of the light pen or tracker ball. The tracking cross can also be moved around by typing in the appropriate x and y co-ordinates on the keyboard, but unless great precision is needed this method is too slow.

Light pens As the picture on the crt screen is produced by scanning the screen at a precise speed in a series of horizontal lines, the computer can calculate the position of any given point on the screen if it is given a signal when the electron beam scans that particular point. This is done by means of a light pen, which consists of a pen-shaped holder containing a PHOTOELECTRIC CELL whose signal is fed to the computer.

When the end of the pen is held against the screen, the photocell detects the short flash of light produced when the electron beam scans past it, and the computer relates this signal to the scanning of the beam to determine the position of the pen.

The tracking cross is generated by a *tracking program* in the

Above: a computer-generated three dimensional graph.

Below: an operator using a light pen on a Russian 'Delta' graphic display, which is connected to the main high speed computer by an 'Elektronika-100' miniature computer.

computer, and the aperture of the light pen is designed so that it can only view a part of the cross at a time. The tracking program moves the cross so that its centre is always aligned with the aperture of the light pen, and so the operator can use the light pen to move the cross around the screen.

There are two methods in which the light pen can be used to produce drawings. In the first of these, the computer displays a grid or matrix of spots on the crt screen. The light pen is used to indicate two of these spots to the computer, and the operator then presses a key on the keyboard and the computer instructs the crt to draw a line between the two spots. By repeating this procedure with the appropriate spots on the screen, a complete drawing can be built up. If a grid of spots is too coarse, a finer grid may be drawn in the area where greater precision is required. Circles and arcs may be drawn by various methods such as by indicating three points, by indicating one point and typing in the required radius on the keyboard, or the ends of an arc and the radius.

In the second method no grid of spots is presented. To draw a line, the light pen is used to move the tracking symbol to indicate each end of the desired line, and the line is drawn when the appropriate keys are depressed. Circles and arcs are drawn in a similar way to that of the first method.

By the use of suitable programs it is possible for the computer to convert a roughly drawn figure into a more precise diagram, and to move a diagram around on the screen to give alternative views and three-dimensional effects.

Tracker balls An alternative method of moving the

tracking cross or spot is by means of a tracker ball, a freely rotating sphere mounted in a socket next to the keyboard of the display unit. The rotation of the ball drives two POTENTIOMETER devices whose settings determine the x and y co-ordinates of the spot. Moving the ball alters the relative settings of the potentiometers and the computer changes the position of the spot accordingly. A 'joystick' type lever control is sometimes used instead of the ball.

Applications Alphanumeric displays are valuable where non-specialist staff must have easy access to information stored in a central computer system. For this reason they are widely used in banking, finance, insurance, stockbroking, and travel and hotel booking agencies.

Graphic displays have many uses in engineering, for example in drawing electronic and integrated circuit diagrams, layouts for petrochemical piping, and many other aspects of computer-aided design. Graphic displays are also useful for presenting difficult character sets, such as Chinese and Arabic, which would be impractical on a purely alphanumeric system.

A permanent record of the images produced on a graphic display screen can be obtained by photographing the screen or by use of videotape recordings. In addition to the scientific and technical applications, this facility has great potential for creative uses, such as producing animated films.

GRAPHITE (see carbon)

GRAVIMETER (see geophysics)

Top right: an IBM 2250 display used by designers at the Pressed Steel Fisher division of British Leyland.

Above right: a computer display of a diseased heart ventricle. This display is part of a medical system developed by NASA.

IBM (UK) LTD

PHOTRI

Below: Cavendish's experiment (1798) to determine the gravitational constant G by measuring the attraction between sets of lead balls. Cavendish placed his experiment in a draught-free room in his garden using a telescope to view the end of the beam.

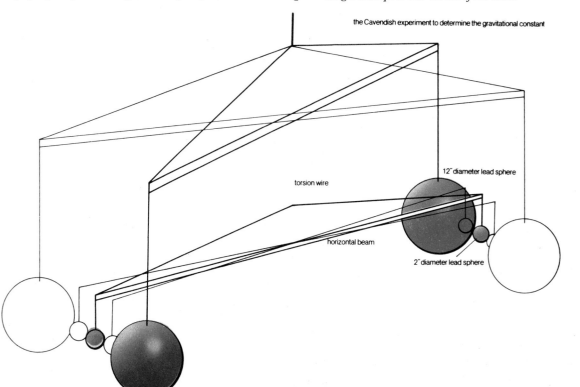

OSBORNE / MARKS

the Cavendish experiment to determine the gravitational constant

12″ diameter lead sphere

torsion wire

horizontal beam

2″ diameter lead sphere

GRAVITATION

We are accustomed to the idea that the force which causes objects to fall to the ground (and which we call gravity) is also the force which keeps the planets moving round the Sun, but this fact was not realized until the 17th century. The ancient Greeks thought that solid bodies fall because they are seeking their natural place (under the 'lighter elements' water, air and fire), while the planets are moved by invisible crystalline spheres. Even Johannes KEPLER, who proved in 1609 that the planets' orbits are ellipses around the Sun, thought that they must be moved by motions in the ETHER.

It was Isaac NEWTON who first realized that the planets would naturally move in ellipses if there was an attractive force between the Sun and the planets which depended on the product of the masses of the two bodies divided by the *square* of the distance between them. He showed that it was the same force which attracts an apple towards the Earth, by comparing the force on the apple with the force needed to keep the Moon in orbit about the Earth. Since the distances from the centre of the Earth to the apple, and to the Moon, were known he could demonstrate that these forces also depended on the inverse square of the distance—that is, the force decreases as the square of the distance *increases*.

Measuring gravity The force of gravity is actually extremely weak (see FIELDS), and it is only because the Earth

Below: this apparatus to detect gravity waves monitors the position of a massive aluminium cylinder, normally in a vacuum. Claims that gravity waves have been detected have not been confirmed.

is so massive that its gravitational effects are obvious. The attractive force between two 20 kg (44 lb) objects 30 cm (1 ft) apart is only the same as the weight of one thirty-thousandth of a gramme (one millionth of an ounce) on Earth. The first measurement of gravitational force between two bodies of known mass was made by Henry CAVENDISH in 1798.

His apparatus consisted of two 2 inch (5 cm) diameter lead balls (each weighing 1.7 lb, 0.75 kg) hung from the ends of a six foot (2 m) long deal beam, which was supported at the centre by a long wire allowing the beam to swing horizontally. Two 12 inch (30 cm) diameter lead balls (each weighing one sixth of a ton) were placed near the small balls on opposite sides, so that the gravitational attraction between each pair of large and small balls caused the beam carrying the latter to swing towards the large balls. The 12 inch balls were then moved to the other side of the small balls, making the beam swing the other way. The total swing measured at the end of the beam was 3/10 inch (8.5 mm), and from this Cavendish calculated the force between the lead balls. He expressed his results as the gravitational force between two 1 kg masses 1 metre apart, a quantity usually called G. Cavendish's value for G was the best for almost a century, and is within one per cent of the best modern value (0.00000000006673 newton, that is 6.673×10^{-11} newton).

Newton's gravitational theory also predicted that all objects at the same place will fall equally fast towards the centre of the Earth. The ancient Greeks, in particular Aristotle, had maintained that heavy bodies always fall faster than lighter ones, but in 1590 Galileo disproved this hypothesis. According

to the legend he dropped two objects of different mass from the Leaning Tower of Pisa, and they hit the ground simultaneously. There is actually a very slight difference in acceleration between light and massive bodies, but the Earth is so much larger that this is unnoticeable.

Variations in gravity The acceleration due to gravity at any place is called 'g', and is about 32 feet per second per second (9.8 m/s²). It changes slightly according to the altitude and latitude of place where it is measured. The Earth acts gravitationally as if all its mass were concentrated at the centre. It is not a perfect sphere, so a change in either altitude or latitude means a change in the distance from the centre of the Earth, and thus a change in the gravitational force (according to the inverse square law). At a height of 100,000 feet (30,000 m) 'g' is 99% of its value at sea level. Even at the altitude of an orbiting spacecraft, about 200 miles (320 km), the gravitational force is still only 10% less than at the surface.

But the spacecraft is given sufficient orbital velocity that CENTRIFUGAL FORCE exactly balances that due to gravity, and the astronauts experience weightlessness.

Einstein's General Theory of RELATIVITY (1915) introduced a new theory of gravity, which for everyday purposes is the same as Newton's, but it explained a puzzling discrepancy in the motion of the planet Mercury. Einstein's theory also predicted that light as well as matter is affected by gravity, and astronomical observations have proved that this effect does occur. Other predictions of the theory, such as the existence in space of 'black holes' (in which the gravitational field is so strong that light cannot escape) and gravitational radiation (in some ways similar to ELECTROMAGNETIC RADIATION) are still being investigated by astronomers. Another, more recent, theory, suggests that the value of G may change very slowly over the duration of the Universe, thus accounting for some of its large scale properties such as its apparent expansion.

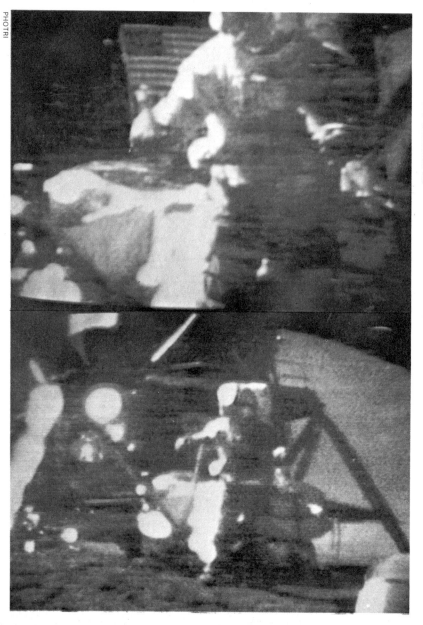

Left: TV demonstration from the Moon's surface by David Scott of Apollo 15. A hammer and a feather, dropped together, fell at the same rate in the airless conditions of the lunar terrain.

GRAVURE PRINTING

Gravure is one of the major commercial printing processes and can be used successfully on papers of qualities ranging from newsprint to fine art. It is used mainly for printing magazines and packaging, but other applications include the production of decorative laminates such as wood grain effects, floor tiles, wallpapers, postage and trading stamps, and fine art reproductions.

In LETTERPRESS PRINTING, ink is transferred to the paper from a raised image; while in LITHOGRAPHY, although the printing surface is all flat, the image area is defined by a water repellent ink allowing the non-image areas to be coated with a film of water which prevents the printing ink from contacting the surface of the plate. Gravure, however, is an *intaglio* process, that is the ink is transferred to the paper from very small *cells* which are recessed into the printing cylinder. Other intaglio processes include ENGRAVING and ETCHING.

In the proofing and revision department a colour proof, which is a sample copy of the page to be printed, is examined for any defects. Where these are found, such as a whitish patch due to some cells not having been etched deeply enough, the cells are located on the copper cylinder and cut deeper, using an engraving tool.

Because the cell depths (and in some processes, the cross-sectional area) can be varied, different amounts of ink may be transferred at different points, allowing subtle variations of tone such as are seen on a single colour postage stamp. The depth of a gravure cell may vary from about 0.001 mm in the highlight areas, to 0.4 mm in the shadows.

Cell structure There are three main types of cell structure, depending on whether the surface is prepared by *conventional gravure, invert halftone* or *electromechanical engraving* methods. In conventional gravure the image is broken up into tiny square cells all of the same area but varying in depth. Invert halftone processes are characterized by varying cell cross-sectional areas; depths may either be kept constant or also varied. This is particularly useful for colour reproduction. In electromechanical engraving, signals from a scanning head, which is moved systematically across the photographic subject to be reproduced, are used to control the movement of a diamond stylus engraving head which cuts out cells in the shape of inverted pyramids with varying depths and areas.

Cylinder preparation Gravure printing surfaces are normally made of highly polished copper, which is often deposited as a thin skin by ELECTROPLATING on to solid steel cylinders. For hard wear on especially long runs this may be chromium faced. Initially the material to be printed must be photographed to provide negatives of high contrast for line work such as text, but only medium contrast for continuous tones as encountered, for example, in a photograph of a scene. If necessary the negative may be retouched to improve the quality of the final job. As in all colour REPRODUCTION IN PRINTING, three photographic separations are taken through three separate colour filters.

Positives and not negatives of both pictures and text are used for producing the image on the cylinders or plates. To do this *carbon tissue* is used, which is a light-sensitized paper coated with a mixture of pigment and gelatin. The carbon tissue is first *screened*, to divide the printing area into small cells, by covering it with a gravure screen (composed of tiny opaque squares surrounded by clear lines) and by exposing it to light in a contact vacuum frame. The ruling of the screen is usually 60 lines per centimetre (giving 3600 cells per square centimetre), but may be up to 160 lines per cm. These rules provide the thin walls of the cells. Next the positives, mounted on a glass plate and in contact with the tissue, are exposed to diffused light. Where the tones are lighter the light passes through the positive freely and the gelatin on the carbon tissue becomes harder than where light reaches it weakly, from darker areas of the positive, while the screened lines remain the hardest.

Now the carbon tissue is ready to be mounted on to the cylinder. After mounting, the backing paper is removed and the cylinder developed in warm water to wash away any soluble (unhardened) gelatin, leaving the hardened gelatin *resist*. This process is followed by drying and the painting out, with a bitumen base varnish, of any areas such as edges to be protected from etchant. Ferric chloride is used for etching and first penetrates the gelatin in the thinnest areas where the printed tones will be darkest, and lastly the highlights where the gelatin is thickest. Etching times vary from ten to twenty minutes and various factors must be controlled, such as the strength of the ferric chloride solution and the temperature of the bath. After etching is completed, the bitumen varnish and any residual gelatin are removed and the cylinder or plate washed and dried. It is now ready for *proofing*, which means printing a sample page. If necessary limited corrections, for example increasing the depth of cells, are made by hand in the revision department.

Gravure printing The cylinder is now mounted in the printing machine. Sheet-fed plate machines handle single sheets of paper and are used mainly for high quality colour reproduction, particularly of fine art work. Reel or web-fed presses require a continuous band of paper and are used for long run colour work to high standards of quality. They are predominantly used in the magazine and colour catalogue field, for postage stamps and for printing on non-absorbent packaging materials such as film and aluminium foil.

On sheet-fed presses the ink is transferred from the ink reservoir by a fountain roller which floods the plate with ink, while on reel or web-fed processes the cylinder may revolve in an ink trough. In both cases the excess ink is removed from the metal surface by a steel *doctor blade*. Because the ink must flow in and out of the minute cells, gravure INKS are thinner than those used in letterpress and lithographic printing and consist of finely dispersed mixtures of pigment, resin and solvent. After transfer to the printing paper or other material, the solvent evaporates, leaving a solid ink film. Some form of drying system is included on most gravure presses to accelerate the evaporation of the solvent. This is particularly important with high speed work. The ink is circulated by pumps to prevent the formation of a skin and to counteract the tendency of some pigments to settle out. A large volume of ink is circulated to reduce the need for constant adjustment of the viscosity by the addition of solvent.

In web-fed presses the printing paper passes at high speed between the copper cylinder and a rubber roller to which pressure is applied by an impression cylinder. A large rotary gravure press comprises a number of adjacent units each printing one colour, so for four colour printing (normal colour printing is done in cyan, magenta, yellow and black) on each side of the web eight units would be needed. At the end of the press is a large unit where the web is cut, folded, collated and stitched or stapled to form the completed magazine. Nowadays there are rotary gravure presses capable of producing 55,000 copies per hour of a 48 page, four colour magazine.

Below: here a printing cylinder, which has been chromium plated for long service, is furnished with ink on one unit of a rotary gravure web-fed press. The surface is wiped clean by the doctor blade, leaving ink only in the cells. The web of paper, travelling at speed, comes into contact with the cylinder and the ink is transferred to the paper before it passes to another coloured ink in the next unit.

Top near right: a photomicrograph shows the cells in detail. These are etched to different depths depending on the areas of light and shade in the original photographic material to be reproduced.

Top far right: the copper plated printing cylinder revolves slowly in the etching bath, operating conditions being carefully controlled to provide the correct depth of cells to produce a full range of tones.

Bottom near right: conventional gravure. A positive is photographed on to screened carbon and light hardens the gel to the correct tonal values. The image is etched on the copper through the pores in the gel.
Bottom far right: electroengraved gravure. The image is monitored on a scanning cylinder, the signal monitoring the engraving head which moves in synchro with the scanning head.

conventional gravure

electro-engraved gravure

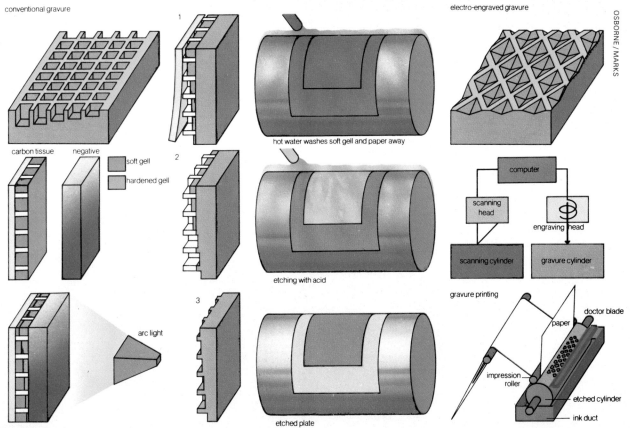

carbon tissue   negative

soft gell
hardened gell

hot water washes soft gell and paper away

etching with acid

arc light

etched plate

computer

scanning head

engraving head

scanning cylinder   gravure cylinder

gravure printing

doctor blade

paper

impression roller

etched cylinder

ink duct

GREEK FIRE

Incendiary devices had been used in warfare for well over two thousand years before the appearance of Greek Fire in the seventh century AD. Such incendiaries had been deployed by the Assyrian and Persian armies, for example, and generally consisted of some form of flammable material—pitch, tow, or naphtha—placed in pots and hurled at the enemy, rather like a Molotov Cocktail. But Greek Fire, which consisted of a stream of burning oil projected under pressure (not unlike a modern FLAME THROWER), was a great improvement on these and was regarded with considerable fear by those who did not possess its secret. It was developed by the Byzantine Empire, the mediaeval successor to the Eastern Roman Empire, and was used both on land and sea.

Although many historians and scientists have attempted to discover the secret of Greek Fire, the search has been hampered by the probably misguided mediaeval opinion that the secret lay in its chemical composition. It is clear that the great majority of Byzantines themselves did not know how the device really worked, and for good reason, since it was a carefully guarded state secret.

The device used The mediaeval sources themselves describe three main parts for the device: a pump, a swivel tube and a brazier. It is known that the material projected was crude oil, obtained from areas to the north east of the Black Sea. This crude oil may or may not have been distilled, for very little is known about the art of DISTILLATION before the thirteenth century; although a twelfth century Arab source states that the Byzantines were famed for their skill at 'cooking' oil. Whatever the case, the principle upon which the device worked, must have been that of preheating the oil, which was placed in an air-tight bronze container. This would have reduced the viscosity of the oil (made it thinner) and increased its volatility. When sufficient pressure had been built up, both by heating the oil and by using the pump, a valve or tap was opened, and the oil was forced out under great pressure through the swivel tube, at the end of which it was ignited.

The heating device, or brazier, consisted not of an open wood fire (rather dangerous on a ship) but of a 'slow match' of smouldering linen, which was brought rapidly up to the required temperature by the use of a bellows. Clearly, this method posed some danger, for heating the oil causes the pressure inside the container to rise, and over-heating could cause an explosion. But it is made clear in the sources that the operator was a skilled man, who presumably learned to judge correctly the amount of pressure required.

Whatever the exact details of the device, it seems certain that the Greek Fire projector worked along these lines, and can be seen therefore as an early flame thrower, which projected burning oil on to enemy vessels or personnel with great force. The discovery of the principle of preheating is quite a significant development, although it seems to have been lost again during the later mediaeval period. It was rediscovered in another form in the nineteenth century, with the development of the blowtorch and the Primus stove.

Below: an illustration of Greek Fire taken from a Byzantine manuscript of the tenth century. The swivel tube can clearly be seen in the illustration and it is apparent that the burning material is being ejected with some force.

GRENADE

A grenade is a small anti-personnel bomb filled with high EXPLOSIVE and used in close range warfare. In the early days of their use grenades took the form of spherical shells filled with large grains of black powder and resembled pomegranates with their seeds, hence the derivation of their name from the Spanish word *granada* meaning pomegranate. In the 17th century each infantry company of the British army included five grenadiers, soldiers armed with grenades.

After about 1750 the grenade began to go out of favour although it was successfully used in many sieges, notably during the Napoleonic Wars and in the Crimean campaign. But later, grenades such as the Mills bomb were extensively used in World War 1 both by the German and the allied armies. During and after World War 1 many improvements were made and the grenade diversified considerably, being launched from rifles, specially designed weapons and even spring operated guns. Modern grenades can be projected to considerable ranges and can be constructed to produce anti-personnel fragments, to penetrate armour plate, to generate smoke or tear gas, or to fire signal and illuminating flares.

Construction

Early grenades of the 14th and 15th centuries were made of bark, glass, clay or earthenware filled with black powder, and were set off by a fuze of corned powder in a quill or a thin tube of rolled metal. Obviously intended to produce an incendiary effect rather than a blast, they were not lethal, and grenades having spherical or cylindrical metal bodies soon succeeded them.

Field use of these grenades tended to be rather dangerous because the fuzes were unreliable, the powder burning

Above: three types of non-lethal grenade. On the left is a smoke grenade which very rapidly produces a local smoke screen, in the centre is a riot control grenade which emits an irritant gas for about 25 seconds, and on the right is a signal grenade which produces red, green, blue or yellow smoke for 25 to 45 seconds.

Below left: a grenadier of the British army Foot Guards of 1745 carrying a grenade and a lighted match to ignite the fuze.

Below: cutaway of a Mills hand grenade. The firing pin is held up by the striking lever. If the safety pin is removed the lever flies free, the spring is released and the firing pin hits the detonator cap. The detonator fuze is activated and ignites the explosive.

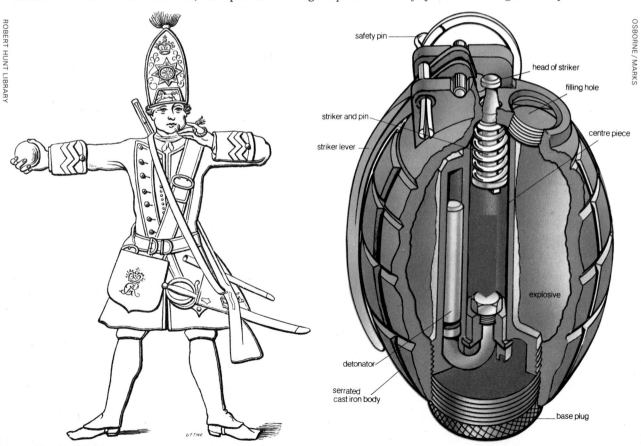

sporadically and sometimes flashing through to the main filling with disastrous consequences for the thrower. It was not until the early 1900s that more consistent fuzes were produced, though the problem of fixing the burning time remained: if it was too long the enemy could throw back the grenade before it went off, and if it was too short the grenade could kill the thrower. Fuzes designed to function on impact were slow to perfect, mainly because of the difficulty of making the grenade land nose-first; so handles with trailing tapes were fitted to ensure a proper strike. Arming these fuzes, that is changing their state from safe to live, was effected in flight by means of vanes, propellers, springs and inertia sleeves.

Modern anti-personnel grenades comprise three main parts: a pyrotechnic fuze and detonator initiated by the action of a spring-loaded striker on a percussion cap and giving about 5 seconds delay; a filling of high explosive; and a fragmenting case made of wire or engraved steel. As they weigh between 140 and 500 grammes (4.9 to 17.6 oz) they can be thrown to about 30 metres or yards, or projected from a rifle to approximately 400 metres. Similar ignition and projection systems are used on smoke, tear gas and signal grenades, but the appropriate filling is usually contained in a simple tinplate body. Anti-tank grenades generally have a shaped charge filling designed to achieve penetration of armour.

GROUND-CONTROLLED APPROACH (see avionics)

GUANO INDUSTRY (see fertilizer)

GUERICKE, Otto von (1602–1686)

Otto von Guericke, German physicist and engineer, is best known for his invention of the air pump, and for his experiments on the vacuum; but science for Guericke was always a leisuretime activity. Destined from the start to be a politician, his education, at the Universities of Leipzig, Helmstedt and Jena, was mainly in law. He continued these studies at Leiden, but there he also attended lectures of mathematics and engineering.

After his studies, Guericke returned to his native town of Magdeburg and became an alderman of the city in 1626. Guericke played an increasingly important role in civic affairs, but he was forced to leave the town after its nearly complete destruction in May 1631, during the Thirty Years' War. He then successively became the official engineer in Brunswick, in Erfurt, and for the electorate of Saxony.

Guericke later returned to Magdeburg and again became absorbed in local politics. During the period 1646–76, he served as mayor of Magdeburg. In 1666, in recognition of his services to the community, he was raised to the ranks of the nobility, and he was given the title 'von' Guericke.

Guericke began his scientific experiments only in 1646, but current arguments about the nature of space and the possibility of obtaining a vacuum had been preoccupying him for some time. There were two theories in vogue: the first, based largely on metaphysical arguments, and held strongly by the seventeenth century French philosopher Descartes asserted that a vacuum is totally impossible and that space is perpetually filled with matter; the second, based on a growing understanding of atmospheric pressure and on experiments carried out by GALILEO, TORRICELLI and others, claimed that a vacuum could exist.

Guericke attempted to resolve the dispute experimentally. First he tried to pump water from a well caulked (sealed) beer barrel using a suction pump, but he found that air leaked in.

He then attempted to pump air directly from a hollow copper sphere, with the result that the sphere caved in and collapsed, thus supporting the idea of the impossibility of forming a vacuum. Not yet satisfied, Guericke devised his own air pump and repeated the experiment, this time succeeding in producing at least a partial vacuum. It was this pump which was improved by BOYLE and used in his famous experiments. In 1657 Guericke first performed the well known Magdeburg experiment, where two large copper hemispheres were fitted together, and the air between them pumped out. Two teams of horses, one attached to each hemisphere, could not pull them apart. This, and other public demonstrations, were made at Magdeburg, Berlin and Regensburg.

Although famous for his experiments on the vacuum, Guericke was interested in a total explanation of the physical universe and its phenomena. In particular he felt that magnetic force might in some way explain the motions of the planets. In an attempt to simulate, on a small scale, the planet Earth and its magnetic properties, he made a sphere of sulphur and, by rubbing it, produced static electricity and noticed its attractive power. He did not, however, clearly distinguish between electrical and magnetic effects.

In 1681 Guericke left Magdeburg, this time to escape the plague. He retired to Hamburg, where he spent the remaining five years of his life.

GUIDED MISSILES (see missiles)

Left: an engraving of Guericke from his 'Experimenta Nova', 1672. In Guericke's famous Magdeburg experiment (below) to demonstrate the power of a vacuum, a team of horses was attached to each half of an evacuated hollow sphere, but they could not separate the two halves.

THE BETTMAN ARCHIVE

GUITAR

The guitar is a member of the fretted instrument family in which the pitch of the strings is altered by pressing them down behind 'frets', which are metal strips attached to the fingerboard. Other members of the same family include the banjo, mandoline, bazouki, balalaika and ukulele. Guitars of whatever type—classic, flamenco, plectrum, acoustic, 12-string, Hawaiian or electric—are all descendants of the instrument which evolved over the centuries, mainly in Spain.

History Among the earliest evidence of the guitar is the illustration of the 'guitarra latina' in the 'Cantigas of Alfonso the Wise' (Spain, about 1270 AD). This is a true guitar; that is, it has a body with incurved sides and a longish neck fitted with frets, carrying 4 strings attached to a bridge fixed to the lower part of the soundboard, which is pierced by a single central soundhole.

Where the ancestor of this guitar came from is still uncertain, due to lack of reliable research, but a Hittite carving (about 1350 BC) depicts an instrument with strong guitar characteristics. Later Persian ceramics show another guitar-like instrument, the Târ, and it is possible it spread as far as the Pillars of Hercules (Straits of Gibraltar) in ancient times and became established in the Iberian peninsula. Even the name of the 4-string Târ, 'chartâr', could have become 'guitarra' in Spanish, particularly since the first guitar of which there is evidence was a 4-string guitar.

In his 'Declaración de Instrumentos' (1555 AD) Fray Bermudo states that the guitar had 4 strings tuned G D g b (capitals are used for the bass strings, and small letters for the treble strings) for playing 'popular music' or A D g b (the middle 4 strings of the modern guitar) for 'serious and composed music'. By 1586, when Juan Carlos y Amat wrote his method for the 'Guitarra Espagnola' it had acquired another string, the first (top) e string, of today's guitar. At the end of the 18th century the sixth (bass E) had become a permanent addition and E A D g b e was established as the standard tuning for the guitar.

Until this time the guitar had been strung with pairs of strings, a custom that has survived on some versions of the guitar in Latin America (and on the mandoline). In fact the popular modern 12-string guitar is almost certainly derived from a large double-strung guitar popular in Mexico. However, single strings were generally adopted around the end of the 18th century, the top three being of gut and the lower three of silk floss covered with a winding of silver or copper wire. Nowadays the three treble strings are of extruded nylon and the basses, of wire-covered nylon floss.

Later development The early years of the 19th century saw a great upsurge of popularity for the guitar throughout Europe and virtuoso guitarist-composers such as Fernando Sór, Dionisio Aguado (both from Spain), Carruli, Carcassi, Giuliani, Molino (from Italy) and Napoleon Coste (Corsica), became the objects of critical acclaim and popular esteem. This fashion for the guitar created a great demand for instruments which was met by fine luthiers (builders) such as Lacote and Grobert (Paris), Stauffer (Vienna) and Panormo (London). Run-of-the-mill guitars could be bought for as little as 7s 6d (then $1.50) but a Panormo guitar 'in the Spanish Style cost from '2 to 15 gns' (then $8.40 to $63.00).

In the 1860s and 1870s, however, the guitar began to wane in popularity as the big sound of the pianoforte and the large orchestra caught the public fancy. In 1833 a German guitar maker, Christian Friedrich Martin, emigrated to the USA and set up a workshop in New York, later moving to Nazareth, Pennsylvania, where C F Martin and Co continue to make fine guitars.

In 1921 the Martin Co produced larger, sturdier instruments to be strung with steel strings and played with a plectrum. These instruments, like those made by other North American makers, were still based on the old Spanish guitar, but a few years later the Gibson Company started to produce large steel-strung guitars with arched fronts and backs carved from solid wood, which became known as 'cello guitars and which produced a crisper, more penetrating sound suitable for use in jazz and in dance-bands. During the 1930s magnetic pickups were fitted beneath the strings of 'cello guitars, thus producing the electric guitar and paving the way for the modern solid and semi-solid instruments.

The classical guitar

In the meantime things had been happening to the guitar in Spain where in 1850 a guitar maker, Antonio Torres, egged on by the guitarist Julian Arcas, evolved a fuller bodied, more powerful yet still refined guitar which became the prototype for all modern classic guitars. An additional advance came from the guitarist Francisco Tarrega who advised a new rational technique which allowed the player to exploit the improved qualities of the Torres model guitar and which became the basis of modern guitar technique.

In the year that Tarrega died (1909) the sixteen year old Andrés Segovia gave his first public performance. Through his artistry, the strength of his personality and a burning desire to advance the guitar, he was largely responsible for the new renaissance of the classic guitar and its full acceptance as a serious instrument in the world of music.

Electric and acoustic guitars

Parallel to the post World War 2 revival of the Spanish and classic guitar, has been the growing popularity of other forms of the guitar such as the electric guitar in the jazz, rock and pop scenes and the flat-top acoustic guitar which has become the folk and blues instrument par excellence, whether single or double-strung.

Basically there are only two types of guitar, acoustic and electric. The sound of the electric guitar is produced by the string vibrating above coil and magnet. The string must be steel or some other suitable magnetic material and under each is positioned a small permanent magnet surrounded by a coil of wire (the PICKUP). As the string moves (vibrates) the surrounding magnetic field is distorted, which induces a voltage in the coil (see ELECTROMAGNETISM). The resulting electrical signals are fed into an electronic AMPLIFIER where they are converted into sound. The body of the electric guitar plays little or no part in the quality or quantity of the sound. Volume and tone controls are used to regulate the power and quality of the sound which comes from a speaker (or speakers) linked to the amplifier.

The acoustic guitar, classic, folk-blues or 'cello built all rely on the vibrations of the strings passing via the bridge

Below left: a six stringed Persian Tàr, probably the ancestor of the guitar. Its guitarlike characteristics include the waisted body, fretted neck and low-set bridge. But it has a parchment front like a banjo instead of a wooden soundboard.

Below: the mandoline (left) and lute (right) are older, round backed instruments.

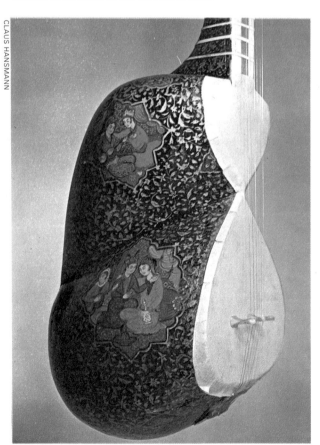

CLAUS HANSMANN

The design of the classical guitar has been intuitively and sensitively evolved over the centuries, producing an extremely versatile instrument with a unique range of beautiful contrasting sounds. Usually spruce is used for the sound table, rosewood for the back and sides with an ebony fingerboard and cedar for the neck.

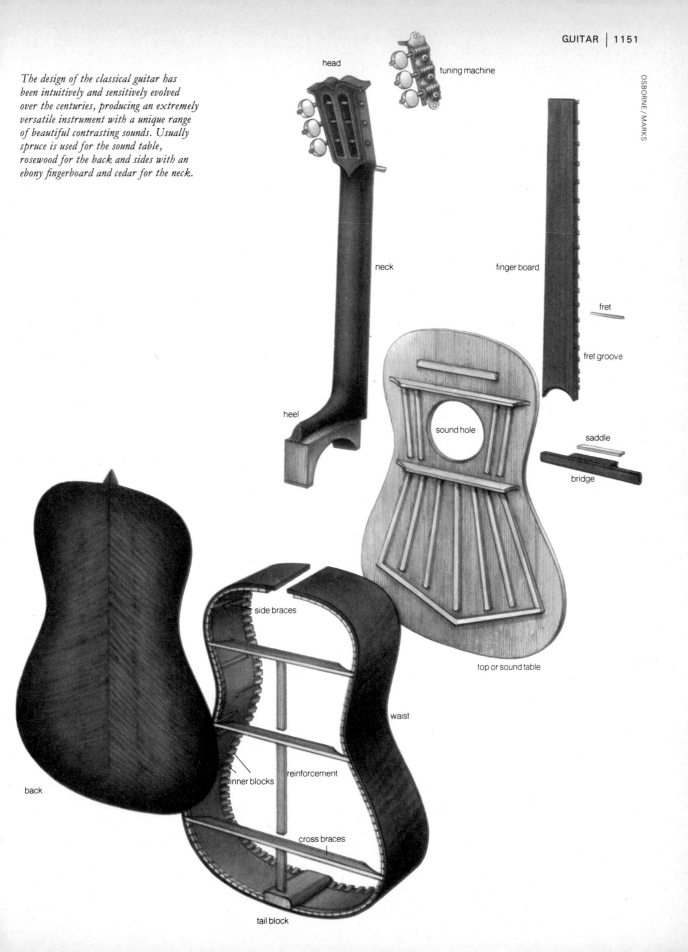

head

tuning machine

neck

finger board

fret

fret groove

heel

sound hole

saddle

bridge

top or sound table

side braces

waist

back

inner blocks

reinforcement

cross braces

tail block

into the soundboard which is then set in motion. The sound produced is amplified by the sound-box. The shape, size, and construction of the body (soundboard and back and sides) determine the quantity and quality of the sound.

Construction Antonio Torres was followed by a group of Spanish guitar makers who established firmly the principles which were gradually adopted by non-Spanish luthiers, most noted of whom was the German maker, the late Hermann Hauser. Nowadays there are fine guitar makers in various countries throughout the world. Every maker has his own version of the Torres design but they all remain close enough to the original to see from whom the tradition stems.

The basic idea behind this design is that the system of fan-strutting beneath the soundboard allows it to vibrate as fully as possible while still maintaining and supporting it. Torres was not a scientist or an engineer. He was a fine craftsman who understood wood and was devoted to making excellent guitars and it must be admitted that the best guitars have been made by craftsmen who have sensed intuitively what was needed to be done with every individual piece of wood.

Attempts have been made to assess scientifically the resonant qualities of woods with a view to improving the guitar but the

Below: three of the principal types of guitar. On the left, a Spanish or classical guitar; centre, a 'cello guitar with arched front and back and f-holes instead of a central soundhole; and right, a Dobro, with metal inserts that give it a resonant, metallic sound favoured by blues singers.

best instruments are still made of the woods which tradition has proved to be best, namely spruce for the soundboard, rosewood for the back and sides, ebony for the fingerboard and Cuban cedar for the neck. The bridge is usually of rosewood. Other woods such as maple, sycamore, algarrobo and walnut are suitable for back and sides but rosewood remains the first choice.

The Flamenco guitar has cypress for the back and sides, a light brittle wood which contributes to the bright tone required by a Flamenco player. Ideally wood for guitar construction, especially the spruce for the soundboard, should be quarter cut, that is, cut from the trunk like slices of a cake, so that the annual rings pass through the wood at right angles. Flat-top acoustic, steel-strung guitars have soundboards of spruce and backs and sides of rosewood or mahogany. The strutting of the soundboard is simpler and sturdier than on a classic guitar. The best 'cello guitars have soundboards carved from spruce and backs and sides of maple. Instead of a soundhole they usually have f-holes like a violin and two longitudinal struts, one on the bass and one on the treble side of the soundboard.

The Hawaiian guitar differs from other guitars. It is played resting flat across the knees, soundboard uppermost, and the pitch of the strings is changed by sliding a round or flat piece of metal, 'the steel', up or down the fingerboard producing, incidentally, the wailing sound typical of the Hawaiian guitar. The right hand fingers are equipped with metal or plastic finger-picks. Various tunings are used which allow chords to be played by simply placing the steel at right angles or diagonally across the strings. A sophisticated version of the Hawaiian guitar is the 'pedal guitar', an important component of the Country and Western group on which various tunings can be selected by the use of a pedal.

In recent years, rock, pop, and folk guitarists have got into the habit of employing different tunings which facilitate special harmonic sequences or personal, or traditional styles. It has always been customary to retune the sixth string to D and sometimes the fifth to G on the classic guitar, but generally speaking the traditional tuning remains the most useful and characteristic.

With the exception of Spain and Latin America, where the guitar has always been the popular folk instrument, it has tended to be an instrument of fashion which has resulted in its development being spasmodic. Today it is enjoying an unprecedented boom and it remains to be seen whether it has achieved a permanent position in the world of music in general.

Below: the use of holographic techniques allows the pattern of vibrations in the soundboard of a guitar to be seen as dark and light bands. This guitar was sounding a note at a pitch of 254 Hz, just below a standard Middle C, which is 261 Hz.

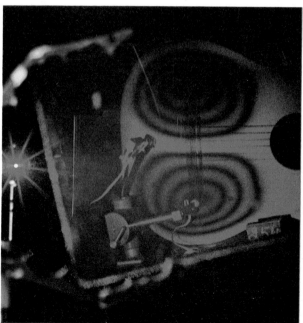

ZEFA

GUN

The term 'gun' in its broadest sense means a projectile-firing instrument where the propellant charge is explosive rather than mechanical. It thus encompasses instruments from the vast CANNON once used to defend fortresses to the smallest pocket PISTOLS. In its more specialist use 'gun' means a smooth bored longarm, that is a firearm intended to be held with both hands and having a barrel whose interior surface, or bore, is without rifling grooves; the most common example is a SHOTGUN. Since most of the individual types of gun will be discussed separately, this article is concerned with the overall development of projectile-firing instruments using an EXPLOSIVE (gunpowder) as propellant.

Guns seem to have appeared first in China about 1250 AD, in a form fired by one or both hands. The projectiles fired from many of these early guns took the form of arrows instead of the more familiar ball or bullet. Larger guns, or cannon, were definitely known in Europe in 1326, and there is some evidence for earlier use of firearms in Europe. From the second quarter of the 14th century there are frequent references to the use of artillery in various forms and sizes, and longarms approaching modern style, that is a barrel attached to a stock intended to be held under the arm or against the chest, are known from literary references dating back to the 1340s. The term 'handgunnes' does not appear for another forty years, and when it does it hardly describes what would today be accepted as a handgun; they could, however, be held in one hand and were favoured by mounted men since the other hand could be used in controlling the horse. FIRING MECHANISMS do not appear until about 1400, and it is because of refinements in these that guns gradually developed into the forms in which we know them.

The role of the gun in warfare did not become significant until the 17th century, although in various forms it had replaced earlier weapons such as the LONGBOW and CROSSBOW during the previous two centuries. Cannon were still largely ineffective against large fortifications, and naval battles were still fought on the basis of boarding the enemy ships, although cannon had been carried at sea in great variety (including breech loaders) since the 15th century. Land battles were, until the Thirty Years' War (1618–48), decided largely on the success of the pikes of the infantry and the lances and swords of the cavalry. Indeed, until the successful development of the metallic cartridge REVOLVER and CARBINE in the third quarter of the 19th century, guns were never held to be a principal weapon of cavalry. When the musket replaced the pike as the principal weapon of the infantry during the 17th century, the bayonet rapidly appeared, to render the musket technically an 'exploding pike', a concept which underwent little fundamental change until the 19th century.

The pistol as a practical handgun became prominent in the 1500s with the development of the self-contained *wheellock* mechanism, and was in extensive use for sporting purposes until the end of the 18th century. The *flintlock* mechanism succeeded the wheellock in the middle of the 17th century.

Multi-shot guns, in all forms from cannon to pocket pistols, were made during all ages since the first appearance of guns. Their practical limitations were dictated largely by the design of the firing mechanism in use at the time, and by the inability to establish an effective gas-seal between one charge and the next. Guns with more than one barrel, revolving barrels, and single barrels with several charges placed one above the other and fired successively either by several locks or by a moving lock, all were tried, certainly as early as the 16th century, but only multi-barrelled guns, particularly pistols, enjoyed much popularity. The double-barrelled sporting gun so popular today, appeared in England about the middle of the 18th century as a flintlock, but did not become typical of sporting guns until the development of the relatively simple *percussion*

FIG. 5.—SECTIONAL PLAN OF FRENCH MITRAILLEUSE.
(WITH THE CARTRIDGES IN THE BARRELS AND THE CLOSER SCREWED HOME).

Above left: a three-barrelled mediaeval handgun. It was mounted on the end of a wooden stock; each barrel was loaded and fired separately by setting a match to the hole.

Below left, top: a cutaway view of a French machine gun used in the Franco-Prussian war of 1870, showing seven barrels loaded and with the breech screwed shut. Below: The American Gatling gun of the late nineteenth century.

Above: the biggest cannon in the world, as of 1903. The production of bigger and bigger guns before World War I amounted to an arms race which contributed directly to the outbreak of that war.

Below: 15 inch naval guns from 'Royal Sovereign' class battle ships used in both world wars. They fired shells weighing a ton.

lock in the 1820s made it more practical.

As with multi-shot guns, breech loaders were made from the earliest days of firearms, breech loading cannon being particularly in evidence. But for exactly the same reasons as those given for the multi-shot guns, breech loaders achieved no widespread success until developments in the firing mechanisms made it possible to construct a safe and powerful gun. This did not occur until the centre-fire metallic cartridge was successfully produced in England and America in the 1860s. From this date the breech-loading gun in all forms developed rapidly, and repeating arms in a bewildering variety appeared over the next forty years. Repeating RIFLES were adopted by almost all military powers during the 1880s and 1890s, and the introduction of a new form of gunpowder, which left almost no residue in the barrel and developed far higher velocities than the original type black-powder, made the repeating and semi-automatic firearm a practical reality. MACHINE GUNS came first, in the 1890s, and by the time of World War I successful experiments had been made with semi-automatic rifles, firing and automatically reloading ready for the next shot with each press of the trigger. Fully automatic rifles appeared in the 1920s along with the sub-machine gun, but not until after World War 2 did the former achieve general adoption by the world's armed forces. The success of such a large variety of semi and fully automatic guns, including an electrically operated aircraft cannon, is based almost entirely upon the production of precision metallic cartridge AMMUNITION, without which most of these intricate designs would not function correctly. In contrast, guns for sporting purposes have changed very little since the 1890s. (See also AUTOMATIC PISTOL, FIELD GUN and ANTI-AIRCRAFT GUN).

GUNNERY TECHNIQUES

The history of gunnery goes back to the early 14th century. Early GUNS were called *vasi* or *pots-de-fer* and they were in fairly general use in Europe by 1350. Gunpowder was placed in a vase shaped receptacle; an arrow, with leather wrapped round its stock, was stuffed into the neck of the vase and then the powder was fired by means of a hot iron applied to a touch hole. This method was used with minor improvements for the next 500 years or so.

As with the gun itself, the technique of gunnery developed very slowly after the initial impetus of the invention had slackened. In 1537 an Italian, Nicolo Tartaglia, published a treatise on the subject of gunnery. His diagram of ballistics (the study of projectiles) shows 'the visual line', which is our present line of sight (an imaginary straight line drawn from the gun to the target), and what he called 'the way of the pellet' is what we would describe as the trajectory of the projectile.

Ballistics Clearly, gunners of Tartaglia's period had already learnt that a projectile tends to follow a curved path in flight, although they may not have known that this effect is caused by gravity and the resistance of the air. It is not enough to point the barrel of the gun straight at the target in order to hit it. That technique would work only if the target were very close and the forces of gravity and air resistance had not had time to take effect. If it were further away the projectile would tend to drop short and the gun would therefore have to be elevated above the line of sight to an angle sufficient for the path of the projectile to reach the target.

The distance between the gun and the target is called the range. To achieve a given range each gun has to be set at a different angle because of gun to gun variations in the diameter of the barrel, called the *calibre*; the length of the barrel; the weight and shape of the projectile, and the amount and type of propellant used to fire it. Even if identical guns use the same propellant to fire identical projectiles, it is extremely unlikely that they will achieve exactly the same range. The minutest variation between guns in, for example, wear on the inside of the barrel, can cause a range difference of one or two percent at the target end.

Once the projectile has left the barrel of the gun its trajectory begins to be affected by wind, air temperature and air pressure; and these will vary according to the different height levels the projectile is passing through. For example, wind speed and direction can vary considerably from ground level to 50,000 ft (15,000 m) which is the height of the trajectory of certain longer range guns. For modern guns, which can fire out to ranges of 15 miles (24 kms) and more, it is important that each individual gun should be extremely accurately aimed and that all the guns in the same battery (usually six guns) should perform consistently. To achieve these standards all the variables, such as propellant and meteorological conditions, are carefully measured and recorded and the appropriate allowances made when individual gun ranges are calculated.

Indirect fire Up until the end of the 19th century gunners had only engaged targets which they could see. This meant that the guns had to have clear lines of sight to the enemy and they often had to be placed in front of their own infantry. The gun positions were thus very exposed and were vulnerable to being overrun and captured.

During the Boer War (1899–1902) the British gunners began to realize the importance of protecting their guns by concealing them but the foliage they used for camouflage prevented them from getting a clear view of their targets. A system of sighting evolved as a result of this whereby fire could be controlled even though the target could not be seen from the gun. This technique became known as *indirect fire*, to distinguish it from the established method of engaging a target by *direct fire*.

When engaging a target by indirect fire, the gunner receives instructions from an observation post, which is sited well forward of the gun position so that the observer has a good view of the area where targets may be expected to appear. The gunner selects an aiming point which he can see and he *traverses* the barrel of the gun to the right or left (with reference to the aiming point) by the number of degrees ordered by the observer. In World War 2 artillery officers were trained to pilot light aircraft so that, where appropriate, they could control the guns from the air, giving them a much greater field of view. This technique continues to be used today although the helicopter has now replaced the light fixed wing aircraft.

The indirect fire method of engaging a target is entirely dependent on good communications between the observation post and the guns. The observer passes target information to

Below left: a detail from the painting by Sir William Allan of the battle of Waterloo. In those days targets were engaged by direct fire; no attempt was made to conceal the gun batteries.

Below right: an illustration from a book published in Germany in 1547 showing gunners calculating the elevation of a piece of artillery using a clinometer (left) and a quadrant marked with shadow scales.

the guns by radio or by field telephone. The information will usually include a map reference of the target and a bearing to it. At the battery command post on the gun position this information is translated into gun data (range, gun bearing and so on) and passed to the individual guns.

A recent development has been the introduction of small digital COMPUTERS into the battery command posts. These computers not only carry out, almost instantaneously, the calculations necessary to derive individual gun data; they also store information about previously engaged targets so that these can be quickly re-engaged if necessary. The computed gun data is passed to each gun by an automatic data transmission system. In the future projectiles containing sensitive guidance systems may be fired from guns. Such a projectile would pick up, during the last part of its trajectory, a LASER beam reflected off a target which was being illuminated by a forward observer. The laser beam would then guide the projectile to its target, such as a tank, with pinpoint accuracy.

Below : the anti-aircraft gun on the right is aimed at the helicopter whose track is calculated by the gun crew as it flies from AA to A. The gun is fired when the helicopter is at A, but is aimed at B to allow for forward movement of the target during the flight of the shell. The battery of two guns on the left engages the anti-aircraft gun by indirect fire. Information about the target's position is radioed from the helicopter to the battery command vehicle where it is fed into field artillery computer equipment (FACE) which then provides the necessary details for aiming the guns. Alternatively, the helicopter can radio information direct to the gun crew, giving the position of the target relative to the church which they can see. The church thus acts as an aiming point. The tank in the left foreground is being attacked by means of laser-guided shells. An observer illuminates the target with a laser beam and the reflected beam is detected by the shells and guides them on to the target. This tank is firing tracer bullets from a machine gun aligned with the main gun. When the tracer bullets hit the target the main gun will be correctly aimed and can then be fired.

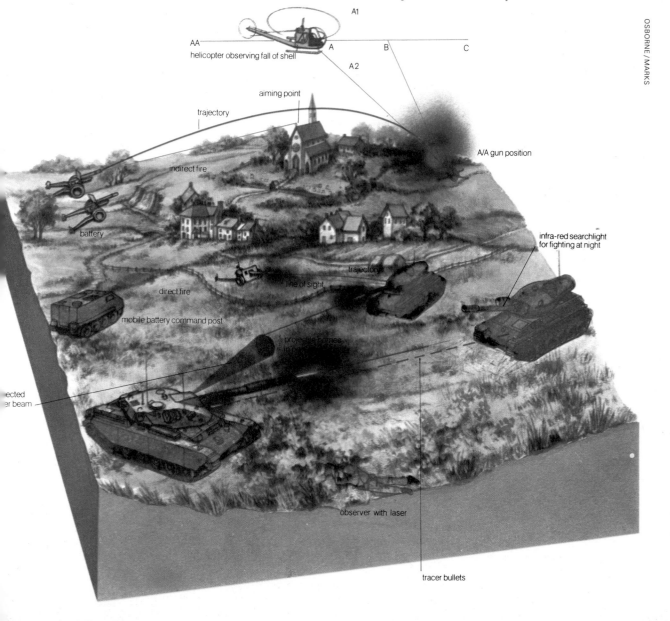

A1

AA

helicopter observing fall of shell

A

B

C

A2

aiming point

trajectory

A/A gun position

indirect fire

battery

infra-red searchlight for fighting at night

direct fire

trajectory

line of sight

mobile battery command post

projectile homes in on

reflected laser beam

observer with laser

tracer bullets

GUTENBERG, Johann (c 1394–c 1468)

Johann Gutenberg was the inventor of printing using movable type, that is, type whose characters are individually cast in metal. He was born probably between 1394 and 1398 in Mainz, at the junction of the Rhine and the Main in Germany. His family belonged to the patrician class, and his father had an interest in the local mint belonging to the Archbishop of Mainz.

Nothing is known of Gutenberg's early life, but he learned the skills of the local goldsmiths of which Mainz was full. In 1428 he had to leave the town after a series of struggles in which the local craftsmen's guilds forced many of the patrician families to leave, and settled in Strasbourg, further down the Rhine. Here he relied for his living on allowances from Mainz, and probably also exercised his skill as a goldsmith. Two years later he returned to Mainz, and in 1436 was accused of breach of promise in an offer of marriage. He lost his case (though he never married) and his hot-headed behaviour at his trial helps to explain the series of lawsuits he was involved in throughout his life.

Until Gutenberg's invention printing was done by using single blocks of wood or brass cut with the design for the whole page. This was a slow and expensive method. The exact circumstances of how Gutenberg first began to experiment with the principle of printing with individual letters rather than with these blocks are not clear; however the introduction of movable type was an important step forward in the development of printing. For the first time type became reusable, simple and cheap to manufacture. Of necessity type sizes began to be standardized. In Strasbourg, Gutenberg went into partnership with Andreas Dritzehn and Andreas Heilmann, undertaking to teach them firstly a new method of making mirrors, and secondly a secret new process. Dritzehn died in 1438 and Gutenberg became involved in a legal battle with Dritzehn's brothers who wanted to be admitted to the partnership. Gutenberg won the case and though the nature of the secret experiments was not admitted at the trial, they were probably trying to cast type with a mould capable of casting individual letters of varying widths.

In 1444 Gutenberg left Strasbourg, unable to find further money for his experiments, and in 1448 entered into partnership with a Mainz lawyer, Johann Fust. During the following years he perfected his new techniques with the help of a calligrapher, Peter Schoeffer, and printed the first books.

Gutenberg agreed with Fust that he would concentrate on printing a Bible, but he also printed popular things for his own profit, including indulgences and school grammars. Angry at this break in their agreement, Fust took Gutenberg to court in November 1455 and, winning the case, obtained possession of Gutenberg's printing materials.

As a result the two men separated, but the first, and possibly the finest, important book was already printed. The Gutenberg or 42 line Bible (so called from the number of lines on each page) took three years, and was probably finished late in 1455.

After parting from Fust, Gutenberg went on printing at Mainz and printed several small popular books. In 1458–9 he printed a second Bible (the 36 line Bible) at Bamberg, using slightly larger type, and then returned to Mainz to work until he retired in January 1465. He died in 1467 or 1468.

Above right : probably the earliest portrait of Gutenberg. This is a copy of the original, which was burned in 1870.

Right : a page from Gutenberg's 42 line Bible of 1455.

THE SCIENCE MUSEUM

SPERRY

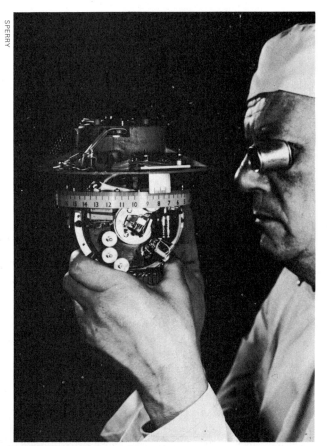

GYROCOMPASS

The gyrocompass is a *true north* directional indicator used extensively in merchant and naval vessels. It is one of the most useful NAVIGATION aids, as it provides a true north indication regardless of any rolling, pitching or yawing of the vessel and is entirely unaffected by any of the disturbances which commonly affect magnetic COMPASSES. The gyrocompass is usually installed below deck and its indication is relayed around the ship to operate ancillary equipment such as steering and bearing repeaters, course recorders and gyropilots.

The basis of the gyrocompass is a GYROSCOPE controlled in such a way that its spin axis is made to seek and maintain alignment with the geographic meridian (north-south line). This is achieved by combining the characteristics of the gyroscope, INERTIA and precession, with two natural phenomena, the Earth's rotation and the force of gravity.

Theory of operation

The Earth rotates about its polar axis from west to east with an angular velocity of one revolution in 24 hours, that is, $15°/h$. At any point on the Earth's surface this angular velocity can be resolved into two components: a component aligned to the local vertical, known as the *vertical earth rate*, and a horizontal component aligned to the meridian and known as the *horizontal earth rate*.

The magnitude of these components varies with latitude. Vertical earth rate varies as the *sine* of the angle of latitude and is $15°/h$ at the poles and zero at the equator, while the horizontal earth rate varies as the *cosine* of the angle of latitude and is zero at the poles and $15°/h$ at the equator (see MATHEMATICAL PRINCIPLES).

The gyroscope used in this gyrocompass is electrically driven and mounted in gimbals in such a way that it has freedom to move about both a vertical and a horizontal axis. The gyroscope can be considered as a *space stable element* because its axes will remain pointed in the same direction with respect to *inertial space* unless acted upon by a force. The Earth is not a part of inertial space but rotates within it, and so the directions in which the axes of a gyroscope point, with respect to an observer on Earth, will appear to change as the Earth rotates although they are in fact remaining constant with respect to inertial space.

Being a space stable element, the gyroscope 'senses' the rotation of the Earth: the vertical axis senses the vertical earth rate and the horizontal axis the horizontal earth rate. For this reason the effect of the Earth's rotation on the axes of the gyroscope varies with the latitude. This can best be appreciated by considering the behaviour of the gyroscope at various geographical locations.

If the gyro is located at the North Pole with its spin axis horizontal, the rotation of the Earth will be measured entirely by the vertical axis, and to an observer using the spinning Earth as a reference the space stable gyro appears to drift about its vertical axis at Earth rate, $15°/h$.

When the gyro is mounted at the equator with its spin axis pointing east to west its horizontal axis is aligned with the meridian (the direction of horizontal Earth rate), and to an

Top: the second gyrocompass made in 1916 by S G Brown, which used a 'ballistic' arrangement to precess the gyro toward the meridian. The rotor diameter is 4 inches (10.2 cm).

Below: arrangement of a gyroscope with gimbal rings, showing how the rotor has complete freedom to maintain any given position. The gyroscope can be mounted on a servo-driven stabilized platform, providing a position sensor and stabilizer for space vehicles.

observer standing on the Earth the space stable gyro appears to rotate about its horizontal axis at Earth rate. This effect is referred to as 'tilting'.

With the gyro still mounted at the equator but with its spin axis pointing north to south, the tilting effect due to the rotation of the Earth is zero since the sensitive horizontal axis is displaced by 90° from the meridian. With the spin axis pointing in an intermediate position, the horizontal Earth rate affects the horizontal axis by an amount proportional to the displacement of the spin axis from the meridian.

Practical gyrocompasses   It is the effect of horizontal Earth rate that makes it possible to apply the force of gravity to convert the space stable gyroscope into a north seeking gyrocompass. When the gyro spin axis is aligned to the meridian there is no tilting effect about the horizontal axis. When the spin axis is east of meridian, horizontal Earth rate causes the north end of the gyro to fall. The rate of tilt of the gyro is directly related to the value of the horizontal Earth rate (15°/h cosine latitude) and the misalignment of the spin axis from the meridian.

At points between the poles and the equator the gyro appears to turn partly about its horizontal axis and partly about its vertical axis because it is affected by both horizontal and vertical earth rates. In general the horizontal Earth rate causes the gyro to tilt and the vertical earth rate causes it to rotate in azimuth (horizontally) with respect to the meridians.

A gravity reference system is used to measure any tilting of

Left: a Sperry CL11 'rotorace' gyro which is used in many aircraft compass systems, including those for the Hawker Siddeley 'Trident' and 'Nimrod' and the BAC 1-11.

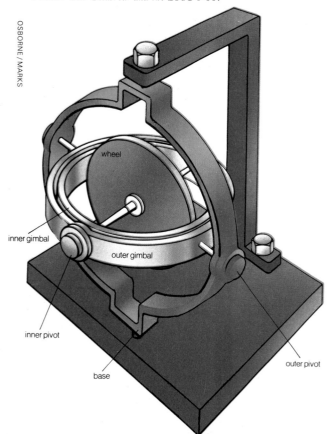

wheel

inner gimbal

outer gimbal

inner pivot

base

outer pivot

the gyro and produce torques (turning forces) to precess the gyro spin axis into alignment with the meridian. Early gyrocompasses used a weight to sense tilt and provide a north seeking force; the weight, being secured to the bottom of the gyro case, forced the spin axis to remain level as a result of its reaction with gravity and the resulting torque precessed the gyro towards the north. The principle was used by Dr Elmer SPERRY on his early gyrocompasses, one of which was successfully demonstrated aboard the USS *Delaware* in 1911 and is now on view at the Smithsonian Institution in Washington DC.

By the early 1920s this weight arrangement had been replaced by a 'ballistic' comprising two containers half filled with fluid, mounted on the north and south ends of the gyro, and interconnected by two small diameter tubes. Any tilting of the gyro caused displacement of fluid from the higher to the lower container and the resulting imbalance precessed the gyro towards the meridian. While improved versions of this system are still widely used today, electrical devices are now extensively used in gyrocompass gravity reference systems because of their great flexibility. Such systems employ ACCELEROMETERS and other devices to detect tilt and the output of the device is amplified to drive the gyro torque motors.

As already mentioned, it is the relatively slow rotation of the Earth that provides the motive power for the north seeking precessional movement of the gyrocompass. When a vessel is travelling over the Earth's surface, however, and therefore about the Earth's centre, the vessel's movement is compounded with that of the Earth and will impair the accuracy of the gyrocompass. Compensation systems have been designed to counteract these errors and leave the gyro accurately aligned to the geographic north.

GYROSCOPE

The term gyroscope (or gyro for short) is generally applied to a flywheel rotating at high speed about its axis. In a scientific gyro the flywheel is mounted so that its axis can take up any orientation in space, whereas in a toy gyro one end of the flywheel axis is constrained in some way. The Earth, Moon and other planets that rotate about an axis also behave like gyroscopes.

Gyroscopic behaviour   Imagine a flywheel spinning about its axis and supported on a pillar at one of its ends. If the axis is vertical, the flywheel will balance on the supported end of its axis like a spinning top. Imagine now that the axis is moved so that it is horizontal; one would expect the force of gravity to topple the flywheel off its support, but this does not happen. The flywheel axis remains horizontal, apparently resisting the force of gravity, and at the same time moves around its point of support in the horizontal plane. This movement is called *precession*. It is a property of all gyroscopes that when a force (gravity in the above example) is applied at right angles to the spinning axis, this will give rise to movement, not in the expected direction, but in a direction at right angles both to the spinning axis and to the applied force. This is because the spinning flywheel has *angular momentum*, and any force applied must alter the direction in which the angular momentum applies.

The scientific gyro   In the scientific gyro, a wheel rotating about, let us say, a horizontal axis pointing north and south, is pivoted in an 'inner ring'—literally a ring of metal. The inner ring in such a case might then itself be pivoted about an axis at right angles to the axis of spin, let us say in this case a horizontal axis east and west. The bearings of the inner ring are held in an 'outer ring' and this second ring is yet again freely pivoted about an axis at right angles both to the axis of spin and to the axis of movement of the inner ring. In this example the outer ring axis would therefore be vertical.

The first amazing property of such a gyro is that if the base on which the outer ring pivots are mounted is tilted in any direction, rotated or displaced, the axis of spin of the wheel will remain fixed—fixed that is relative to the framework of the so-called 'fixed star' or 'inertial space' network. Thus, if a gyro mounted in 'gimbal rings'—the name given to the outer and inner rings—is allowed to remain on the ground, or on a bench or table, the axis of spin will *appear* to make a complete revolution in 24 hours. It is of course merely recording the fact that the Earth has turned 360° on its own axis in this period.

The second and even more baffling phenomenon of a gyro as described is that if a twisting force is applied to the outer ring so as to try to turn that ring on its pivots it *resists* such movement—but, the *inner* ring turns about the inner ring pivots so long as the twisting force continues to be applied to the outer. The motion of the inner ring under these conditions is precession. The action can be reversed. A twisting force (torque) applied to the inner ring will move the outer.

There is a simple rule which allows us to predict in which direction precessions will take place. Imagine the twisting force applied to one ring to consist of a pair of parallel 'straight-line' forces pushing on the edge of the wheel perpendicular to the *faces* of the wheel but at opposite ends of the appropriate diameter of the wheel and in opposition to each other. Then imagine that each of these forces has been carried round 90° (a right angle) by the spinning wheel *in the direction of spin*. The resulting pair of imaginary forces indicate the direction of turning motion that actually occurs.

The toy gyro A toy gyroscope is usually nothing more than a simple wheel with its axle mounted in a metal ring. On the outside of the ring, opposite the two bearing points, there are usually small, nearly spherical knobs, one of which may carry a slit into which a steel ruler or piece of string may fit. The many quite amazing 'tricks' which may be performed with a toy gyro exhibit both types of gyroscopic behaviour—that is, the tendency to maintain a fixed axis of spin and the torque-precession relationship. A small model of the Eiffel Tower is often supplied with the gyro so that an end knob may be supported in a cup-like socket on top of the tower with the wheel axis horizontal. When released the wheel will 'gyrate' in a horizontal plane without falling off or pulling over the tower. A spinning gyro can balance on a 'tight-rope' of string or wire, or on a sharp blade. Use of these properties are to be found in the stabilizing of ships (in large sizes) and as measuring devices for navigation (for example in the GYROCOMPASS and INERTIAL GUIDANCE SYSTEMS), in small sizes. Wheels of 2 to 3 inches (5.1 to 7.6 cm) in diameter have been rotated at 50,000 rpm or more in the latter applications.

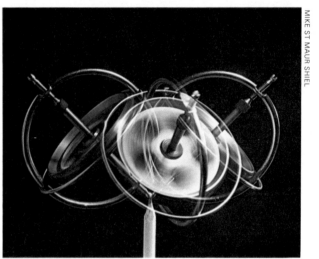

Top right : these gyroscopes, shown in a 19th century textbook, have electromagnets to keep them spinning continuously.

Centre: a toy gyroscope, with its flywheel set spinning by pulling string wound round the axis, shown precessing slowly in a multiple exposure shot. The Earth's precession takes 25,800 years.

Right: an attachment for steadying binoculars and small cameras on board helicopters or moving vehicles. It contains two gyros set at an angle, so that precession does not make tracking too difficult.

HAIR WAVING and STRAIGHTENING

The idea of putting waves and curls into straight hair dates back to ancient Egyptian and Roman times; Cleopatra is said to have set her hair in rollers made of baked mud. Early methods, which involved wetting the hair, winding on to rollers and then drying, achieved only a temporary set, in other words the hair would return to its original shape if it were rewetted. It is the ability of hair to stretch when it is wet by as much as 20 to 50% of its original dry length that makes temporary setting possible.

Permanent waving was invented by Charles Nessler in 1905. Nessler's method involved winding the hair on to rods or rollers, applying an alkaline chemical (usually borax) to soften it and then heating to fix the hair in its new shape. In the early days permanent waving was a long and somewhat hazardous process because the action of the alkali was difficult to control; if it were too vigorous or was allowed to continue for too long damage to the hair would result. Nevertheless, Nessler's invention was an important advance on previous processes; for the first time the chemical structure, rather than just the physical shape of the hair, was altered during waving.

Hair structure   Hair is composed of three layers, a thin outer layer of semi-transparent overlapping scales called the *cuticle*, an inner layer, called the *cortex*, composed of thin thread-like fibres of the protein *keratin*, and a central 'marrow' called the *medulla*. It is the cortex which is important in hair waving and straightening processes. The fibres of the cortex are held together by means of chemical linkages called *disulphide* (or *cysteine*) linkages which, as their name implies, each contain two sulphur atoms.

Permanent waving   The principle of permanent waving is to break these linkages so that the individual fibres in the cortex can move relative to each other as the hair is put into its new shape, and then to reform the linkages to fix the fibres in their new positions. In modern permanent waving the breaking and reforming of the disulphide linkages is achieved chemically and is usually carried out at room temperature, hence the term *cold-waving* sometimes applied to this process. A *reducing agent* (a chemical which can donate hydrogen or remove oxygen in a chemical reaction), usually *ammonium thioglycollate*, is used to break the disulphide linkages while an *oxidizing agent* (a chemical which can remove hydrogen or donate oxygen in a chemical reaction) is used to reform them. Until fairly recently hydrogen peroxide was the most commonly used oxidizing agent, but other more stable oxidizing agents are now preferred. Thus, permanent waving comprises three steps: applying a softening solution (containing the reducing agent), shaping the hair and applying a neutralizing solution (containing the oxidizing agent) to 'fix' the wave. The number of rollers used and their size depends on the result required and the type of hair—coarse or fine.

The softening and neutralizing solutions often contain

Below: a photomicrograph showing damage to a human hair resulting from bleaching followed by permanent waving. The hair is tied in a knot to accentuate any irregularities in the structure.

Bottom: a photomicrograph of a normal, untreated human hair.

Below right: applying the softening solution in permanent waving. The solution attacks most metals, so plastic curlers are used.

Bottom right: applying the neutralizing solution in permanent waving. The solution is in the form of a foam so that it does not drip.

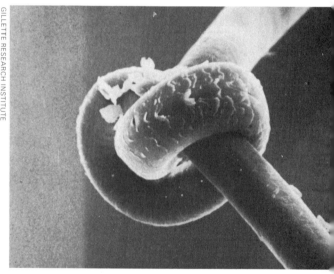

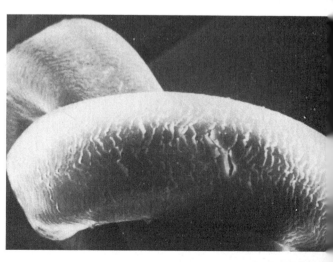

additional chemicals such as wetting or swelling agents which improve penetration into the hair fibres. In order to avoid damaging the hair, the softening and neutralizing solutions are normally neither acid nor alkaline although the action of the softening solution is sometimes enhanced by adding ammonia, which makes it slightly alkaline.

Straightening Hair straightening is simply the reverse to permanent waving. As far as is known it was first introduced in the USA for straightening the 'frizzy' hair of the coloured population. The first hair straighteners were based on caustic soda, a vigorous alkali, but these were generally unsatisfactory because unless they were applied with great care damage to the hair would result.

Modern methods of hair straightening employ similar chemicals as are used in permanent waving. The softening agent is normally applied in the form of a cream which tends to hold the hair against the scalp while it is being straightened. The straightening is done by stretching the hair, preferably with the hands rather than a comb. After stretching, the hair is fixed using a conventional neutralizing solution. In recent years hair straightening has become increasingly popular for, once hair has been straightened, it can be temporarily set into any desired style.

ELIDA GIBBS LTD

HALOGEN

The five elements fluorine, chlorine, bromine, iodine and astatine form the seventh group in the PERIODIC TABLE of elements. They are called halogens, from the Greek words meaning salt producers, because they readily form salts, such as sodium chloride, by simple chemical combination with metals. The halogens each have seven electrons in the outer shell of their ATOMS and will thus readily accept a further electron (as in salt formation) to give the stable eight electron configuration.

Fluorine Fluorine (F) is a light yellow gas at normal temperatures; it is the most chemically active element and reacts very vigorously with most substances, including organic materials and many metals. It will even form compounds with the INERT GASES xenon and krypton. Traces of fluorine exist in sea water, bones and teeth, and it is widely distributed in such minerals as *fluorspar* and *cryolite*.

Fluorine is produced commercially by the ELECTROLYSIS of hydrogen fluoride made electrically conductive by the addition of potassium fluoride. One of the chief uses of pure fluorine is in the manufacture of uranium hexafluoride (UF_6) which is used in the separation of the uranium ISOTOPE U235 (used in NUCLEAR REACTORS and in the A-BOMB) from the more common isotope U238. Most fluorine compounds, however, are manufactured from hydrogen fluoride and not fluorine itself. Hydrogen fluoride is made by heating finely powdered fluorspar with concentrated sulphuric acid. When dissolved in water it forms a weakly acidic solution which is used for etching and polishing glass.

Nearly three quarters of the hydrogen fluoride produced is used in making organic fluorine compounds (compounds containing both fluorine and carbon atoms). Examples of organic fluorine compounds include fluothane, a nontoxic and non-flammable anaesthetic, polytetrafluoroethylene (PTFE), a plastic used as a non-stick coating for kitchen utensils, Freons, low-boiling liquids used as refrigerants and aerosol propellants, and BCF (bromochlorodifluoromethane), a chemical used in FIREFIGHTING.

It is known that tooth decay is less common in areas where fluoride salts are present in the drinking water supply. For this reason fluoride is sometimes added to water supplies that are deficient in fluoride salts, and stannous fluoride (a fluoride of tin) is a constituent of some toothpastes.

Chlorine Chlorine (Cl) is a heavy, greenish yellow gas with an irritating smell, which was first isolated by Scheele in 1774. It achieved notoriety in World War I when it was used as a poison gas. Chlorine is the twelfth most common element in the earth's crust, its chief sources being sea water and rock salt, where it occurs as sodium chloride.

Chlorine is prepared industrially by the electrolysis of brine in a *diaphragm cell* or a *mercury cell*. In the diaphragm cell chlorine gas is released at the anode and sodium hydroxide forms at the cathode. Because chlorine will react with sodium hydroxide, it is important to provide a barrier between the cathode and the anode which will prevent mixing of the two products but allow the electric current to pass between the cell electrodes. A porous diaphragm, usually made of asbestos paper, is used for this purpose. In the mercury cell a stream of mercury is used as the cathode. Chlorine gas is liberated at the anode as in the diaphragm cell, but the sodium, which migrates to the cathode, dissolves in the mercury to form an *amalgam*. The mercury-sodium amalgam is removed from the cell and passed through a water bath where the sodium reacts to form sodium hydroxide and hydrogen. The purified mercury is then pumped back to the electrolytic cell.

As in the case of fluorine, most of the chlorine produced is used in making organic chlorine compounds such as *vinyl chloride*. This is an important compound because it can be polymerized to give the widely used plastic *polyvinyl chloride* (PVC). Chlorine is contained in certain weedkillers and insecticides such as DDT, though the future of these compounds is uncertain because of possible long term harmful effects on animals and humans. The chemical *perchloroethylene* is a commonly used DRYCLEANING fluid. Chlorine compounds are also used for bleaching, especially in the paper and textile industries. Chlorine itself is a useful bactericide and for this reason is added in very small quantities to swimming pools and drinking water. It is also used as a *quenching gas* in some GEIGER COUNTER tubes.

Bromine

Bromine (Br) is a dense volatile liquid at room temperature, giving off a highly poisonous brown vapour. Most of the world's bromine is extracted from seawater which has a bromine content of 0.14 lb/ton. The high concentration of salts in the Dead Sea makes it the world's richest source of bromine. Brine is taken from the sea, treated with dilute acid and chlorine, and passed down a tower into which air is blown. This releases bromine from the bromide salts present in the seawater.

The chief use of bromine in industry is in the manufacture of *ethylene bromide* which is added to petrol [gasoline] together with the antiknock agent *tetraethyl lead*. The ethylene bromide prevents lead deposits from building up in the engine by converting it to lead bromide which is volatile at the operating temperatures of petrol engines and thus passes out through the exhaust system. The increasing use, however, of lead-free petrol is likely to reduce drastically the demand for ethylene bromide. Silver bromide is an active constituent of photographic FILM; crystals of this compound become activated when exposed to light. When treated with a photographic developer the activated particles are *reduced* to black metallic silver while the unactivated particles remain unchanged.

Iodine

Iodine (I) is not an abundant element, but is widely distributed in nature, its salts being found in rocks, soils, seawater and animal and plant tissue. Iodine salts are found in relatively high concentrations in certain sea organisms such as corals, sponges, seaweed and in codliver oil. Most of the world's supplies of iodine come from northern Chile, where it is found in association with the ore of Chile saltpetre. Iodine itself is a black solid at room temperature which vaporizes easily to give a violet vapour.

Iodine is used in medicine as an external antiseptic, both as the free element and in the compound *iodoform* (CHI_3). It is essential in the human body, and deficiency of iodine leads to the disease known as *goitre*. Some iodine compounds are opaque to X-rays and are used in radiography to distinguish various parts of the body. The radioactive isotope $I131$ is used in medicine to study liver, kidney and thyroid disorders. Certain iodine-containing dyes are used in colour photography, and silver iodide is used for impregnating photographic film.

Astatine

Astatine (At) is the least important of the halogens. Its most stable isotope, $At210$, has a half life of only 8.3 hours. As far as is known, astatine resembles iodine in its chemical properties.

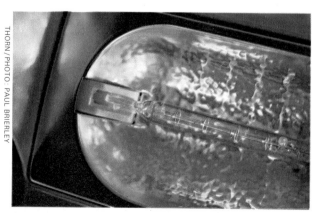

Above left: a view of the cell room in a brine electrolysis plant. The cells are mercury cells and the plant produces chlorine and sodium hydroxide.

Above: spraying grapevines with the chlorine-containing compound copper hydroxychloride to control fungus infections.

Left: a tungsten halogen lamp. The presence of halogen molecules in the lamp envelope allows the tungsten filament to be operated at a higher temperature than normal and the lamp emits a correspondingly brighter light. It is more efficient than normal filament lamps.

HANDICAP AIDS

People suffering from physical disabilities often require the assistance of some mechanical or electrical aid to enable them to enjoy some pleasure and independence in life. Types of disablement vary enormously and aids for them range from simple homemade gadgets to complex electromechanical systems. For severely disabled people it is important to make communication and moving about easier, and an essential feature of all handicap aids is that they be of good ERGONOMIC DESIGN.

Page turner The electric page turner is a machine for turning the pages of a magazine or book and is designed to help those people who have lost the use of their hands or whose hands are weak and unsteady. The equipment has a bookrest that is capable of accepting a magazine, paperback or hardback book. Switching is operated by mouth, using the blow-suck method, a hand squeezer, or by pressing a microswitch. This causes a small motor to traverse a metal arm, pivoted above or below, across the page. At the end of the arm is a serrated wheel or sticky pad which engages on the corner of the page. The page is pushed ahead of this finger until it compresses enough to flick over. The moving arm then continues to smooth the page down, finally stopping in a position such as to hold it for reading or to turn it back again should a situation such as turning two pages at once occur.

The page turner has built in illumination and an adjustable reading angle, and stands on any normal bed table. It requires to be set up by someone other than the disabled user, especially in the case of the model which is mounted on a stand and is intended for use by people who have to be flat on their back. Electrical safety has to be a feature of the page turner and one model works entirely from a three volt torch battery. One alternative to the page turner is a MICROFILM projector displaying on a screen, or on the ceiling, successive pages of a book which has been previously photographed on a reel of film.

POSSUM A more complex piece of equipment for the severely disabled is the Patient Operated Selector Mechanism (POSSUM). This electronic robot responds to the commands of the disabled user, which may be lifting a little finger or blowing into a tube. The switches used are microswitches, which need very little pressure to operate them. The blowing or sucking action can be used to operate a diaphragm covering a pocket inside which is the microswitch. As the diaphragm moves, it presses the switch. This can then be used to operate a motor driven rotary selector switch.

This system can handle quite a large number of functions. It can, for example, open the front door, operate the TV, room lights and radio, electric blanket or room heater, SOS loudspeaking telephone, intercom or bell system. With a suitable mouthpiece, such as a pipe stem, a plastic tube is supported in a convenient position to the person's mouth. A light sustained suction or pressure causes a white light to illuminate each panel of the indicator in turn in a steady sequence of steps until the

Above left: this chair enables disabled or elderly people to travel up a flight of stairs at the touch of a button. Its track is laid over the stairs, and a one third horsepower electric motor winds the chair up or down. The chair can rotate through 90° so that if there is a bend at the top of the stairs the user can step off easily.

Left: going to the toilet can present problems to the disabled. This design has a pedal operated douche of water at body temperature, followed by a flow of warm air; the bowl is flushed simultaneously. The unit has a manual control so it can also be used conventionally.

selected device is reached. Release of the suction or pressure causes the selected device to be switched on and the background green of the panel changes to red to indicate the 'on' stage. The control then returns to the start in a fraction of a second so that each selection begins from the same place. To switch off, the selection procedure is repeated, to control working on the 'first time on, second time off' principle.

A more advanced system, using two or more 'levels' of switch, can be coded to control an electric typewriter with a speed capability of up to 100 words per minute—faster than an expert high speed typist.

Moving around
To restore the function of mobility, aids such as the wheelchair and car have been produced and modified.

There are three basic types of wheelchair: a fixed frame, manually propelled chair; a folding frame, lightweight, manually propelled chair; and an electric powered chair for indoor use only.

The fixed frame wheelchair with its comfortable upholstery is designed for use indoors. The lightweight folding type is designed as a transportable general purpose chair, and with its pneumatic tyres gives a much better ride over uneven surfaces. The powered chair is intended for the more severely disabled who are too weak or too deformed in the upper limbs to provide their own power. The propulsion comes from a low voltage, low power motor, the voltage being derived from a car battery. The chair is controlled by a joystick which can be easily operated by the weakest hand. This control can be located on one of the arms of the chair or in between the user's

JOHN WATNEY

Above right: many everyday operations which we take for granted, like peeling potatoes, need two hands. This simple device to hold the potato in place makes life simpler for the one-handed person.

Below: this sewing machine requires only one hand for its operation. The usual accelerator-type foot pedal has been extended so that it can be pressed by the elbow, while the hand is used to hold the material. The controls for setting the stitching type and size have also been enlarged so that they do not need a strong grip.

Right: an alternative to the POSSUM system of typing uses a small projector strapped to the person's head. The keyboard is on the opposite wall and each letter is represented by a light cell. The light spot must dwell on each letter for a short time.

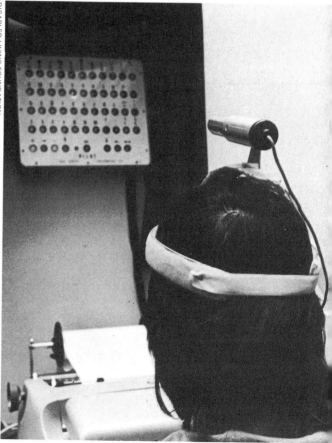

DISABLED LIVING FOUNDATION

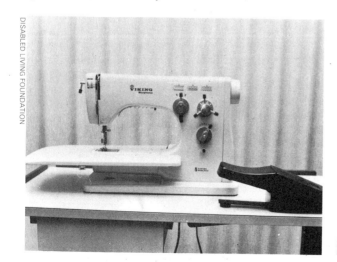

DISABLED LIVING FOUNDATION

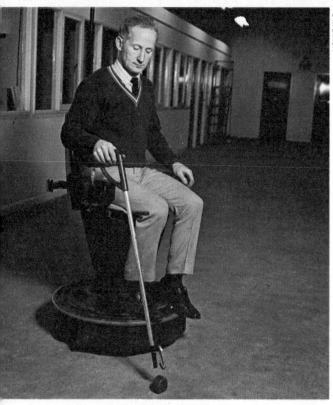

legs on a column in the centre of the chair, which is the style of the 'sleigh ride' or Snowdon chairs.

For those people who have lost the use of their legs or who have severe chronic lung or heart conditions, purpose built and modified production vehicles are available for getting from place to place. In Britain, purpose built three wheeled electric or motor vehicles are available free of charge. The saloon model electric tricycles have a centre tiller with a horizontal bar twist grip control, which controls the forward and reverse speeds, steering, service brake and electric braking. They have provision for a folding transit wheelchair alongside the driving seat, and are powered by one or two 36 volt batteries, depending on the model.

The motor tricycles are similar in most respects to the electric types but are fitted with 197 cc two-stroke blower cooled engines with a four speed gearbox and electric starting.

Available in most countries, at some cost, are modified production vehicles ranging from commercial vehicles to the lightest cars. Hand operated controls for throttle, brake and clutch are conveniently grouped within reach of the driver at gear lever and steering wheel positions. One type of equipment fitted is based on standard vacuum power components and effective control of brake, clutch and throttle requires only finger light pressure, since the power necessary is provided by vacuum servo units drawing power from the engine.

By having the functions of mobility and communication restored, the disabled gain confidence and independence.

HARDBOARD (see manufactured board)

Above left: a variety of powered chairs have been devised for disabled people to use at work or in the home. This one is suitable for kitchen work, and includes a grip for picking up objects.

Left: conversions of ordinary production vehicles for use by disabled drivers require automatic transmissions, doing away with gear changing. Both accelerator and brake are provided by the lever to the right of the steering wheel. It is in the mid position at the moment: moving it down operates the accelerator, while moving it up applies the servo-operated brakes. The car has power steering.

Below: this range of cutlery is for use by people with little or no grip. The implements have larger handles, or moulded plastic clamps which fit over the palm of the hand.

HARGRAVES, James (c 1720–1778)

The parish register of Stanhill church near Bolton in Lancashire records the marriage in 1740 of James Hargraves, inventor of the spinning-jenny, to one Elizabeth Grimshaw. The name is very definitely Hargraves and not Hargreaves, as is so often quoted, and while we know the date of his marriage the precise date of his birth is a mystery.

As a young man it is very likely that James Hargraves was well versed in the art of WEAVING cloth using a hand LOOM. Hargraves lived on a farm and it was very common for farm-workers to weave at home in their spare time in order to supplement their agricultural wages which were very low. Hargraves is supposed to have been a good carpenter as well.

About 1760 James Hargraves was asked by Robert Peel to make a *carding* engine. Robert Peel, the grandfather of Britain's first prime minister, was a neighbour of Hargraves and interested in textile weaving and printing designs on calico, a rough and cheaply made cotton fabric. A carding engine was required in order to mechanize the process, known as carding, by which the tangled fibres of cotton in its natural form are straightened and re-arranged prior to SPINNING the cotton into long, thin threads. Hargraves' carding engine was the first of a series of improvements made in the eighteenth century to the carding process.

In 1733 John Kay had invented a device called the fly-shuttle. The fly-shuttle was used on weaving looms to pass the threads of wool or cotton more rapidly from side to side of the width of cloth being made. The fly-shuttle carries a thread called the weft which is passed back and forth between a set of threads called the warp threads.

John Kay's fly-shuttle made it possible for textile weavers to work very much faster and to produce much more cloth. An important consequence was that spinning became a serious bottleneck in the textile industry. The old fashioned method of making threads by hand-spinning carded wool or cotton simply could not produce enough thread to keep the weavers supplied.

The need to mechanize spinning became critical and in London in 1761 the Society of Arts decided to offer a prize, worth £50, to anyone who could invent a spinning machine capable of making six threads at once with only one man to work it. James Hargraves and Robert Peel may or may not have known of the competition but at any rate Hargraves invented a spinning machine in about 1764, which he patented in 1770. How he arrived at a suitable design is not known but there is a story that he got the basic idea when an old-fashioned spinning wheel was knocked over and as the machine revolved on the floor Hargraves saw how to make a device capable of spinning lots of threads all at once.

Hargraves' spinning machine was basically quite simple; it was made of wood and hand operated. It was called a spinning-jenny, which is probably not a reference to a person's name but rather a local way of saying spinning engine.

As a spinning machine Hargraves' jenny was such a success that many people who earned a living using spinning wheels in their homes became fearful for their jobs. Hargraves' home and his store of machines were attacked and many things were broken. Probably about 50 years old at the time and, so we are told, 'a stout, broadset man of five feet ten inches high, or rather more', James Hargraves left Stanhill and went to Nottingham in order to escape further persecution. In Nottingham Hargraves manufactured spinning-jennies and, together with a man called Thomas James, set up a mill to spin cotton mechanically.

Another man was spinning cotton mechanically in Nottingham. Richard Arkwright, a native of Preston, had also been impressed by the need to mechanize the spinning process and in 1769 he patented his so-called water-frame. This name was used because Arkwright's spinning machine could be driven by water-power, so allowing a much bigger spinning machine handling many more threads to be operated. Moreover Arkwright's machine worked on a somewhat different principle to Hargraves'; both men's machines had their good and bad features. It was logical, therefore, that the next development in spinning machines should feature an amalgamation of the two types. The result was the famous spinning mule of Samuel Crompton of 1779; apparently the name derives from the fact that Crompton's machine was a hybrid of those of Arkwright and Hargraves.

In the eighteenth century textile production in Britain changed from being a small scale domestic affair to a mechanized factory-based industry. Men like Richard Arkwright and James Hargraves were influential in bringing about these changes. But whereas Richard Arkwright became wealthy and famous—he was knighted in 1786—James Hargraves died in obscurity in 1778 at the age of about 60.

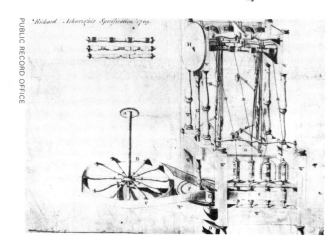

MARY EVANS PICTURE LIBRARY

PUBLIC RECORD OFFICE

Above left: an improved version of Hargraves' spinning jenny.

Left: a drawing of Arkwright's water-frame from his 1769 patent specification. The wheel on the left is driven by water power.

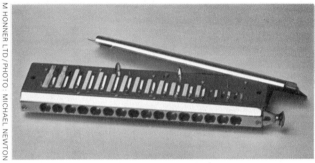

Top: one of the first Trossinger harmonicas, made in Germany about 1830. The plates are cast lead, the wood carved by hand, and the reeds hammered from brass wire.

Above: a modern chromatic harmonica. The sliding knob on the left changes the scales. The top of the case is removed.

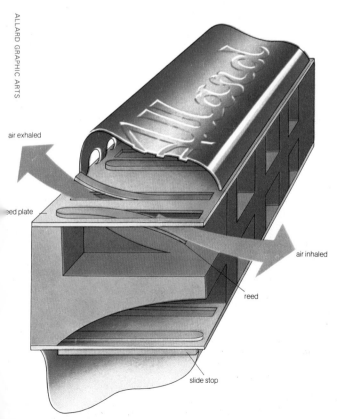

air exhaled

eed plate

air inhaled

reed

slide stop

HARMONICA

When Sir George Grove was compiling his massive *Dictionary of Music and Musicians*, he wrote that although the lowly *mouth organ* was being called the harmonica, the name would not stick, because there was already a noble musical instrument of that name. In music history there are indeed at least two instruments called the harmonica, but today the mouth organ is by far the best known.

The original harmonica, also called *armonica* and *glass harmonica*, evolved from an older instrument which consisted simply of a set of tuned water glasses. These were tuned by filling them to different levels with water, and were played by rubbing moistened fingertips on the rims. Benjamin FRANKLIN in 1761 made the glasses of different sizes, fitted them inside one another in a row, and installed them in a cabinet horizontally so that they could be turned by means of a handle or a foot treadle. They were kept moistened by turning through a bath of water in the lower part of the cabinet. Franklin named his instrument the armonica, or harmonica, after the Greek goddess *Harmonica*, who personified order and symmetry and also gave her name to the musical discipline of *harmony*. Beethoven and Mozart wrote music for Franklin's instrument, which has a tonal purity rather like that of a small pipe organ played softly.

The much better known harmonica, or mouth organ, has been quite popular for more than a hundred years because it is portable, cheap and fairly easy to play. It consists of a set of metal reeds, fixed at one end but freely vibrating when acted upon by the breath of the player. The pitch of each reed is established by its length, rather than from an enclosed air column, as in the pipe organ, the oboe, and other reed-pipe instruments. The reeds are arranged in two rows closely together, and the enclosing case is made of wood covered with a light gauge of sheet metal, which is usually embossed with a decorative design and the name of the manufacturer. The instrument is small enough to be held in one hand while being played, and is played by alternately blowing and drawing the breath to sound the notes of the diatonic scale. The player uses his tongue to cover up the reed chambers he does not want to use. Chromatic models are available which have two sets of reeds pitched a semitone apart, with a finger operated device for separating them.

The British firm of Wheatstone, in 1829, was among the first to produce mouth organs, calling the instrument the *Aeolina*. It is said to have been invented by C F L Buschmann in Germany in 1821, who called it the *Mundaoline*. (Buschmann also had a hand in the development of the ACCORDION, another instrument which employs free-beating reeds, as does the HARMONIUM.)

In countries like the United States, the mouth organ was especially popular in the nineteenth century, when pioneers on the frontier with no musical training could carry their instruments in their pockets. Since World War 2, especially in Chicago, the most important development of harmonica playing in the instrument's history has occurred among black people, who have evolved a particularly intense style in the context of their musical idiom. Among these players the instrument is called the *mouth harp* or just *harp*.

Left: a chromatic harmonica. The sound is made when air, blown from the mouth, passes the reeds and valves of the reed plate. The upper half of the instrument gives the naturals and the lower, opened by the slide, the sharps and flats.

Above: a nineteenth century British harmonium made by Boosey and Ching. This engraving was used in their advertisements.

Below: cutaway of a harmonium. When the treadles are operated air is drawn into the wind chest via the feeders and chimney. If the expression pallet is open the wind is stored in the reservoir giving a strong continuous tone but if it is closed the tone can be controlled directly from the treadles.

HARMONIUM

In the eighteenth century in Europe, scholars began to study other, earlier cultures in search of the origins of Greek fire, gunpowder, and other things of which they sometimes possessed only fragments of information. Among the other discoveries they studied was an ancient Chinese musical instrument called the *sheng*. This was a small wind chest which employed a set of reeds which were free-beating reeds, that is, fixed at one end and vibrating freely when air flowed over them. The pitch of each reed was determined by its dimensions, rather than by a stopped column of air. (A pipe organ has columns of air of various lengths, and a clarinet or an oboe, for example, has a fixed reed in a column of air whose length is determined by the player's fingers on the keys.) These investigations into free-beating reeds resulted in the development, early in the nineteenth century, of several popular musical instruments, among them the ACCORDION, the HARMONICA (mouth organ), and the harmonium.

The harmonium is a small keyboard instrument in which a foot treadle operates a bellows which supplies air to a wind chamber or air reservoir. Pressing a key allows air to flow from the chamber on to the appropriate reed. A knee lever or an expression 'stop' allows air to bypass the chamber from the bellows, giving an increase in volume. (Free-beating reed instruments keep a steady pitch whatever the volume of air; the only effect of increasing the air supply is to increase the volume of the sound.)

The harmonium as it is known today was developed by a Frenchman, Alexander Debain, in 1840, from earlier instruments called the physharmonia, the seraphine, and others. The American version, called the American organ, was developed

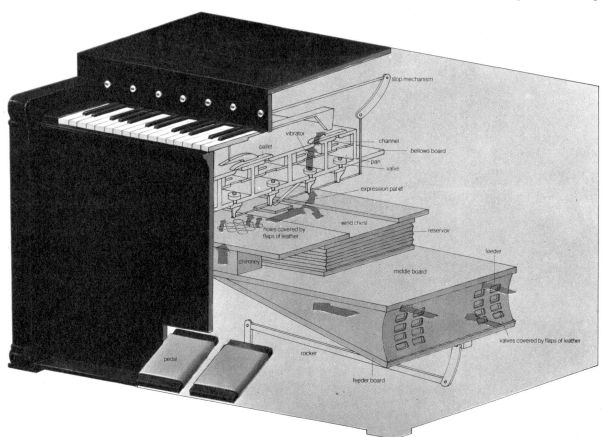

stop mechanism

vibrator

pallet

channel

bellows board

pan

valve

expression pallet

wind chest

reservoir

holes covered by flaps of leather

feeder

chimney

middle board

valves covered by flaps of leather

pedal

rocker

feeder board

shortly before the Civil War (1860–65), and differs chiefly from the European version in that the air is sucked into, rather than pushed out of, the bellows.

The American version of the harmonium was carried west by the pioneers, and accompanied the hymns in many frontier churches. It was also prominent in American parlours. The harmonium was carried by settlers and missionaries to tropical areas, where it possesses the advantage (over the piano) of not going out of tune in a humid climate. The Bohemian composer Antonin Dvorak (1841–1905) composed a set of bagatelles for harmonium and string trio.

Below : this unusual harmonium was built in 1872–73 in London. It divides the octave into fifty-three equal intervals, allowing more perfect representation than the standard twelve intervals.

HARPOON, explosive

The EXPLOSIVE harpoon has been in use now for over 100 years for killing whales on a commerical scale. The simple hand-thrown type is not now used by the WHALING INDUSTRY, but is still used in some areas, such as by the Eskimos and Azores islanders, for killing small whales, seals and walrus. Small non-explosive harpoons are widely used for fishing in many parts of the world.

Until the middle of the nineteenth century the whaling harpoon was generally a simple shaft with a double barbed head, but this was greatly improved on in 1848 by Lewis Temple, a blacksmith from New Bedford, Massachusetts. His design was an adaptation of the Eskimo harpoon, and had a pivoted barb which swivelled inside the whale's flesh so that it would not fall out. The barb was 7 inch (17.8 cm) long, mounted on a stud at the end of a 3½ ft (1.1 m) shaft attached to a 6 ft (1.8 m) wooden pole. The barb was held in line with the shaft by a small wooden peg, and when the barb entered the whale the peg was sheared by pulling on a line attached to the harpoon, allowing the barb to turn sideways.

Harpoon guns The first harpoon gun was probably invented by the Dutch in 1731. Many designs were produced in the following hundred years, and the most successful of these was the Greener gun, followed by the large bore Brand shoulder gun in the 1840s.

Below : a harpoon gun used in modern whaling. The gun is aimed by means of the sight along the top, and fired by the trigger lever beneath the handle at the rear. Whaling fleets often use sonar equipment to track the whales, and ultrasonic transmitters to scare them so that they get exhausted from fleeing and are easily caught.

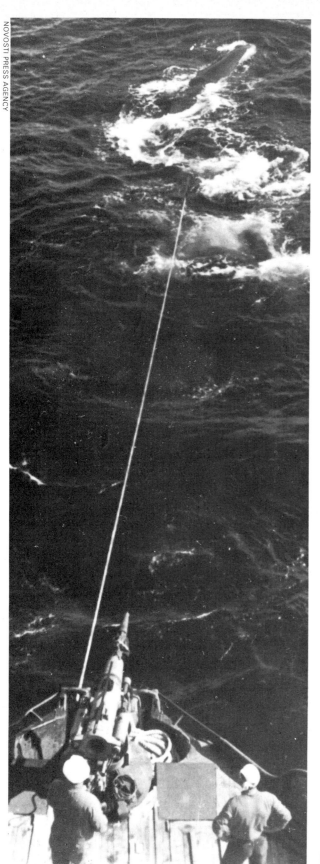

NOVOSTI PRESS AGENCY

The forerunners of the explosive harpoon were developed in the 1860s by Captain Pierce in America and Svend Foyn in Norway. The Pierce 'darting gun' consisted of a stockless gun barrel fixed to the shaft of the harpoon. A thin iron rod attached to the barb of the harpoon ran back along the shaft to the gun's trigger mechanism, and when the barb entered the whale the gun went off, firing an explosive-tipped lance into the whale. This gun was first used in the Arctic in 1865.

Svend Foyn is regarded as the most important pioneer of modern whaling, having introduced the first steam driven whaling boat in 1863, the bow mounted harpoon gun firing an explosive harpoon (1868), the factory ship (1890), and the first Antarctic whaling expedition in 1893.

Foyn's harpoon had a set of hinged barbs which spread out within the whale, and as they opened they broke a small glass tube of sulphuric acid that ignited a fuze, setting off a charge of gunpowder.

Modern harpoons . The modern harpoon gun is mounted in the bows of the whaler, and weighs about 1000 lb (454 kg). It is charged with black powder and wadding, which is ignited by a 0.32 inch (8 mm) calibre blank pistol cartridge loaded into a hole in the gun's breech and fired by a trigger mechanism.

The harpoon itself is 4 to 6 ft (1.2 to 1.8 m) long, and weighs between 160 and 180 lb (72.6 to 81.7 kg). The shaft is made of iron and has a strong line attached to it, and the end of the shaft carries four barbs and a pointed, grenade-like explosive head. Upon impact the explosive head is embedded in the flesh of the whale and held in place by the barbs. The force of the impact fires a percussion cap that sets off a short fuze train which ignites the main charge of black powder (see AMMUNITION). The force of the explosion kills or stuns the whale, and the carcass is winched back to the whaler by means of the line attached to the harpoon.

The whale carcasses are inflated with air to prevent them sinking, and are marked with a flag so that they can be collected later and towed to the factory ship for processing.

HARPSICHORD (see piano)

Left : a whaler about to fire a second harpoon into a sperm whale, which is still alive despite the impact of the 8 kg (17.6 lb) of explosive carried by the first harpoon. Sperm whales grow to over 60 ft (18 m) long, and feed mainly on cuttlefish.

Below : whaling in the Arctic, 1881, using 'javelin-bomb' explosive harpoons fired from open boats.

MARY EVANS PICTURE LIBRARY

H-BOMB

A hydrogen bomb is a device in which energy from nuclear FUSION reactions between ISOTOPES of hydrogen is released in an uncontrolled, explosive manner. Nuclear fusion is a process in which nuclei of small atoms combine to form the nucleus of a larger atom, and energy is released because the BINDING ENERGY holding together the particles in the large nucleus is less than the sum of the binding energies holding together the small nuclei. The energy set free by the almost instantaneous fusion of many millions of nuclei results in an explosion of enormous power. Indeed, the hydrogen bomb is the most destructive device ever produced by man, being many times more powerful than an atomic bomb (see A-BOMB).

Fusion Nuclear fusion cannot occur spontaneously. Normally two nuclei will tend to repel each other because they both carry a positive electric charge, so if they are to fuse, they must be forced together. In order to force nuclei together, favourable conditions are required: the nuclei must be as close together as possible to start with and they must be moving towards each other at very high velocities. High velocities can be achieved by heating the components to temperatures of several hundred million degrees, and for this reason the hydrogen bomb is often called a *thermonuclear bomb*. Once the *critical* temperature is achieved, fusion will begin, and the energy released will maintain the temperature, and hence the reaction, until either all the fusionable material has been used or the whole reaction *mixture* has expanded to such an extent that the temperature has fallen below the critical level. This whole process takes place so quickly that it is almost instantaneous.

Two isotopes of hydrogen—deuterium and tritium—are used in hydrogen bombs, rather than ordinary hydrogen. Deuterium occurs in nature, for example as deuterium oxide (D_2O or heavy water) to the extent of about one part in 5000 of ordinary water, from which it can be extracted and purified. Tritium, a radioactive isotope, does not occur naturally and must be produced artificially: it is made by bombarding lithium-6 (an isotope of the ALKALI METAL lithium with atomic weight 6) with neutrons, when it splits into helium and tritium.

Development of hydrogen bombs Primitive hydrogen bombs consisted of an A-bomb and a supply of hydrogen isotopes in liquid form. The A-bomb acted as a trigger by supplying the heat necessary to initiate the fusion reaction. (This is still the only practical means of supplying the enormous heat required, although the possibilities of using LASERS as triggers are being explored.) Liquid isotopes were used because atoms are closer together in a liquid than in a gas, but because liquid hydrogen isotopes are very unstable and dangerous, this type of hydrogen bomb could not be stored safely.

Modern hydrogen bombs consist basically of an A-bomb trigger surrounded by a lining of lithium deuteride, a compound of deuterium and lithium (lithium-6). Lithium deuteride has two main functions. First, it serves to hold deuterium nuclei very close together (atoms are even more closely packed in a solid than in a liquid) so that they are in a favourable position to undergo fusion when heat is supplied. Second, the lithium-6 will produce tritium when bombarded with neu-

Right: the mushroom cloud produced by the testing of a hydrogen bomb in the atmosphere. A similar cloud would be produced even by a non-nuclear explosion of the same size: it is caused by the hot gases, which initially rush upwards in a column until their pressure equals atmospheric pressure at that height, then spread out.

trons, and the tritium can then fuse with the deuterium. Neutrons for this process are supplied by the A-bomb, so that the trigger also has more than one function. In addition to the main reactions—deuterium with deuterium and deuterium with tritium—other fusion reactions may contribute to the explosion. For example, a lithium nucleus can fuse with a deuterium nucleus to release energy.

This type of hydrogen bomb is said to be relatively 'clean', meaning that it produces only small quantities of radioactive debris, or 'fallout'. The fallout, which can remain radioactive for months or years, is composed chiefly of radioactive fission products from the trigger—but only in limited amounts as only a small A-bomb is used—together with unburned tritium. Often, however, a hydrogen bomb is surrounded by a layer of uranium (uranium-238). As well as acting as a 'container' to keep the bomb together and the fusion reaction going a little longer, this uranium, when bombarded by fast neutrons generated by the fusion reaction, is a further source of fission energy. This type of bomb—called a fission-fusion-fission bomb—produces considerable amounts of radioactive fallout, and is therefore described as 'dirty'.

The explosive power of a hydrogen bomb is much greater than that of an A-bomb, for two main reasons. First, because hydrogen is the lightest of all elements, a given mass of deuterium or tritium contains many more atoms than the same mass of uranium or plutonium and thus, weight for weight, there are more deuterium or tritium nuclei available for fusion than there are uranium or plutonium nuclei able to undergo fission. In fact, the complete fusion of a given mass of deuterium would theoretically yield almost three times as much energy as the complete fission of the same mass of uranium-235. Second, the size of a hydrogen bomb, unlike that of an A-bomb, is theoretically almost unlimited. The self-sustaining chain reaction of an A-bomb can only continue if more than a certain mass of fissionable material is present, but when the bomb explodes, much of the fissionable material is blown away unused and, because the required mass is no longer present, the chain reaction stops. In the hydrogen bomb, fusion will continue as long as fusionable material is available, in however small amounts, provided the temperature is high enough, and so a larger proportion of the fusionable material is used. Hydrogen bomb size is therefore limited only by the weight that an aircraft or missile delivery system can carry.

Testing of hydrogen bombs The first hydrogen bomb test explosion was carried out by the United States on 1 November 1952, at Bikini Atoll in the Pacific: it had an explosive yield of five to seven megatons (equivalent to the explosion of between five and seven million tons of TNT). The Soviet Union tested its first hydrogen bomb on 21 August 1953. Since then Britain, France and China have also developed and tested their own hydrogen bombs. The largest hydrogen bomb ever exploded—by the Soviet Union on 30 August 1961—was estimated to have had a yield of some 60 megatons (equivalent to 60 million tons of TNT). For comparison, the A-bombs exploded over Japan at the end of World War 2 had a yield of about 15 kilotons (equivalent to 15,000 tons of TNT), and the maximum size of an A-bomb is probably a few hundred kilotons.

Although hydrogen bombs have never been used in war, test explosions have many undesirable effects. In particular, radioactive fallout can contaminate food, milk and so on, and could cause serious diseases such as cancer. It was at least partly to minimize such dangers that in August 1963 the United States,

the Soviet Union and Britain signed a treaty banning nuclear weapon tests of any type in the atmosphere, in outer space or underwater: such tests are permitted only if they are carried out underground and only if adequate precautions are taken to prevent the escape of radioactive debris into the atmosphere. Since then, many other countries have signed this treaty, even though they are not themselves in a position to carry out nuclear tests. But two countries—France and China—have not yet signed, and are still carrying out tests in the atmosphere, despite strong protests from countries such as Australia and New Zealand who claim that their territories are being contaminated by radioactive fallout.

At the present time, moves are being made to persuade France and China to stop their atmospheric testing and also to limit the size of test explosions carried out underground. While these moves will not themselves affect the numbers of hydrogen bombs currently stockpiled by the nuclear-weapon countries—many thousands of them are already fitted into intercontinental ballistic MISSILES and carried on long-range bombers and nuclear SUBMARINES—it is hoped that limiting and eventually abolishing nuclear testing altogether will be at least a first step in ensuring that these terrible weapons will never be used in war.

Right: a post-boost controlled multiple warhead missile. When the main rocket stage has reached its destination the 'bus' carrying the warheads continues onwards. The first warhead at 2 is dropped. The bus then performs a series of manoeuvres by firing its own rocket motor and another warhead is ejected at each stage. The warheads can either be aimed at different targets or at the same target after a predetermined time lapse.

1

2

3

warheads

bus

final rocket stage

4

3

1

2

4

post-boost control of a multiple warhead missile MIRV

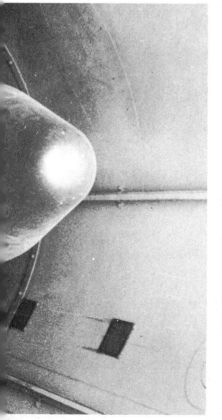

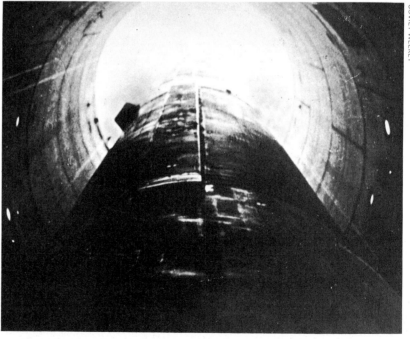

A French atomic weapon, the SSBS (sol-sol ballistique stratégique), a ground to ground missile. This has a simple atomic 150 kiloton warhead, but the missiles are to be equipped with hydrogen warheads.

A Soviet missile in its underground silo. The USSR has over 1500 of these hydrogen armed missiles ready for launching, and the USA 1000. Each side has over 600 subs, probably with 16 H-bomb missiles each.

HEARING AID

The development of the electronic hearing aid was the biggest advance ever made in helping deaf people, and hearing aids are now used by millions of people all over the world. All hearing aids are fundamentally simple acoustic amplifying systems and consist of four basic parts: a MICROPHONE to pick up the sound and convert it to a very small electrical signal; an AMPLIFIER to increase the size of the electrical signal; an earphone (often called a receiver in hearing aid circles) to turn the electrical signal into an acoustic one which is then fed into the ear through an earmould; and a source of power for the amplifier, usually a small BATTERY. The earmould is not part of the hearing aid but is essential for fitting the aid to the user. It is made of plastic and moulded from an impression taken of the user's ear.

Hearing aids can be divided into three groups: body worn, head worn and educational aids such as group hearing aids and auditory training units. Because of their larger size body worn aids are capable of the widest possible performance and can cater for all types and degrees of deafness. They are, however, large and many people do not like to be seen wearing them, preferring the smaller head worn aids. These can be divided into three main groups: those worn behind the ear, in spectacle frames, and completely in the outer ear itself. Head worn aids are not capable of producing the high output of body worn aids, but otherwise have very similar characteristics. The smaller the aid the more restricted is its performance. Group hearing aid equipment is used in schools for the deaf and partially hearing units where size is unimportant. The large high quality microphones and earphones used ensure the best possible performance and exceed that obtained with aids worn on the body or head.

Performance   The performance of a hearing aid is largely controlled by the transducers, that is microphone and earphone. The performance of the transducers can be indicated by means of a frequency response curve which shows graphically how the microphone or earphone responds over a range of frequencies from 100 to 10,000 Hertz (Hz). At low frequencies the limitation is largely due to the microphone, while at high frequencies it is the earphone that restricts the performance.

The amplifier consists of three or more transistors, depending upon the amount of amplification required. The frequency response and power output from the amplifier is such that it places almost no limitation on the performance of the aid. The amount of noise, however, generated by the first transistor stage is important because if it is too high the listener will hear a continuous background rushing noise. The maximum amount of sound available from the aid, called the maximum acoustic output, will depend upon the power handling capability of the output transistor and earphone; in addition the power available will be limited by the current that can be drawn from the battery. The smaller the battery the smaller the current that can be taken while still giving a reasonable battery life, and the lower the maximum amount of sound available from the aid. The amount of acoustic amplification required depends upon the degree of deafness which the aid is required to help and may vary from 40 decibels (dB) that is 100 times, to 80 dB, that is 10,000 times. Because the transducers have less than 100% efficiency, the electrical amplification necessary is considerably greater than the acoustic amplification. Amplification varies with frequency and most hearing aids amplify high frequencies more than low ones. It has been found that this gives better intelligibility of speech.

The earphone will alter the performance of the aid in terms of frequency response, gain and maximum acoustic output, and on body worn aids this is used as a means of altering the performance and then fitting the hearing aid to suit individual requirements. The main limitation on earphones is at high frequencies.

Frequency response curves   The performance of hearing aids can be roughly divided into three groups in terms of the maximum acoustic output or power; that is, low, medium and high power. Low power aids will have maximum outputs of around 110 dB sound pressure level (SPL), medium 120 dB SPL and high power aids 130 dB SPL or more. It should be remembered that the noise from a jet engine close by is only about 130 dB SPL and that some deaf people are not able to hear at this level, but can hear something at 135 dB SPL or more.

On many hearing aids there is a switch which disconnects the microphone (marked M) and switches in an inductive pick up coil (marked T because it was originally designed for telephone use). This coil enables the user to pick up alternating magnetic signals produced by an electric current flowing through a loop of wire around the room, enabling him to move anywhere in the loop and hear the signal without direct connection to the amplifier. Such a system can be used in schools and in the home where it is used for listening to the radio and television. This system has the advantage that speech picked up by a microphone near the speaker's mouth is effectively fed directly into the hearing aid without the interfering effects of distance and background noise.

In order to measure the performance of a hearing aid, a constant acoustic signal over the frequency range 100 to 10,000 Hz is fed in and the output measured by an acoustic coupler.

Left: the earliest type of hearing aid, the ear trumpet, had a large mouth which collected more sound than the ear by itself. Seen here are Beethoven's ear trumpets.

Below: examples of early aids. They had carbon microphones and large batteries in leather holders. They were not amplifiers in the conventional sense, but similar to telephones.

Top left: a device called a laryngograph enables a profoundly deaf person to modify his own voice patterns. Two tiny electrodes are placed on the front of the neck of the deaf person. These record every movement of the vocal cords, analyze them and show the result as a simple pattern on an oscilloscope.

Top right: a class of partially deaf children working solely with body worn hearing aids. The desks, however, are also equipped with 'goose neck' microphones, which are for use with headphones where each aid is interconnected for maximum benefit to each child.

Below: head worn aids—spectacle frame and behind ear types. 1 microphone, 2 earphone (receiver), 3 battery compartment, 4 volume control, 5 circuitry, 6 earhook, 7 on-off switch, 8 tone control, 9 audiological adjustment, 10 adjustable temple extension, 11 earphone spout.

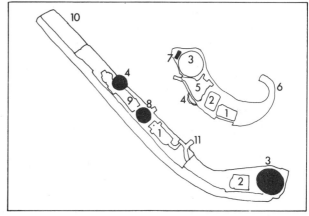

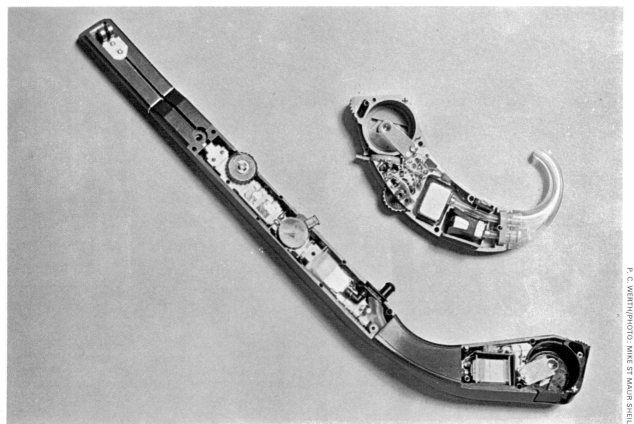

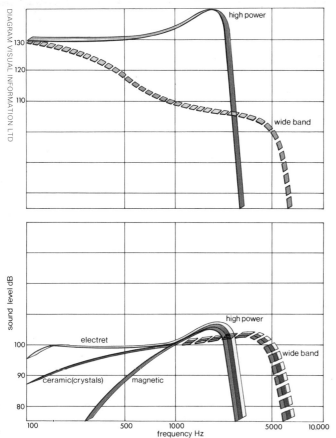

DIAGRAM VISUAL INFORMATION LTD

HEART-LUNG MACHINE

Heart-lung machines are used in all major heart operations to maintain the function of the heart and lungs during surgery.

The heart pumps blood between the lungs, where it picks up oxygen, and the various parts of the body, where the oxygen is consumed. Oxygenated blood flows from the heart in arteries and deoxygenated blood flows back to the heart in veins. The heart consists of four chambers: the *right atrium* and *right ventricle*, which pump the deoxygenated blood to the lungs, and the *left atrium* and *left ventricle* which pump the oxygenated blood from the lungs to the rest of the body. The functions of the lungs and the heart are thus intimately associated with each other.

A heart-lung machine performs two main functions: it introduces oxygen into the blood received from the veins, and it pumps the oxygenated blood to the patient's arterial system

Right: a heart-lung machine equipped with a membrane oxygenator. On the left is an exploded view of the oxygenator. The venous blood is passed to the oxygenator, partly through a by-pass tube inserted close to the heart and partly through a peristaltic pump from the heart itself. After leaving the oxygenator, the blood passes through a pump and a heat exchanger before being returned to the heart.

Below left: a heart-lung machine with a bubble oxygenator, which is made of transparent plastic and is disposable. The machine has three pumps, a temperature control unit and a monitoring unit mounted on the vertical pole at the right of the machine.

Below right: a heart-lung machine with a membrane oxygenator. Oxygen inlets and outlets (blue) can be seen on one side of the oxygenator.

Above: frequency response curves measured at the earpiece after amplification. The lower curves are obtained using a low level acoustic signal input to the aid. The maximum acoustic output is shown in the upper curves. Different microphones alter the low frequency responses (black lines) while different earpieces affect the high frequency responses. The earpieces also affect the maximum acoustic output of the aids as can be seen from the curves for a wideband and a high power earpiece. It is not yet possible to have a wide frequency band and high output.

Below: sound is picked up by the microphone, converted into electrical signals and amplified by the three amplifying stages. The acoustical output signal is detected by the ear mechanism (right).

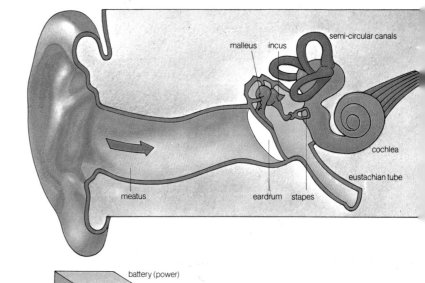

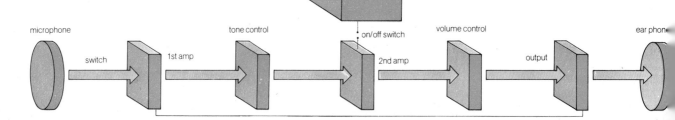

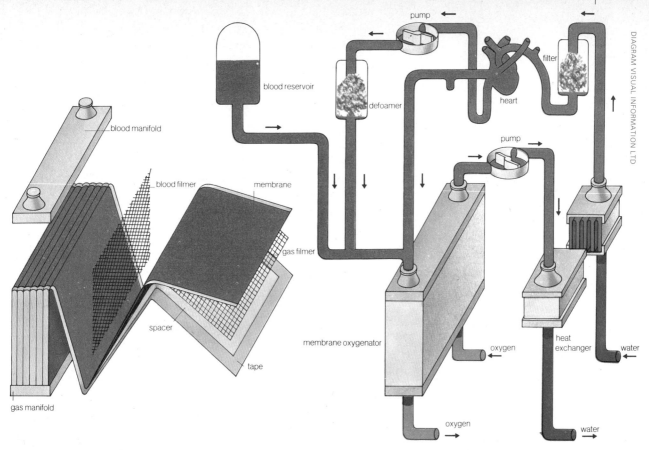

blood manifold

blood filmer

membrane

gas filmer

spacer

tape

gas manifold

blood reservoir

pump

pump

defoamer

heart

filter

membrane oxygenator

oxygen

heat exchanger

water

oxygen

water

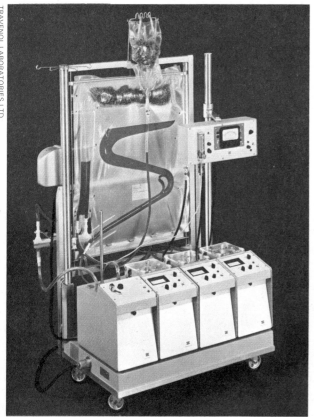

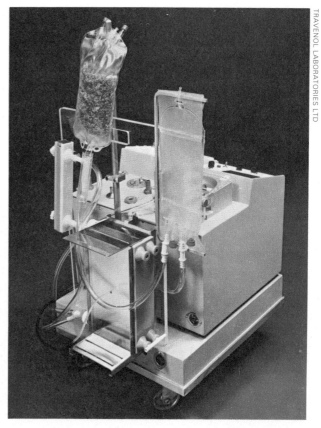

at a rate similar to that of the patient's own heart. It must also keep the patient's blood volume and temperature at acceptable levels and maintain the correct chemical balance of the blood. The machine comprises speed controlled roller pumps to maintain the circulation, an oxygenator to introduce oxygen into the blood, filters to remove particulate debris from the patient's blood, a HEAT EXCHANGER and controller to maintain the required temperature, reservoirs for blood and chemical solutions interconnected with tubing, and stopcocks. The entire system is mounted on a mobile trolley.

The heart-lung machine in action

During major heart surgery a time is reached when the action of the heart and lungs needs to be bypassed by the machine. Tubes called *catheters* are introduced into the major veins close to the heart and the blood flows into a reservoir in the heart-lung machine and is pumped to the oxygenator. The blood gives up carbon dioxide and takes up oxygen in the oxygenator and is passed through a filter and heat exchanger. The freshly oxygenated blood is then pumped at the desired pressure through a catheter to a major artery. Once the bypass is functioning correctly the vessels of the heart may be clamped off and the surgery commenced.

Introducing the machine into the circulation requires an extra priming volume of blood which allows the machine to function directly it is connected to the patient.

The ability to perform major heart surgery is due to the technical progress in developing oxygenators and pumps. It was discovered that blood would give up its carbon dioxide and take up oxygen if it was spread as a film on to surfaces exposed in an atmosphere of oxygen. A metal plate dipped into venous blood (blood from the veins) and exposed to oxygen produces the desired effect and a successful oxygenator is based on this principle. The *rotating disc oxygenator* comprises many thin metal discs separated by spacers supported on a shaft. This assembly is housed in a glass cylinder held between two metal end plates. Entry and exit ports for oxygen and blood are fitted. The venous blood enters one end and the rotating discs allow a thin film of blood to be exposed to the oxygen atmosphere and return it to the pool. The appearance of the blood in the oxygenator becomes progressively a brighter red, and with sufficient discs in the cylinder the blood being pumped from the outlet is fully oxygenated. A cylinder possessing a larger number of discs will oxygenate more blood in a given time but will require a higher priming volume of blood so a compromise size must be selected. The speed of rotation regulates the rate at which blood is oxygenated and needs to be controlled. For an adult the oxygenator needs to deliver up to four litres of blood per minute. The temperature of the blood in the oxygenator is measured and a temperature controller can be set to regulate the heat exchanger to produce the required value.

Rotating disc oxygenators, however, suffer from two drawbacks. Firstly, the shearing forces set up as the blood comes into contact with the rotating discs tend to rupture the blood cells, and secondly, direct contact between the blood and the oxygen causes some of the protein molecules in the blood to be destroyed, or *denatured*. This means that the quality of the patient's blood deteriorates progressively while the heart-lung machine remains connected. The period of use of such machines is thus limited to a few hours.

These drawbacks are to a large extent overcome by the *membrane oxygenator*. In this device the oxygen and the blood flow along opposite sides of a membrane made of silicone rubber. Gas molecules, that is the oxygen in one direction and the carbon dioxide in the other, can pass through the membrane while the blood cannot. The blood is thus oxygenated without any direct oxygen-blood contact and without mechanical agitation.

Pumps

The pumps used in heart-lung machines must be able to transport blood through the machine and the patient without mechanically damaging the cells. Damaged cells and the subsequent reduction in their number can cause immediate and long term problems in the patient's circulation. Pumps with a *peristaltic* action (the blood is squeezed gently along a length of silastic tubing by rollers, cams or fingers) are found to be superior in performance and possess the important advantage that no mechanical parts come into direct contact with the blood. The rate of rotation of the pumps must be carefully controlled to ensure minimum mechanical damage to the cells while maintaining adequate circulation.

To prepare the machine for use all components must be clean and sterile, all connectors and edges should be free from burrs and during the assembly of the system great care should be taken to preserve the sterility of all parts. Correctly matched blood in the correct quantities should be added to the machine to prime the oxygenator. At the conclusion of surgery the patient's condition is carefully checked before releasing the main vessel clamps.

Right: an inductively coupled pacemaker, which consists of an implanted wire coil with leads to the heart, and an external, battery powered coil which generates a current in the internal one by electromagnetic induction, like a transformer.

Far right: an implantable pacemaker with a nuclear battery. The design of the battery ensures protection from radiation.

Below: a heart-lung machine with a rotating disc oxygenator. The oxygenator can be seen in the centre of the picture and has a number of discs fixed to a horizontal shaft rotating in a cylindrical container. Three peristaltic pumps can be seen in the foreground.

KEN MOREMAN

HEART PACEMAKER

The heart pacemaker maintains the steady pumping action of the heart by delivering a regular stimulation. Any muscle is sensitive to electrical excitation, but the heart is even more sensitive than most.

Heart pacemakers are divided into three categories: the natural pacemaker possessed by all animals, from the most primitive to the most complex; the external electronic pacemaker, located outside the body and used by hospitals in emergency and temporary situations; and the miniature pacemakers, driven by batteries, which can be surgically implanted in the body. The pacemaker adjusts the rate of stimulation according to the demands of the body; for example, during sleep, the adult human heart slows to approximately 55 to 65 beats per minute, and during hard work or exercise speeds up to more than 100 beats per minute. During temporary periods of great exertion the heartbeat may exceed 200 beats a minute. A failure of the pacemaker to communicate its signal to the heart results in the failure of the heart to pump blood, a condition known as *heart block*.

Natural pacemaker The natural pacemaker is a *sino-atrial node* (lump of small fibres) located near the top of the heart, which receives its instruction from outer masses of muscle tissue in the heart, according to the body's need for oxygen, its temperature, nervous excitation, and other factors.

Biological experiments have shown that each cell of heart tissue seems to beat at its own rate, and that the instructions to the natural pacemaker are a consensus. In experiments with the salamander and similar creatures, grafted pacemakers from other animals can take over the function of the natural pacemaker without difficulty, but in man such a graft results only in scar tissue, so the function of the human natural pacemaker must be replaced when necessary by an electronic device.

External pacemaker The external pacemaker, used in emergency and temporary situations, works by means of a *catheter* (a tube inserted by a surgeon) extending through a vein to the right ventricle of the heart. The catheter contains electrical sensing and stimulating devices.

Implantable pacemaker Several types of 'portable' pacemakers have been developed since the 1950s. One model requires the implantation only of electrodes, with the device itself taped to the patient's chest. This device can be powered by a battery small enough to be worn on the chest or by batteries which are worn in a pocket or in a holder which clips to the patient's belt. Pacemakers which are entirely implanted in the body, battery and all, have been in use since the late 1950s and information on their long-term performance is still being collected.

Implantable pacemakers must meet certain design requirements. They must have long term reliability, measured in years.

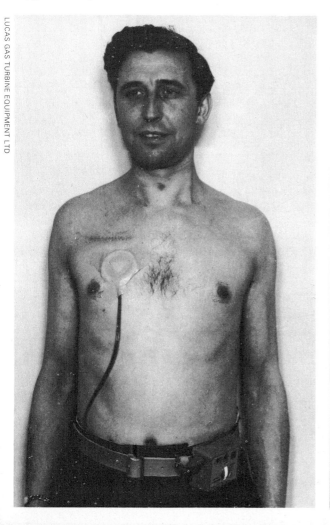

They must have long battery life (currently three years). The circuitry must be designed to operate at a low current drain, whose output pulse must remain unaffected by battery and load variations. The enclosure of the device must offer maximum protection from the ingress of body fluids, and the electrode system must be mechanically and electrolytically stable.

Batteries Pacemakers commonly used mercury cells, which are small enough and offer an excellent power to volume ratio and are capable of maintaining a constant output voltage for 90% of their life span. Other recent developments include an *isotope source generator* and the *metal-oxygen cell*. The ISOTOPE generator converts the heat generated by plutonium-238 into electrical energy using a *thermopile* (see THERMO-ELECTRIC

Left: an implantable pacemaker with five batteries.

Below left: a close-up of the nuclear battery, which is about 2 inch (5 cm) long. A small quantity of plutonium-238 generates electricity in a semiconductor thermopile. The battery is licensed for production in both the USA and Britain.

Below: an isotope battery of the type used in heart pacemakers. The isotope, 0.18 gm of Pu-238, decays radioactively, thus heating the sides of the capsule one end of which touches the thermopile which is itself in contact with the outer capsule at its lower end. The battery is filled with a low conductivity gas such as xenon or is evacuated, and must be well insulated both thermally and against escape of radiation. A voltage is generated in the battery due to the heating of the thermopile.

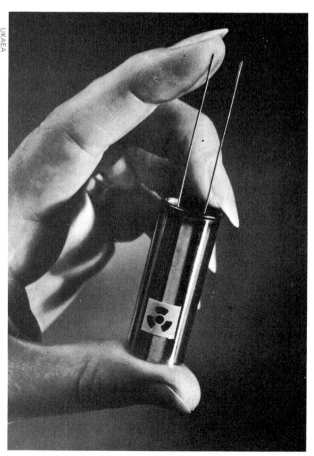

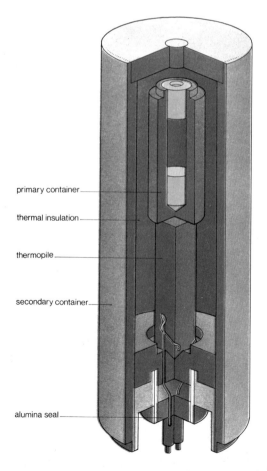

primary container

thermal insulation

thermopile

secondary container

alumina seal

DEVICES), with the constant deep body temperature of 37°C (98°F) acting as a cold junction. Although a life of ten years is predicted, extensive testing is needed to ensure completely safe packaging. The metal-oxygen cell relies upon the oxygen content of the body tissue to supply it with energy; problems to be overcome include the level of oxygen present and the ability to maintain suitable rates of diffusion.

Circuitry The *blocking oscillator circuit* still in use in many pacemakers is satisfactory, but because it needs a TRANSFORMER it is unacceptable for *thin film* circuit construction, which has been found to be best for long term stability. *Complementary pair* pulse generators have been tried; their advantage is that they do not place a constant strain on the battery, but they are particularly sensitive to line and load variation. *Monostable* and *bistable* circuits (see LOGIC CIRCUITS) have been adapted for pacemakers; difficulties have been overcome in achieving the required pulse repetition rate and width without unacceptable differences in timing components.

The *demand* pacemaker possesses, in addition to the pulse generator, a frequency selective amplifier which controls the pulse generator *inhibitor*. The electrode that stimulates the heart also monitors the ECG (electrocardiogram). The amplifier inhibits the generator except when heart block occurs, thus stimulating the heart 'on demand'.

The patient suffering from heart block is admitted to hospital, and his heart is assisted by an external pacemaker while he undergoes minor surgery to have the subminiature device implanted. He will be discharged from hospital, attend out-patient clinics for check-ups, and be able to lead a normal life.

HEART VALVES, artificial

Artificial heart valves are devices implanted by surgery to replace natural heart valves which have become diseased and are gradually failing to operate properly.

The heart is a hollow muscular pump which is divided into two by a wall or *septum* to make a right half and a left half. These are again divided into upper chambers or *atria* and lower chambers or *ventricles*. The right side of the heart collects the impure blood from the body through veins leading into the right atrium, which contracts and sends blood through the *tricuspid valve* into the right ventricle. This in turn contracts to drive the blood through the *pulmonary valve* and the *pulmonary arteries* into the lungs where the blood is reoxygenated. The oxygenated blood returns to the left atrium, passes through the *mitral valve* and into the left ventricle, where it is pumped through the *aortic valve* and then round the body.

In order for the heart to pump blood efficiently it has to develop a high pressure in each of its chambers, and therefore its valves must be capable of allowing the blood to flow freely in one direction and not let any leak-back occur.

Much research is still going on today in order to improve the design of the artificial heart valve. Firstly it must be accepted by the body and not cause irritation to the surrounding

Below : a human heart fitted with a Starr-Edwards mitral valve. In the left diagram oxygenated blood from the lungs flows through the artificial valve into the left ventricle. The left ventricle then contracts, closing the Starr-Edwards valve and opening the aortic valve so that the blood is pumped into the aorta.

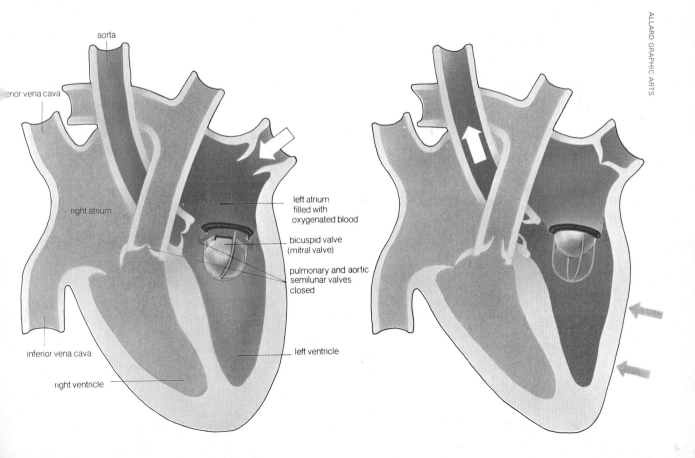

ALLARD GRAPHIC ARTS

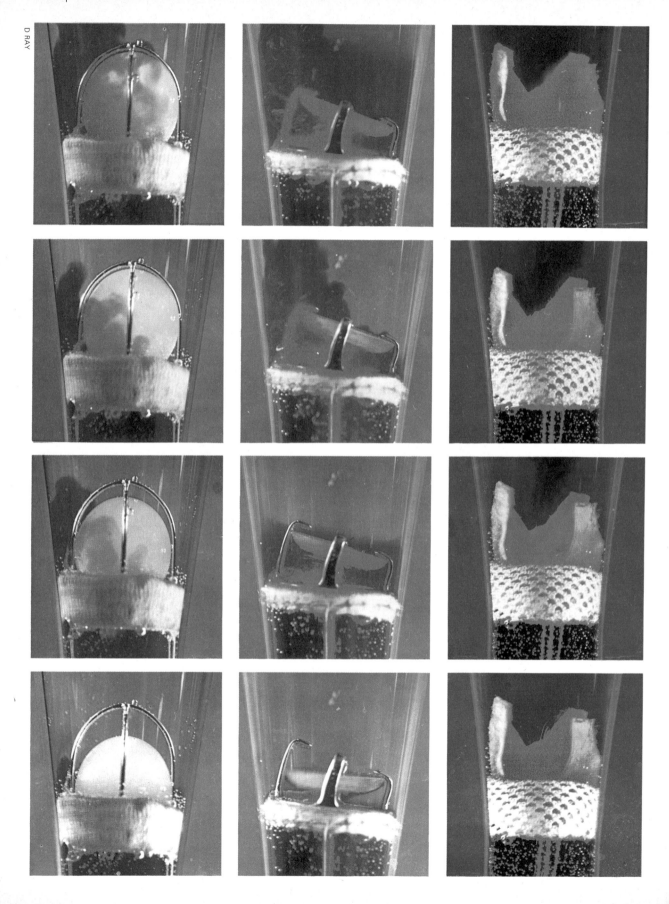

tissue. It must also be capable of performing its function for many years without the need for replacement or repair.

The most commonly used artificial valve is the Starr-Edwards valve. This valve has a ring around the base and a metal cage which encloses a silicone plastic or, more recently, a hollow metal ball. The metal used is an alloy of cobalt, chromium, tungsten, molybdenum and iron, which is hard and inert. The ring and cage are covered with a cloth; this forms a framework into which tissue can grow. Each time the heart contracts, the ball is pushed upwards and blood escapes around the ball; when the heart relaxes the ball falls back into the ring to make a leakproof seal.

Two main problems exist in the use of artificial heart valves. The first is the risk of clots forming around the valve: therefore, patients with these valves must have medication to lower the ability of the blood to clot. Secondly, the present design of heart valves still gives a fairly high resistance to flow. Nevertheless, artificial valves are much more efficient than the damaged natural valves they replace, and patients who were virtually invalids can now live a full life.

Many other types of valve have been made, all with their particular advantages and limitations. They all use the same principle of action, the contractile force of the heart ejecting blood and lifting a disc or ball to allow flow in one direction.

Many attempts have been made to build leaflet valves that have a hinge or flap similar to the natural heart valve, but unfortunately the repeated hinging or flexing action causes the valve to break up. Until technologists can develop materials capable of withstanding this high degree of stress, leaflet type valves are not likely to gain wide acceptance.

HEAT (see calorimetry)

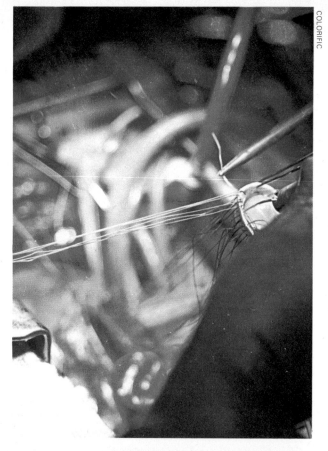

Opposite page: experiments comparing the performance of three types of heart valve; the Starr-Edwards valve (left), an experimental disc valve (centre) and a natural homograft valve (right). The pictures show how the valves cause turbulence in the red fluid, which represents blood, as it flows through them. The flow through the natural valve is virtually non-turbulent whereas the Starr-Edwards valve introduces significant turbulence.

Above right: a Starr-Edwards valve being inserted into a heart. The surgeon's sutures can be seen passing through a Dacron collar around the valve.

Right: an X-ray photograph showing a Starr-Edwards valve in position. Only the metal parts of the valve can be seen because only these are opaque to X-rays. The plastic ball does not show up in the picture.

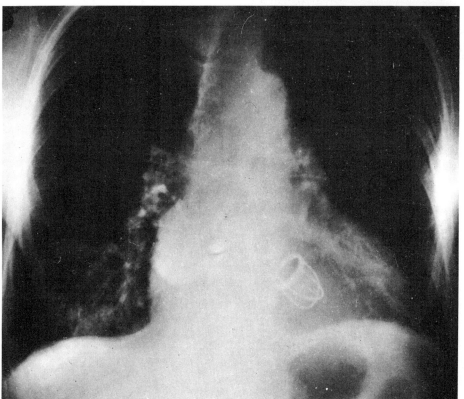

HEAT ENGINE

The term heat engine is used by engineers in two entirely different ways. First it is used loosely and generally to include any engine which produces work or power continuously from the combustion of a fuel in air. In this sense, any of the following are heat engines: petrol [gasoline] engines, diesel engines, gas turbines and jet engines and steam turbine power plants.

The second sense is the precise one used in the science of THERMODYNAMICS. In thermodynamics, a heat engine is a device which receives literally *heat* and produces work or power from this. By this definition, a petrol engine is not a heat engine because it does not take in heat but a mixture of petrol and air. A distinction like this may appear at first to be splitting hairs—after all, burning petrol in air produces a mixture of hot gases and these gases are used in the engine to drive the pistons and produce work. Nevertheless, it is more satisfactory for both engineers and scientists if engines which burn fuel internally are given their correct name—INTERNAL COMBUSTION ENGINES.

Steam turbines There are few practical types of heat engines and the most important example is the steam turbine power plant used in electricity generating stations. This heat engine consists of a boiler in which water is evaporated into steam using heat transfer from hot gases, a turbine which produces power as the steam flows through it, a condenser in which steam is converted back into water again, and a feed pump which pumps the water back into the boiler. The working fluid (in this case steam or water) flows continuously round in a closed circuit.

Other types of heat engine have been devised, for example, the STIRLING and Carnot engines, but these have achieved little practical importance so far.

The efficiency of heat engines The importance of the thermodynamic concept of a heat engine derives from the fact that it is essential to our understanding of the conversion of heat into work. Heat is available from the combustion of fossil fuels such as coal and oil and from nuclear fuels as well. But fuel is expensive and it is important to know that the maximum amount of power is being obtained from a given quantity of fuel. By examining the behaviour of a 'perfect' heat engine the answer can be found.

Suppose there is a reservoir of heat at a temperature T_1 (a reservoir is used in thermodynamics to mean a *store*—of heat, in this example) and a cold reservoir at temperature T_2. Also, suppose that an amount of heat Q is taken from the hot reservoir to the engine, thereby producing an amount of work W. From this generalized description of the working features of a heat engine it is possible to determine the highest value of W that can be obtained.

The first law of thermodynamics states that it is not possible to get something for nothing, or put another way, that the best that can be done is to turn the whole of Q into work W. If both Q and W are measured in the same units (as mentioned in CALORIMETRY, this is possible, and the international unit of heat and work is the *Joule*) then W can be related directly to Q. When W equals Q the ratio W/Q is unity—this ration is called the *efficiency* and is usually expressed as a percentage, in this case 100%. An efficiency greater than this is impossible because it would break the first law of thermodynamics.

When the efficiency of a power station as a heat engine is measured, its efficiency is found to be much lower—around 45%. In other words 55% of the heat is 'lost' to the cold reservoir, (that is, to the cooling water in the cooling towers).

At first sight, it would seem that engineers are not doing a very good job. This is, however, a false impression which can be explained by the second law of thermodynamics. This states that the efficiency of even a *perfect* heat engine must be less than 100% and that it is related to the temperatures of the reservoirs. The efficiency is given by $(T_1-T_2)/T_1$ provided that the temperatures T_1 and T_2 are expressed on a special (absolute) scale of TEMPERATURE and measured in Kelvins (K)—0°C is 273 K.

Suppose that T_1 on this scale has a value of 800 K and T_2 a value of 300 K. The maximum efficiency of any heat engine operating between these temperatures would be (800–300)/800 which is 0.625 or 62.5%. If the actual efficiency of the real heat engine is 45% then the engineers are really doing quite well.

Right: construction of a 660 megawatt turbine designed to operate at 3000 rpm. In the foreground is the high pressure turbine shaft followed by the intermediate pressure shaft and three low pressure shafts. The turbine is driven by steam, which is fed to the high pressure section at a temperature of 1050°F (566°C) and a pressure of 2300 psi (159 bar).

Below: heat engines convert the heat flowing from a hot reservoir to a cold reservoir into mechanical work. The efficiency of this conversion process improves as the temperature difference between the two reservoirs increases. The steam turbine power unit in a power station is a good example of a heat engine. Superheated steam is forced under pressure into the turbine chamber where mechanical work is generated through the rotation of the turbine blades.

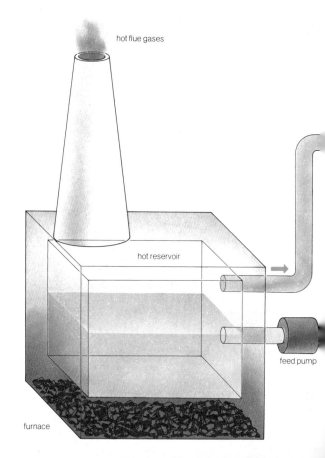

hot flue gases

hot reservoir

feed pump

furnace

REYROLLE PARSONS

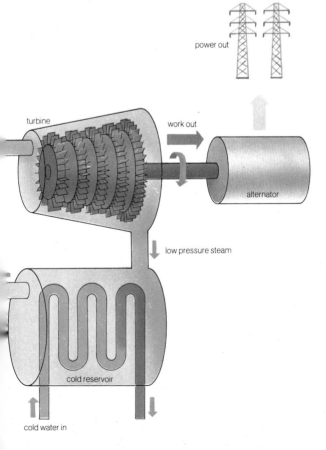

power out

turbine

work out

alternator

low pressure steam

cold reservoir

cold water in

HEATER

Because man has refused to be restricted in his movements by climate, he has had to protect himself against the cold by clothing and by the heat produced from burning fuel. As housing developed so did domestic heating. The Romans had their floors warmed by the products of combustion from underground fireplaces (see HYPOCAUST). In colder climates open fires were superseded by closed stoves with extended flue pipes, and these were the forerunners of the more advanced methods in use today.

Heat transfer   There are three ways in which heat is transferred from a hot body to a cooler one: *conduction, convection* and *radiation*. Conduction is the transfer, or flow, of heat through a body when part of it is heated or brought into contact with something hot. The handle of a poker becomes hot by conduction. Convection is the transfer of heat through a liquid or gas by the mixing effect of convection currents which are set up when the gas or liquid is heated. The water in a domestic hot water tank fitted with an electrical immersion heater heats up largely by convection. Radiation is the name given to direct heat transfer from a hot body to a cooler one spaced apart from it. Heating by the sun's rays is an example of radiation.

Domestic heaters generate heat by burning a fuel, such as gas, oil, coal or coke, or by passing an electric current through an electrical element. Such heaters can be broadly divided into two types, those which require a secondary system to distribute the generated heat, as in central heating systems, and those which do not, such as electric 'bar' and fan heaters and free standing paraffin [kerosene] heaters.

Central heating   Central heating is the term used for a system which distributes heat throughout a building from a single heat source. The heat is generated by burning a fuel such as coke, oil or gas, in a boiler if the heat transfer medium is water, or a HEAT EXCHANGER if the medium is air.

ALLARD GRAPHIC ARTS

In a domestic boiler the heat generated is used to heat (but not boil) water which is then circulated to the various radiators in the system. The radiators are connected to each other and to the boiler by means of piping, nowadays usually small bore copper tubing, so that the heated water flows in a circuit from the boiler through each successive radiator and then back to the boiler to be reheated. Modern systems include electrically driven pumps to circulate the water at the rate required to maintain a suitable temperature difference between the input and output pipes of the boiler. For domestic systems this temperature difference is normally about 10°C (18°F). The system must also allow for the expansion of the water as it is heated. In an *open system* the extra water volume is accommodated in an open expansion tank. In a *sealed system* the increase is taken up by the compression of air in a closed expansion vessel. Whether the system is open or sealed, it should be connected to a mains water supply so that any loss of water can be made good. The radiators in a water circulating system emit heat partly by radiation and partly by conduction to the adjacent air. The heat is distributed throughout the room by air convection.

In 'warm air' central heating systems, air is passed through a heat exchanger by an electrically driven fan and is kept separate from the combustion gases which are discharged to the atmosphere. The warmed air is distributed via ducts to the rooms through grilles having regulating dampers, and is returned to the heat exchanger for reheating, usually via grilles in the doors but sometimes through separate ducts. Air for ventilation may be introduced from outside through a fresh air inlet and the rate of recirculation reduced accordingly.

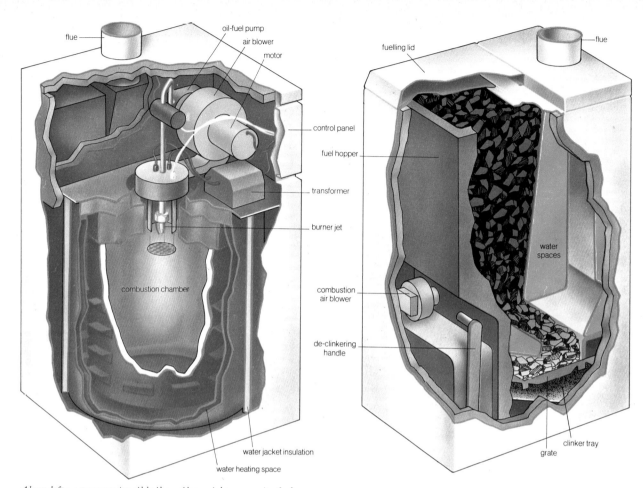

flue

oil-fuel pump

air blower

motor

control panel

transformer

burner jet

combustion chamber

water jacket insulation

water heating space

fuelling lid

flue

fuel hopper

water spaces

combustion air blower

de-clinkering handle

clinker tray

grate

Above left: a pressure jet oil boiler. Above right: a gravity feed coal boiler.
Below: gas and coal convector heaters and an electric radiant fire.

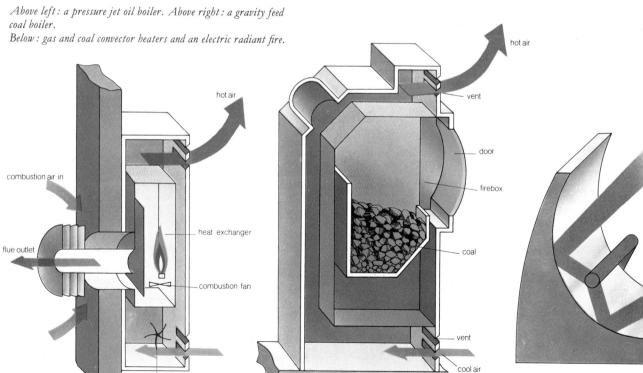

hot air

hot air

vent

door

firebox

coal

combustion air in

heat exchanger

flue outlet

combustion fan

vent

cool air

convector fan

ALLARD GRAPHIC ARTS

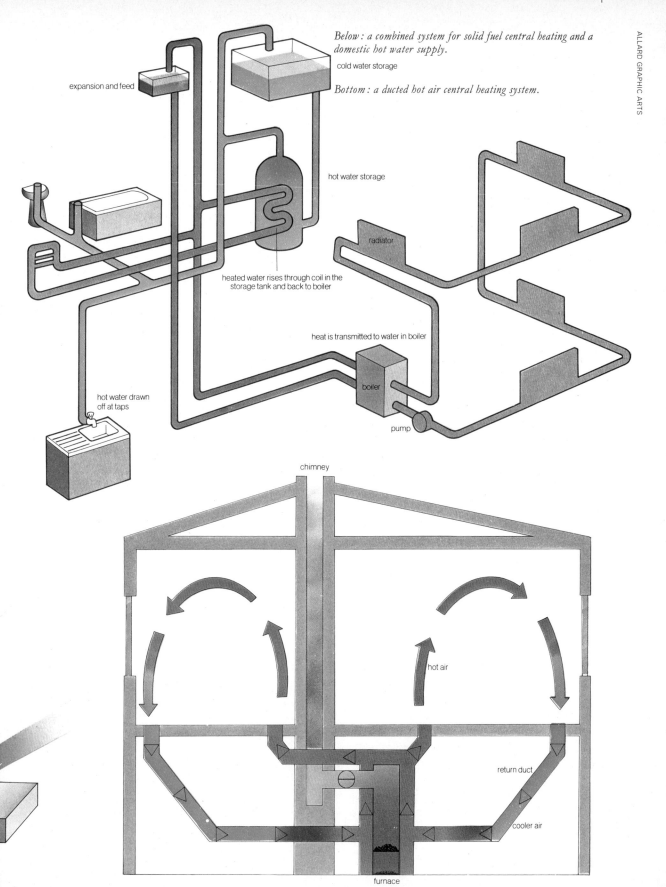

Below: a combined system for solid fuel central heating and a domestic hot water supply.

cold water storage

Bottom: a ducted hot air central heating system.

expansion and feed

hot water storage

heated water rises through coil in the storage tank and back to boiler

heat is transmitted to water in boiler

radiator

hot water drawn off at taps

boiler

pump

chimney

hot air

return duct

cooler air

furnace

Boilers and heat exchangers

In domestic boilers, the water to be heated passes through a series of waterways located above the combustion zone and designed to present a large surface area to the hot combustion gases. This ensures that the maximum amount of heat is passed to the circulating water.

The burners in oil-fired boilers can be of the *vaporizing*, *rotary* or *pressurized* type. In vaporizing burners the oil is fed by gravity along a supply pipe and into a *burner pot* located inside the boiler. Air for the combustion is drawn in or blown by a fan along a *draught tube* positioned around the oil supply pipe. After ignition, the heat from combustion heats up the burner pot causing the incoming oil to be vaporized immediately prior to combustion. In rotary burners the oil is fed on to a spinning *oil cup* situated inside the boiler and air is blown in by a fan. The spinning cup throws droplets of oil outwards on to a burner ring where it is ignited electrically. Once the ring has heated up, the combustion is self-sustaining. Because the flame in a rotary burner is cylindrical in shape and 'wipes' the internal walls of the boiler, rotary burners are sometimes called *wall flame* burners. In the pressurized type of burner, the oil is pumped under pressure to a nozzle inside the boiler, from which it emerges as a very fine spray. As in the vaporizing burner, a draught tube is positioned around the nozzle and air is blown into the combustion chamber by a fan. Combustion is started by means of a spark generated between two ignition electrodes located close to the nozzle.

Gas boilers have a series of gas jets inside the combustion chamber and a pilot jet for ignition. Air for combustion is drawn in from the room in which the boiler is located or from outside through a draught tube. It is not normally necessary to use a fan to blow in the combustion air.

Solid fuel boilers are fed from a hopper above the combustion zone. A fan is sometimes used to blow the combustion air in beneath the grate of the boiler. Solid fuel boilers require a brick chimney or a well-insulated flue pipe carried to above roof level. For small central heating systems having only three or four radiators and where a chimney breast is available, a combined unit comprising a back boiler fronted by an open fire or by a gas or oil-fired incandescent radiant fire can be used.

Domestic heat exchangers are of two general types: *direct* and *indirect*. In the direct type the air to be warmed is blown directly through ducts above the combustion chamber of the heat exchanger whereas in the indirect type a radiator, similar in construction to a car radiator, is fed with hot water from a boiler and air is blown through the radiator. Domestic heat exchangers use the same fuels as boilers and also, sometimes, electricity.

The heat output of boilers and heat exchangers is usually regulated by a THERMOSTAT. In the case of oil and gas burners, the thermostat operates a magnetic valve which restricts the fuel supply to the burner. In solid fuel burners the thermostat controls the fan.

Some countries, notably the United Kingdom, offer electricity at a lower price if it is taken 'off-peak', that is during hours of reduced demand. Since these occur mainly at night, off-peak heaters must be able to store the generated heat. The usual method is to enclose the electrical heating elements within blocks of a special high density refractory clay. With water circulating central heating systems the heat transfer can be directly to the water by an integral pipe coil or indirectly using an air to water heat exchanger. For warm air systems the heat storage unit operates in a similar manner to a direct-fired air

Above: a solid fuel central heating boiler designed to burn smokeless bituminous fuel. The unit not only provides domestic hot water and feeds up to eight radiators, but also heats the room by radiation from the glowing fuel and convection of air through the grille above the boiler grate.

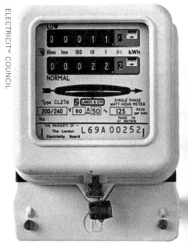

Right: a meter which measures consumption of electricity both at off-peak and standard rates.

Below: a 50 gallon storage water heater which operates on off-peak electricity.

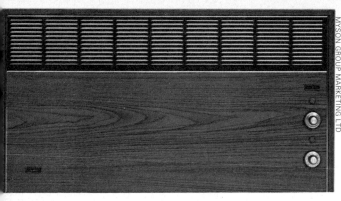

Above: a radiator for a hot water central heating system. Air is blown by means of a fan through a water-to-air heat exchanger situated inside the heater. The fan is thermostatically controlled.

heater. Off-peak electricity can also be used with individual room storage heaters. In the simplest type, heat emission is unrestricted and close control is not possible. Better control is given by units which have dampers for regulating the convection air flow through the heater. Further improvement is possible by using a multi-speed fan to blow air through the airways of the heater.

Another method of heating buildings is to use underfloor heating cables. These usually consist of an electrical wire heating element wound on a rayon core and fitted in a flexible PVC tube. Such cables are easy to install under wooden floors and can even be embedded in concrete floors.

Room heaters   In electric room heaters an electric current is passed through a coiled wire element to generate heat. Radiant heaters have elements which are designed to glow red during operation and the heat radiates directly into the room from the element. In bar heaters a reflector is positioned behind the glowing element to project heat into the room by reflection. The element of a convector heater operates at a lower temperature and is mounted in a housing which has an air inlet beneath the element and an air outlet above it. Air next to the element is heated and expands so that it becomes less dense than the surrounding cooler air. Being less dense, the hot air rises up through the heater body and out through the air outlet; it is replaced by cool air drawn in through the air inlet. A current of air is thus set up through the heater which distributes the heat throughout the room. Fan heaters are similar to convector heaters except that an electric fan is used to drive the air past the heating elements. Another form of electric room heater is the oil-filled type. An immersion element mounted inside the heater at its base heats up the oil in the radiator and, like a radiator in a central heating system, the heat is transferred to the adjacent air by conduction and then throughout the room by convection.

Free standing paraffin [kerosene] heaters are useful in applications where economy is important or an electricity supply is not available, for example in the heating of greenhouses. These usually have an adjustable cylindrical wick situated at the base of a chimney tube so that as the hot combustion products pass up the tube, air for combustion is drawn in around the wick. The wick dips into a tank of paraffin [kerosene] at the base of the heater. With proper adjustment of the wick the heater will operate efficiently with a smokeless blue flame.

Hot water supplies   Domestic hot water supplies are usually derived from a central heating boiler or from an electrical immersion heater. In the former case, heat is transferred from the boiler to the water tank by means of a water-to-water heater exchanger so that the hot water supply is kept separate from the water circulating through the radiators. An immersion heater consists of a metal tube enclosing an electrical heating element. The heater is generally fitted at the base of the hot water tank and the heat distributed throughout the tank by convection. Some hot water heaters, usually operated by gas or electricity, heat the water only as it is required. Such heaters simply require connection to the cold water mains.

Heaters of various types are widely used in industry. For example, FURNACES are used in the steel industry and steam-generating boilers are an important part of POWER STATIONS.

Left: the heating unit for an off-peak warm air central heating system. The electrical heating elements are sandwiched between the refractory bricks which store the heat.

HEAT EXCHANGER

A heat exchanger is a device in which heat is transferred from a stream of hot fluid (either gas or liquid) to a stream of cold fluid without any mixing of the two streams. A common example of a heat exchanger is the car radiator. Here, heat is taken from the engine in the form of heated water which is cooled in the radiator by the passage of cool air over the radiator surface.

Engineering principles
Heat is a form of energy measured in such units as Btu's (British Thermal Units) or joules (the international unit of energy) and represents an amount of energy taken from a hot body to a cooler one. *Energy transfer* (or heat transfer) only results where there is a *temperature difference* and always from the higher temperature to the lower temperature. In the process, the temperature of the hotter body drops because energy has been removed from it and conversely the temperature of the cooler body increases. This continues until there is no temperature difference left to cause any heat transfer.

An engineer wishing to maximize the heat transferred from a hot fluid to a cooler fluid will use a heat exchanger. The features which affect the design of such a device to obtain maximum heat transfer are the temperature difference between the fluids and the *area* of surface interaction. The designer may not have much control over the temperature difference, which is fixed by the nature of the job to be done, so he must incorporate a high area of surface contact to achieve the best heat transfer.

The fins on the cylinder of an air cooled motorcycle engine deliberately provide a large surface area to remove unwanted heat. In electronic circuits, high power transistors are fixed to finned heat sinks to keep the transistors cool in operation. In both these examples the emphasis is more on the removal of heat rather than heat exchange between fluids but the principle of incorporating a large surface area is a basic design feature.

Double tube heat exchanger
This consists of one tube placed concentrically inside a second large tube. To transfer heat from a hot fluid, such as the lubricating oil from an engine, to a cold fluid, for example the cooling water, one fluid is passed through the inner tube and the other through the annular space between the two tubes. Because of the temperature difference between the two fluids there will be an exchange of heat through the wall of the inner tube which separates them. Such types are also called concentric tube or tube-and-annulus heat exchangers. In the above example of an oil cooler, the oil would most probably be passed through the inner tube, which would be more capable of withstanding the high oil pressure than the outer tube, but in general the hotter fluid could be passed through either tube.

Parallel and counter-flow types
When the two fluids flow in the same direction through a double tube heat exchanger it is known as a *parallel flow* type and in the *counter flow* type the fluids flow in opposite directions. Counter flow heat exchangers are intrinsically more efficient and must be used where maximum heat transfer is required.

To explain this, consider a hot fluid, such as oil, at a temperature of 90°C and a cold fluid, say water, at a temperature of 10°C. The greatest possible heat transfer occurs when either the temperature of the oil drops to 10°C or the water rises to 90°C. The relative magnitudes of the two flow rates determines which of the two occurs. If the water flow rate is considerably higher than that of the oil, the temperature rise of the water will be less than the drop in temperature of the oil.

In a parallel flow heat exchanger the two fluids leave at the same end. Given any amount of heat transfer, the hotter fluid will get colder and the colder fluid get hotter as in the counter flow type, but the best that can be achieved from the exchanger is when the fluids leave at the *same* temperature. This will be somewhere in between the two extremes, depending on the two flow rates.

Other designs
The double tube heat exchanger is an extremely simple design but does not leave much room for improvement to the interacting surface area, which is determined solely by the surface area of the inner tube. For larger surface areas more elaborate designs are necessary.

One of these is the *shell-and-tube* heat exchanger which consists of a bundle of parallel tubes passing between the flat ends of a cylindrical casing or shell. One fluid flows through the tubes while the other flows through the shell. This type is widely used in the chemical process industry.

The *plate* heat exchanger is another important type consisting of a multi-layer sandwich with hot and cold fluids flowing through alternate layers. Some air heaters for cars are made in this way; they use hot water from the car's cooling system.

Top: rebuilding a large shell-and-tube heat exchanger for use in a chemical plant. The tube bundle consists of 1618 U-shaped stainless steel tubes welded to the 8 inch (20 cm) endplate. The whole will be enclosed in a cylindrical casing (the shell) and one fluid circulated through the shell while the other passes through the tubes.

Bottom: heat exchanger of fused aluminium in a car's cooling system.

ROBERT JENKINS & CO LTD

B A TECHNICAL CENTRE/PHOTO: PAUL BRIERLEY

HEAT PUMP

It is a basic law of nature that heat will flow from a hot body to a colder body, but not the reverse. With a heat pump, however, this reverse operation becomes possible: that is, heat is taken from the colder body and 'pumped' to the hotter body. In the process, the hot body becomes hotter and the cold body colder.

Reverse heat engines

This does not mean that a heat pump violates any laws of nature, because, to achieve this, power must be supplied to the pump to make it work. It therefore operates like a HEAT ENGINE in reverse.

A heat engine operates between a hot body and a cold body (these are usually called *reservoirs*) and part of the heat, as it flows from the hot reservoir to the cold reservoir, is converted into mechanical work. To conceive the reverse of this process, imagine work being put into the 'engine' and heat flowing in the opposite direction. This is the basic principle of the heat pump.

A heat pump is therefore identical in operation to a REFRIGERATOR—differing only in purpose. A refrigerator is used specifically to cool down still further a colder body by removing heat from it, whereas the heat pump places the emphasis on where the heat is going to—namely, increasing the temperature of the already warmer body.

Working principles

The term heat pump is somewhat misleading since heat is not a fluid like air or water and cannot in fact be pumped—except in a metaphorical sense. Some medium is required for this transfer of heat to take place.

A heat pump functions rather like a steam power plant (which is a heat engine) working backwards, except that steam is unlikely to be the working fluid. A vapour or refrigerant is more likely. The fluid flows round a closed circuit driven by a COMPRESSOR or PUMP. The fluid enters the pump as vapour and experiences a rise in pressure and temperature. The vapour then enters the *condenser* (which is a HEAT EXCHANGER) and heat is transferred to the warm reservoir, which is cooler than the vapour entering the condenser. Here the vapour condenses and leaves as a liquid, still at a high pressure.

The liquid then flows through a *throttle valve*—a restricted passage which the liquid spurts through into a low pressure area. This reduction in pressure causes the liquid to partially vaporize and is accompanied by a reduction in temperature. The liquid vapour mixture now flows through the *evaporator,* which is situated in the cold reservoir (this is the second heat exchanger in the system). Because the liquid-vapour mixture is now colder than the cold reservoir, it takes heat from the reservoir and leaves at a higher temperature than when it went in. This is the complete cycle.

Coefficient of performance

A typical application of a heat pump might be to take heat from a cold reservoir, such as a river, and transfer this to a building which requires heating (this is the warm reservoir). In the process, work or power must be supplied to the pump to drive it. The heat pump might, for example, receive 1000 Btu from the river, absorb 400 Btu in power from an external source to drive it and deliver 1400 Btu to the building. (One Btu is 1.1 kJ, that is, 1100 joules—the Btu is a common unit of heat used by heat engineers

Below: diagram of a heat pump arrangement used to heat a building. Heat from the soil is absorbed into a brine solution passing through a grid under the surface, and is transmitted to the interior of the building by a cycle opposite to that of refrigeration.

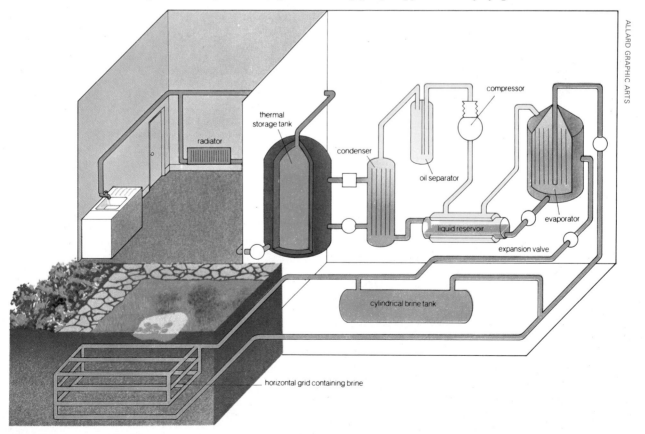

although the joule is the international unit of energy used by most physicists and engineers).

The performance of the heat pump is measured by the ratio of heat delivered to the warm reservoir to the work absorbed by the pump to drive it. For the above example this ratio is 1400/400, which works out to 3.5; this figure is called the *coefficient of performance*.

The best coefficient of performance that can be achieved is determined from the temperatures of the hot and cold reservoirs. If the hot reservoir is at temperature T_1 and the cold reservoir at temperature T_2 then the maximum coefficient of performance that can be achieved is $T_1/(T_1 - T_2)$. This relationship is determined from THERMODYNAMIC principles and is similar to the expression for maximum efficiency of a heat engine.

The heat pump is at first sight a most attractive proposition—we seem to get something for nothing. If the coefficient of performance is 3.5 it means that we get 3.5 kW of heat by supplying 1 kW of electric power to the heat pump—a considerable improvement over the electric fire. The remaining heat is obtained from the river where it was not wanted. But as always there is a snag. From the above temperature expression for maximum coefficient of performance it can be shown that as the hot reservoir heats up through the action of the heat pump, the maximum coefficient of performance will automatically fall. Furthermore, the heat pump is a costly device. So far this has proved too high to make the system economically attractive except in certain instances. But if fuel costs continue to rise it may be that the system will become economically viable.

Below: this man has installed his own heat pump to warm his house from the heat in the ground. It has 1500 ft (457 m) of copper pipe filled with a liquid which takes the heat from the ground to his house.

HEAT TREATMENT

The term heat treatment covers a wide range of procedures carried out at elevated temperatures in which the properties of METALS and ALLOYS are changed in order to facilitate efficient processing or to develop suitable service performance. Since the material involved in the manufacture of most metallic items undergoes at least one heat treatment at some stage, it is an important part of modern industrial technology.

In metal, atoms are arranged in a regular pattern called a *lattice*. The structure of an alloy, viewed under the microscope, usually consists of a mixture of two or more *phases*, that is, constituents of different lattice types. The principle of heat treatment relies upon the fact that this *microstructure* can be modified by controlled heating and cooling in order to alter the overall properties of a material. Microstructure dictates the material's hardness, strength, toughness, and ductility, and its ability to be worked and machined. Other properties such as electrical and magnetic characteristics and corrosion resistance are also directly related to structure.

The important factors in heat treatment which influence the structure obtained, and which therefore must be controlled, are composition of material, heating rate, process temperature, treatment time, cooling rate and process medium. Nearly all heat treatment processes are carried out in specially designed furnaces; these may be of the continuous type, having different temperature zones which the work passes through, or the batch type. Cooling may occur within the furnace or outside.

Ferrous materials Because STEEL has a wide range of chemical compositions and properties, it is the most important alloy when considering heat treatment and the processes involved fall broadly into three categories: *annealing*, *hardening* and *surface hardening*.

Annealing This term covers a range of processes aimed at softening steel in order to facilitate further working or machining. The treatments involved, however, can also homogenize the steel composition, refine its grain size and relieve stresses induced by working operations. Forgings, castings and cold-worked products such as sheet steel, strip and wire, often undergo annealing.

Full annealing of steels with up to 0.85% carbon involves heating to temperatures above Ac_3 (see diagram) in order to convert the structure completely to *austenite*, the high temperature lattice form of iron in which up to 1.7% of carbon is dissolved. On slow cooling in the furnace, this transforms to a mixture of *ferrite*, the low temperature lattice form of iron which has only slight solubility for carbon, and coarse *pearlite*, a plate-like mixture of ferrite and *cementite* (iron carbide). This structure facilitates efficient machining of low and medium carbon steels. Higher carbon and alloy steels are frequently subjected to a *spheroidize anneal* by prolonged *soaking* (holding) at temperatures just below Ac_1. In this case austenite is not formed but a structure of ferrite containing cementite in the form of spheroidized particles is promoted, a more easily machineable structure than that which would result from full annealing. *Isothermal (cyclic) annealing* gives a similar structure to full annealing but permits greater control over the form of pearlite produced and can allow shorter cycles in which the slow cooling from austenitizing temperature is eliminated. Again the steel is heated above Ac_3 but is cooled rapidly to, and held at, an intermediate temperature (600 to 700°C, 1112°F to 1292°F) until transformation is complete.

Cold-worked materials such as low carbon steel sheet and strip become harder as the degree of working increases.

Efficient processing demands that they be annealed so that the deformed grain structure is replaced by new, strain-free grains (*re-crystallization*). This is the principle of *process-interstage annealing* normally carried out at temperatures just below Ac_1.

Heating conditions for *normalizing* are similar to those for full annealing but cooling, normally in air, is somewhat faster and results in a finer structure. Normalizing is usually carried out in order to refine the grain size (this imparts desirable metallurgical properties) of forgings such as gear blanks, improve machineability and, where further heat treatment is carried out after machining, to promote good response to hardening treatments with minimum distortion. Normalizing may soften low carbon or low alloy steels but may actually become a hardening treatment when applied to higher carbon or alloy steels.

Hardening and tempering

By rapid cooling of steel (*quenching*) from the austenite phase region, the non-equilibrium phase, *martensite*, which is hard and brittle, can be produced. The depth of hardening of a quenched component depends upon its *hardenability*, which is a function of steel composition and grain size. A steel of a given hardenability will harden to a greater depth the faster the cooling rate, which in turn is dependent upon the quench medium, the degree of agitation and the section size involved. Quenching is done by plunging the heated articles into a quench tank which may contain, in ascending order of severity, oil, water or brine. Increases in the steel's content of carbon and alloying elements, such as manganese, chromium, nickel, molybdenum, vanadium and tungsten, promote greater hardenability; and some materials (for example some tool steels) are so highly alloyed that they harden fully when merely cooled in air.

Because the product of hardening is brittle, it is normal practice to then *temper* in order to impart toughness at the expense of some hardness, because this is more important for the finished product. This involves reheating to temperatures between 400 and 700°C (752 to 1292°F), depending upon the steel involved, and soaking (holding at that temperature), when further structural changes occur. Typical components subjected to hardening and tempering range from bolts, seat belt buckles, springs and spanners [wrenches] to crankshafts, gun barrels and die blocks.

Surface hardening

Many components require a hard, wear-resistant surface coupled with overall toughness, a combination which use of a high carbon or alloy steel would not allow. Techniques whereby only the surface of a component is fully hardened fall into two categories: those involving no change in surface chemistry encompass *flame* and electric *induction hardening* in which only the surface layers of a medium carbon steel are heated to austenitizing temperatures to form a hardened 'case' on quenching, and *thermochemical (case hardening) treatments*, in which elements such as carbon and nitrogen are introduced into the surface of plain and low alloy steels, usually containing less than 0.3% carbon, in order to improve surface hardenability. Because heating to elevated

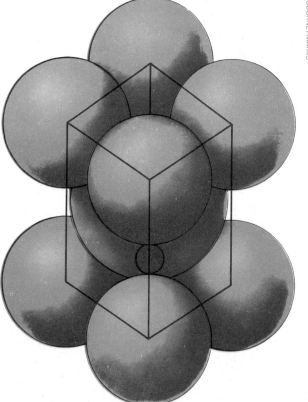

Top: a pallet of castings being transferred from the furnace behind is reflected in the oil quench tank below.

Right: at high temperatures iron has a face-centred cubic structure and can hold more carbon. On rapid cooling it reverts to body-centred cubic and forms very hard martensite (seen here) owing to distortion because now there is not enough room for the carbon atoms.

temperatures in air promotes oxidation and removal of carbon at the steel surface (*decarburization*)—effects which can be detrimental and expensive to rectify—treatments described under annealing and hardening are often carried out in a neutral, protective environment from which air is excluded. The protective medium may be solid (*pack*), molten salt or gaseous (controlled atmosphere). In thermochemical treatments, it is essential to surround the workpieces with a chemically active medium which provides a source of the elements to be diffused into the steel surface.

Carburizing is the most common treatment of this type, being widely used, for example, in the manufacture of automobile transmission gears. Components are heated to around 925°C (1697°F), when carbon diffuses into the austenite lattice at the steel surface. The depth of carburized case is determined by the soaking time but, for automobile gears, the effective hardened case after quenching is typically of the order of 1.0 mm.

Carbonitriding is a similar process to carburizing, usually carried out at 850 to 900°C (1562 to 1652°F), in which nitrogen as well as carbon is introduced into the steel surface. Nitrogen increases the case hardenability, so that cheaper steels can be employed than in straight carburizing; conversely, a less severe quench is needed to promote full case hardness, thus reducing the risk of distortion of parts during heat treatment.

In *nitriding*, components manufactured from special grades of medium carbon alloy steel, previously fully hardened and tempered, are subjected to treatment in a nitrogen-bearing

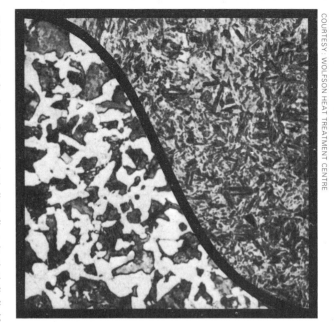

COURTESY: WOLFSON HEAT TREATMENT CENTRE

BIRLEC

Top right: microstructures of 0.35% carbon steel. When cooled slowly (left) the relatively soft phase mixture of ferrite (white) and pearlite (dark plate-like structure) results; water quenching yields the hard brittle, needle-like martensite (right).

Right: case hardening of automatic transmission gears in a high-output continuous gas carburizing furnace.

Below: the microstructure of a plain carbon steel depends on its carbon content and temperature. The diagram (left) acts as a guide to structural changes on slow heating and cooling. When a 0.35% carbon steel is cooled slowly from the austenite phase region it should yield a ferrite and pearlite structure at room temperature. Usually non-equilibrium conditions apply and other phases result, so the continuous cooling transformation graph (right) is more accurate.

formation of various microstructures in steels during heat treatment

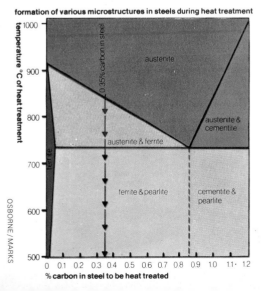

OSBORNE / MARKS

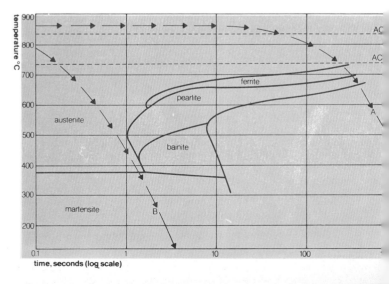

medium at relatively low temperatures, typically 500°C (932°F). Nitrogen diffuses into the ferrite phase promoting the formation of hard nitrides in the steel surface. The process involves minimal component distortion, since quenching is unnecessary, but treatment times are long compared with the other thermochemical treatments described.

Non-ferrous alloys Although many non-ferrous metals and alloys are annealed in order to restore softness after cold working, few are capable of being heat treated to improve strength and hardness. Exceptions are alloys such as aluminium-4% copper, copper-0.5% chromium, and copper-1.8% beryllium, which respond to *precipitation hardening treatments*. For example, the aluminium-copper Duralumin-type alloys, widely used in the aircraft industry, are *solution treated*, by holding at approximately 500°C (932°F), and cold water quenched. The quenched material is only slightly harder than a slow-cooled alloy and can be cold worked. On resting, however, at room temperature (*ageing*) the hardness increases to a maximum value over 4 to 5 days. *Artificial ageing*, by heating the material again to about 150°C (302°F), accelerates the hardening process.

HELICOPTERS

Helicopters belong to a class of AIRCRAFT known as *rotorcraft*, the other members of which are AUTOGYROS (or *gyroplanes*) and *convertiplanes*. Helicopters and autogyros are superficially similar to one another in that both are wholly sustained in flight by the lift generated as a result of the rotation of long thin wings, or *rotor blades*, in a horizontal plane (see AEROFOIL).

The blades of an autogyro, however, are caused to rotate by the action of air blowing through them, in the manner of a WINDMILL, while those of a helicopter are driven by an engine. Autogyros cannot therefore land or take off vertically in calm air. Helicopters, on the other hand, can take off or land vertically, hover, fly forwards, backwards or sideways irrespective of the wind.

The principles of helicopter flight have been known for centuries. Leonardo da VINCI designed one, and many helicopter models were made by early flight pioneers such as Sir George Cayley (in 1792). The first helicopter capable of carrying a man was built by Paul Cornu in France in 1907, powered by a 24 hp engine, but insurmountable stability and engineering problems held back helicopter development compared with that of conventional aircraft.

It was not until January 1942 that the world's first practical helicopter, the VS-316A, was built by the Russian-born American engineer Igor Sikorsky. This machine, designated the R-4 by the armed services of the USA and Britain, had the simplest possible configuration for a helicopter and one that is still the most widely used today.

Construction The main structural element of a helicopter is the fuselage, housing the crew, payload, fuel and powerplant, which until the mid-1950s was a piston engine but is now usually a gas turbine. The output shaft from the engine, turning at several thousand revolutions per minute, is connected to a main gearbox, which steps down the speed to between 300 and 400 revs/min to drive the rotor (the assembly carrying the hub and attached blades).

The reaction of the rotor spinning in one direction would cause the rest of the helicopter to rotate uncontrollably in the opposite direction. In order to prevent this a secondary rotor, of smaller diameter, is mounted on the rear end of the fuselage and driven by a second shaft from the gearbox at such a speed

that it exactly neutralizes the turning action of the main rotor.

Each of the blades of the main rotor (modern helicopters have any number from two to seven) is inclined (with its leading edge upwards) so that it meets the air at a small angle to the horizontal. This is the *pitch angle*, analogous to the pitch of a PROPELLER or a screw thread.

Pitch control When in hovering flight the combination of rotor speed and the pitch of the blades provides a lift force which exactly balances the weight of the helicopter. In order to climb, the rotor has to generate more lift, and this is achieved not by increasing the speed of the rotor (the rotor speed of a particular helicopter at all times remains virtually constant, irrespective of what the aircraft is doing) but by increasing the pitch of the blades. More lift, however, also means more *drag* (wind resistance) and so extra power is needed from the engine.

The pitch of the blades is controlled from the cockpit by means of the *collective pitch lever*, so called because it changes the pitch of all the main rotor blades by the same amount. This lever is mounted on the floor, and is one of the very few differences between the cockpit of a helicopter and that of a conventional fixed-wing aircraft. Operated by hand, it is moved up to gain height and down to descend.

Since most manoeuvres, including climbing and descending, necessitate changes of power, the collective pitch lever has a twist-grip throttle control at the top so that engine power and blade pitch can be controlled and co-ordinated with one hand.

Flight control Helicopters have no wings or tailplane and so the main and tail rotors are required to generate between them not only the forces needed to provide lift but also those needed to control it. In order to make the helicopter travel forward, or in any other horizontal direction, the rotor has to be tilted in that direction. Its reaction, or total lifting force, is then inclined away from the vertical and can be considered as being made up of two components: one acting vertically to balance the weight, and the other, much smaller force, acting along the direction in which the pilot wishes to travel.

To make the helicopter travel faster, the rotor blade has to be tilted further so that more of the reaction of the rotor acts in the desired direction. At the same time the vertical component of lift must be maintained, so more engine power has to be applied.

Above: an early Austrian helicopter, a 1915 Karman-Petroczy which was powered by three Le Rhône engines driving a pair of fixed pitch contrarotating rotors.

IMPERIAL WAR MUSEUM

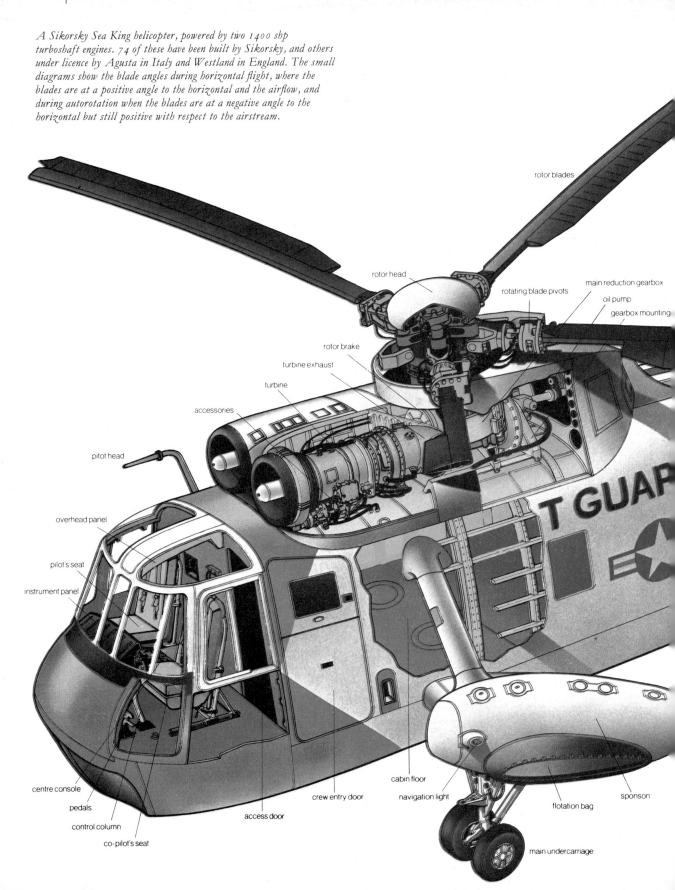

A Sikorsky Sea King helicopter, powered by two 1400 shp turboshaft engines. 74 of these have been built by Sikorsky, and others under licence by Agusta in Italy and Westland in England. The small diagrams show the blade angles during horizontal flight, where the blades are at a positive angle to the horizontal and the airflow, and during autorotation when the blades are at a negative angle to the horizontal but still positive with respect to the airstream.

rotor blades

rotor head

main reduction gearbox

rotating blade pivots

oil pump

gearbox mounting

rotor brake

turbine exhaust

turbine

accessories

pitot head

overhead panel

pilot's seat

instrument panel

centre console

pedals

control column

co-pilot's seat

access door

crew entry door

cabin floor

navigation light

flotation bag

sponson

main undercarriage

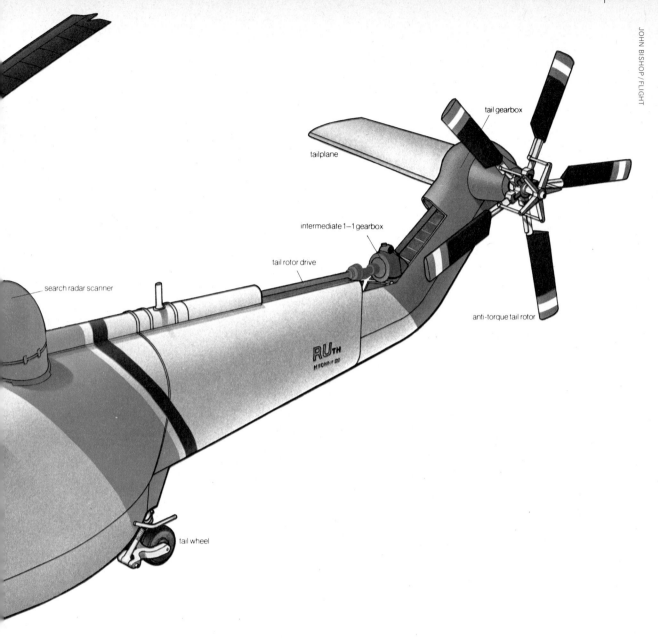

tail gearbox

tailplane

intermediate 1–1 gearbox

tail rotor drive

search radar scanner

anti-torque tail rotor

RU_{TH}

tail wheel

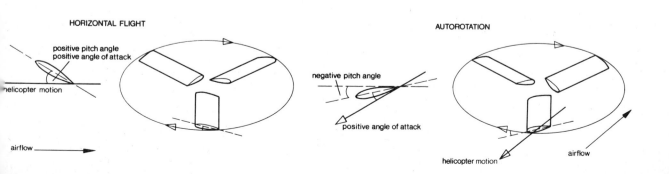

HORIZONTAL FLIGHT

positive pitch angle
positive angle of attack

helicopter motion

airflow

AUTOROTATION

negative pitch angle

positive angle of attack

helicopter motion

airflow

The rotor is made to tilt by arranging that one half of the disc traced out by the rotating blades generates more lift than the other half, and this is achieved by increasing the blade angle on one side and decreasing it on the other. Thus the pitch of a blade goes through a complete cycle, from maximum to minimum and back again, during one revolution.

The *cyclic pitch control*, which determines where on the rotor disc the variations of lift shall occur to perform the desired manoeuvre, or change the speed, is commanded by a conventional control column in the cockpit. Changes in heading (the direction in which the helicopter is pointing relative to north) are made by collectively altering the pitch of the tail rotor blades by means of conventional rudder pedals.

Maximum speed As the forward speed of the helicopter increases, the velocity of the forward-moving blade is increased by an amount equal to the speed of the aircraft, while that of the rearward-moving blade is decreased by the same amount. Eventually a situation is reached when the forward-moving blade is approaching the speed of sound over a considerable portion of its travel. Undesirable aerodynamic effects then cause the drag of the blade to increase rapidly and its lift to decrease. At the same time the relative velocity of the retreating blade, travelling momentarily in the opposite direction to that of the helicopter itself, is too low to provide useful lift and it may become stalled. These effects limit the speed of a conventional helicopter to about 250 mile/h (400 km/h).

Autorotation If engine power is suddenly removed, the rotor slows very rapidly, lift is lost, and the helicopter begins to drop. To prevent loss of rotor speed the collective pitch lever has to be rapidly lowered, so as to set the blades at a negative pitch angle. This means that the leading edges of the blades are inclined slightly downwards from the horizontal, but as the air is moving upwards through the rotor, the blades still meet the airflow at a small upward angle.

As the helicopter begins to descend, usually in a forward glide, the air blowing up through the rotor disc generates forces on the blades which keep them spinning. This situation is known as *autorotation*, and is the basis of the operation of the autogyro.

As the helicopter nears the ground the collective pitch lever is raised slightly so as to reduce the rate of descent, using the kinetic energy stored in the rotor to provide, for a short time, the extra lift necessary to decelerate the machine for touchdown.

Rotors The use of two smaller main rotors in place of a single large one can be an advantage, particularly with bigger helicopters. The rotors are arranged to spin in opposite directions so that the reaction torque of one cancels that of the other. There is thus no tendency for the fuselage to rotate, so the tail rotor can be dispensed with. This reduces the weight somewhat and enables all the power developed by the engines to be put to useful work in lifting and moving the aircraft.

The rotors may be mounted transversely across the fuselage as on the Mil-12, the world's largest helicopter, or they can be located at either end of the fuselage as on the Boeing Vertol CH-47 Chinook. They may be set one above the other and driven by concentric shafts, as on the Kamov Ka-26, or they may be carried on separate shafts mounted at a slight angle to one another; in this case (as with the Mil and the Boeing) the rotors intermesh with each other and the drives to them have to be synchronized so the blades do not collide with one another.

Powerplant The general adoption of gas turbine propulsion for helicopters in place of piston engines in the mid-1950s resulted in a tremendous improvement in performance.

Nowadays piston engines are only to be found on the older or very smallest helicopters. Instead of generating a high-velocity stream of hot gases to thrust the aircraft through the air, as in the JET ENGINE, the power of the engine is extracted mechanically by fitting it with extra turbines and connecting these to the shaft which drives the rotor. This type of powerplant is known as a *turboshaft* engine, and only a small proportion of the gas energy emerges as thrust.

Uses Helicopters have developed into useful and in many cases indispensable machines. As 'air taxis' they can cover 100 mile (160 km) journeys inside an hour, taking up and setting down passengers in confined spaces close to their destinations.

They have many applications in rescue work, particularly at sea, and every year hundreds of swimmers and seamen are saved around the world's coastlines. They have greatly assisted the operation of offshore oil and gas rigs, as crews may be changed and spare drills and essential supplies may be ferried out irrespective of sea conditions.

In inaccessible areas of the world they have many uses, such as the supply of outposts and the maintenance of telephone and power lines.

In FIREFIGHTING, helicopters are frequently used for dealing with forest and bush fires, and in large cities for rescuing people from high buildings. Large helicopters are often used in difficult construction situations, for example for lifting church steeples into position.

In wartime they confer tactical mobility, transporting troops, guns and materials rapidly into the battle zone, and ferrying out casualties and equipment which might otherwise have to be left behind. They may be equipped with cannon and rocket launchers and used as 'gunships'.

Development work is currently aimed largely at increasing the speed, and this may come about as a result of advances in compound helicopters. If the rotor can be made sufficiently stiff, it can be slowed down as the helicopter's forward speed increases, without becoming uncontrollable. The lift could then be provided by small wings mounted conventionally on the fuselage, and the forward thrust provided by conventional propellers or jet engines.

Convertiplanes The convertiplane is basically an aircraft with an engine and rotor mounted at the end of each wing, with the plane of the rotor discs at 90° to the plane of the wings. For take off and landing, the wings are rotated so that the rotors are horizontal, as in a helicopter, to provide the necessary lift. When the aircraft is airborne, the wings are rotated back to the conventional position, so that the lift is provided by the wings and forward propulsion by the rotors, which are then operating as ordinary propellers.

HENRY (see inductance)

Top left: a Westland Whirlwind HAR 10, used by the RAF for coastal rescue work. It is powered by a Rolls-Royce Gnome turboshaft engine and carries a crew of three and up to ten passengers.

Top centre: the main rotor hub and pitch control mechanism of a Westland-Aerospatiale Gazelle.

Top right: the shrouded tail rotor of the Gazelle.

Right: a view of the cockpit of a Bell 206A, showing the cyclic control sticks, the rudder pedals, and the collective pitch lever at the right hand side of the seat.

JOHN WATNEY

HART ASSOCIATES

AUTAIR LTD

HERO of Alexandria (1st century AD)

Hero of Alexandria is such a mysterious figure that until recently there was considerable disagreement about when he lived. It is now known, however, that he must have been alive in the first century AD because a lunar eclipse which Hero describes has been shown by modern calculation to have occurred in 62 AD. Otherwise we know nothing of Hero's dates of birth and death, his life, or even what he looked like.

In Hero's time the city of Alexandria was the intellectual capital of the ancient world. Named after Alexander the Great, Alexandria retained its Greek traditions and institutions even under Roman rule. It is probable that Hero was connected with the University of Alexandria and it was there that he wrote, in Greek, his various studies of mechanics and mechanical technology.

The ancient Greeks' interest in mechanical technology ranged from automatic toys and gadgets to heavier but simple machinery for doing useful work. Unfortunately, very few of the original Greek descriptions of these machines have survived. Of the handful which are known, Hero's descriptions are the most important because his considerable writings are mostly in the original Greek. The works of other authors only exist in fragments and these bits and pieces are mainly in the form of later translations into Latin and Arabic.

One of Hero's works, probably the most famous, is called *Pneumatics*. It contains details of nearly 80 gadgets and devices utilizing not only pneumatic principles but mechanical and hydraulic ones as well. Compressed air is a feature of lots of the items described. The HYDRAULIC siphon is often used to move water from one place to another and in a few instances geared drives are illustrated for the first time. Occasionally Hero depicts applications of steam pressure.

In the *Pneumatics* and another work called *Automatic Theatres* Hero emphasizes toys, novelties and devices intended primarily to entertain. The themes of his other writings are more practical and useful. *Dioptra* is about surveying and contains a description of the construction and use of an instrument designed by Hero himself. A dioptra was an instrument combining the functions of a theodolite and a level. In the least well known of Hero's works, *Belopoiica*, he discusses catapults for throwing missiles in warfare.

The last of Hero's works, *Mechanics*, is only known in an Arabic version prepared long after Hero's time. In many ways this is the most interesting work of all because it deals with the basic machinery of lifting and haulage: the windlass, lever, pulley, wedge and screw. Many applications are analyzed, notably the use of the screw press to crush grapes and olives.

For many centuries after his death, Hero's works remained unknown. About 500 years ago they began to be studied with increasing interest in Western Europe and they became established as basic sources of information about technology. This phase passed rapidly, however, as European mechanical engineering progressed and improved. Nowadays, Hero of Alexandria is important mainly as our principal source of information on the scope and character of Greek mechanical technology, the principles which were understood, the ways they were used and the tasks to which they were applied.

Above right: Hero's whirling aeolipile, the first-ever reaction turbine, was turned by jets of steam piped up from the boiler.

Below right lighting a fire on the temple altar above created pressure that forced water into the bucket, which fell, opening the doors.

HERSCHEL, F W (1738–1822) & J F W

If William Herschel were not famous for his discovery of the planet Uranus, he would be well known as the discoverer of INFRA-RED RADIATION, or equally as the 'father of stellar astronomy'. His son John was a brilliant scientist in his own right, a pioneer in many branches of physics and chemistry as well as astronomy. Yet William Herschel started his career as a musician in the Hanoverian Guard, and until he was 35 showed no signs of becoming anything more than a successful, if rather obscure, musician.

William Herschel was the son of an oboeist in the Guards band of the state of Hanover, in Germany. After an elementary education at the garrison school, William also became an oboeist in the band, which followed the regiment on a number of encounters. Eventually, the situation in Europe became sufficiently warlike for the band to be forgotten, and William

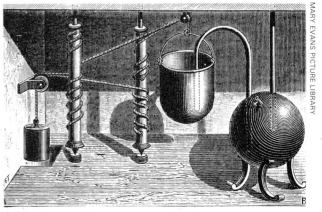

was able to leave the regiment without any trouble. He made his way to England, where life was quieter, to make his career as a musician.

In this he was quite successful. He had a fine musical talent, and held a number of posts in Durham, Leeds, Newcastle and other northern cities. At the age of 28, he was offered the post of organist at a private chapel being opened at Bath, then the centre of the fashionable world.

The next few years were hectic with composing, playing and giving music lessons. When he was 35, William also became deeply interested in astronomy, which had long fascinated him. Finding that hiring telescopes was costly, he set about making his own, and began a complete review of the sky, searching for double stars.

He found plenty of these, but in March 1781 he found one very unusual object which his telescope showed as a small disc.

Right: Sir William Herschel at the age of 81. He was well known for his benign personality, and was always tolerant of the constant flow of visitors to his home, allowing them to gaze through his telescopes. His patron, George III, was interested in science and awarded him a grant on the basis that Herschel would demonstrate the wonders of the skies whenever required. Herschel wanted to call the new planet 'Georgium Sidus', the 'Georgian Star', but continental astronomers not surprisingly preferred the more classical Uranus.

Below: Herschel discovered Uranus with a telescope of 6.2 inches (16 cm) aperture and 7 feet (2.1 m) focal length from the garden of 19 New King Street, Bath. He made many telescopes of this size, but kept the one with which he made the discovery. This one is still owned by his descendants: it is a Newtonian reflector, with a metal concave mirror at the lower end, and is still in good working order.

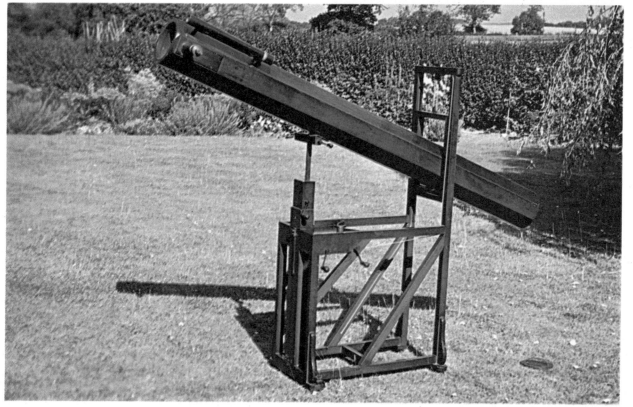

It moved from night to night, and Herschel reported it as a new comet. It was soon realized that this was no comet but a new planet, orbiting the Sun beyond Saturn. The discovery was unexpected because Uranus was the first planet to be actually discovered: all the others had been known since earliest times.

The discovery, which was largely due to the ability of his telescope to show the tiny disc, brought Herschel fame. The King, George III, awarded Herschel an annual grant, enabling him to give up his musical life and move near Windsor. Telescope making became a profitable sideline.

At last William was able to devote all his time to astronomy, observing every hour when stars were visible and making telescopes by day. He built what was for many years the largest telescope in the world, the 'Forty Feet', of 48 inches (1.2 m) aperture, though this was rather cumbersome and was not used regularly.

Left: a photograph of Sir John Herschel (1792–1871) aged 75, taken by Julia Cameron, who was a family friend. Herschel was not always as unkempt as this picture suggests: he had just washed his hair and Mrs Cameron deliberately tousled it to create a dramatic effect.

Below: William Herschel's great telescope, of 48 inches (1.2 m) aperture and 40 feet (12 m) focal length. It was dismantled in 1839 when it became unsafe.

As a result of his sky surveys and other work, Herschel deduced that the Milky Way, the band of faint stars which stretches round the sky, is actually a flat lens-shaped structure with the Sun not at the centre but some way towards one edge. He showed that double stars are not chance alignments but are binary systems, with the stars orbiting each other, and also found that the Sun has its own motion through space in a particular direction.

While trying to find a filter that would block out the heat from the Sun, but not the light, Herschel discovered that the region beyond the red end of a prism's spectrum (the infra-red) has a strong heating effect, and realized that this invisible radiation obeys the same laws of refraction as visible light.

Throughout his observing, Herschel was aided by his devoted sister Caroline, who patiently recorded all his observations so that he would not have to look away from the eyepiece. Caroline was an observer in her own right, and was later awarded many scientific honours for her work. Observing was done outside, rather than in a dome—on some occasions, Hershel found that his feet were frozen to the ground and even the ink was solid.

In 1788, when he was 50, William married a local widow, Mary Pitt, whose husband's private library he had often visited. They had one son, John.

John Herschel eventually graduated as Senior Wrangler at Cambridge, awarded to the top graduate in mathematics each year. His famous name played little part in his success: his less successful colleagues included Charles BABBAGE, the pioneer of the calculating machine, who remained a lifelong friend.

In addition to his mathematical work, John Herschel also became interested in chemistry. One of his discoveries was that sodium thiosulphate ('hypo') will dissolve silver salts—to become useful later on.

John chose to help his father, who had been knighted in 1816. When Sir William Herschel died at the age of 83, John was continuing his reviews of the sky, later extending these to the southern hemisphere by moving to the Cape of Good Hope with his telescopes.

When, in 1839, he heard of DAGUERRE's recent photographic discoveries, after many years of experimentation, Herschel applied his knowledge of chemistry to the subject. Within days he had successfully used a process of his own, involving a glass plate coated with silver halide, to photograph the old Forty Feet telescope, which was shortly to be pulled down. Remembering his earlier discovery, he used hypo to 'fix' the plate, producing what he called a 'negative'. The 'positive' was made in a similar way on paper. Although his first results were inferior to Daguerre's, this is basically the process used today.

When he was in his early thirties, John Herschel's scholarly career was beginning to wear him down. Friends realized that marriage would help, and introduced him to a family which had two eligible daughters. The plan worked, and Herschel became devoted to his clever young wife and the family which soon arrived. They eventually had three sons and nine daughters, and the family happiness of the Herschels became well known.

Although Sir John Herschel's work cannot be tied down to many specific discoveries, he played a major role in the development of science in the nineteenth century, being regarded as one of the most distinguished scientists of the period. Like Newton, he became Master of the Mint, and he was buried near Newton in Westminster Abbey.

HI FI SYSTEMS

'Hi fi' is short for 'high fidelity', and the term is used because a hi fi system tries to reproduce recorded or broadcast sounds with as much fidelity, or faithfulness, to the original sounds as possible.

The heart of any hi fi system is the AMPLIFIER, which produces the output signals to drive the LOUDSPEAKERS or headphones, or provides the input signals for a TAPE RECORDER. The input signals to the amplifier are produced by a record deck, tape deck, radio tuner, TV sound adapter or MICROPHONE. Although most true hi fi systems today are stereophonic or, increasingly, quadraphonic (see STEREO RECORDING, STEREO RADIO), these terms refer to the use of two or four channels to provide a spatial distribution of the reproduced sound and not to its actual quality; there are countless cheap systems on the market which are by no means of hi fi quality despite the claims of their makers. This situation has arisen largely because there are no legally agreed standards for hi fi equipment, although minimum standards have been formulated by several organizations, and work is in progress with a view to the introduction of official British Standards for equipment described as 'hi fi'.

Broadly speaking, the essential requirements for high fidelity sound reproduction are that the equipment should have a good *frequency response*, low levels of *distortion* and *noise*, and an adequate *power output*.

Frequency response The range of frequencies audible to the human ear is roughly between 20 and 20,000 Hz, and so a hi fi system should ideally be capable of reproducing all of these frequencies equally, without unduly emphasizing or

Right: this tone arm has a geometrical configuration which changes as it travels across the record, lowering tracking error, as well as a magnetic anti-skate device and other special features.

Below: an elaborate hi-fi system, including four two-way speaker systems, a stereo open-reel tape deck, matching AM/FM tuner and integrated stereo amplifier, a belt-driven turntable with a die-cast platter and hysteresis-synchronous motor, and a de-coder for unmixing the four-channel signal from 'quad' records.

diminishing any of them. The frequency response of a piece of equipment is usually expressed as the upper and lower frequencies that it will usefully handle, together with the maximum variations from a 'flat' or 'linear' response (all frequencies reproduced equally) quoted in *decibels*. The decibel (dB) is an expression of the relationship between two voltages, currents or power levels, and is a multiple of the LOGARITHM (to base 10) of the ratio between them. Where voltages or currents are being compared the log of the ratios is multiplied by 20, and for power ratios by 10.

For example, if a power level rises from 50 W to 100 W, in terms of decibels it has increased by $10 \times \log (100/50) = 10 \times \log 2 = 3.01$ dB. If a voltage rises from 50 V to 100 V the *gain* is $20 \times \log 2 = 6.02$ dB. Where there is a decrease from one level to another a negative dB number may be quoted, for instance -3 dB represents a drop from 100 W to about 50 W.

POPULAR HI FI

SONY

One method of measuring the frequency response of an amplifier is to set it up so that it produces 1 W output at 1000 Hz with a SINE WAVE input. This output level is taken as the 0 dB standard, and then the output power is measured at a range of different frequencies. The power output figures obtained are then related to the 0 dB standard to give an indication of the linearity of the amplifier's frequency response and its effective upper and lower frequency limits. The frequency response can then be quoted, for example 25 Hz to 20 kHz ± 1.5 dB. Changes in output level of less than ±1 db are virtually undetectable to the human ear, and many people would not be able to detect changes of ±2 dB.

Power bandwidth figures are also widely quoted, and these indicate the frequency range over which the amplifier will produce at least half of its nominal output power, within its specified distortion limits.

Distortion

As well as having a wide and flat frequency response, hi fi equipment must also be as free from distortion as possible. There are many forms of distortion, but basically it is any sound appearing in the output of a system or component that was not present in the input signal.

Harmonic distortion is caused by the unwanted generation of harmonic frequencies within the equipment. A harmonic frequency is a multiple of the *fundamental* frequency, that is, the frequency of the signal passing through the equipment. If the fundamental is 1000 Hz the *second harmonic* will be 2000 Hz, the *third harmonic* will be 3000 Hz, and so on.

Harmonic distortion is a result of *amplitude distortion*, which is mainly due to the non-linear transfer of the signal from one section of the equipment to another, such as from one stage of the amplifier to the next. This occurs when the amplitude of the output signal from the section at a given instant is not exactly proportional to the amplitude of the input signal. Amplitude distortion is also a source of *intermodulation* (IM) *distortion*, where the equipment, when handling two or more input signal frequencies, generates frequencies which are the sum or difference of the input frequencies.

Harmonic and intermodulation distortion are often quoted as percentages of the output signal; for instance if the total harmonic distortion (THD) is stated as 0.1% then that percentage of the output signal will be the harmonic distortion content. Distortion causes a harshness in the sound quality, and intermodulation is probably worse in its effect than harmonic distortion.

If the input signal level is too high it will cause *clipping distortion*, where the tips of the signal waveform become 'clipped' because they are trying to peak at amplitudes greater than the equipment can handle. Overload distortion figures are sometimes quoted by manufacturers, for instance 0.1% distortion for 20 dB overload means that if the input signal level rises 20 dB above that recommended it will result in 0.1% distortion.

Two forms of distortion found in disc reproduction are *tracking distortion* and *tracing distortion*. Tracking distortion is caused where the pickup stylus is unable to follow the modulations of the groove precisely, either because the playing weight is too low or because of excessive mechanical impedance (resistance to motion) in the stylus assembly or pick-up arm mountings. Tracking error is the angle between the centre line of the stylus and a line drawn at a tangent to the groove at the

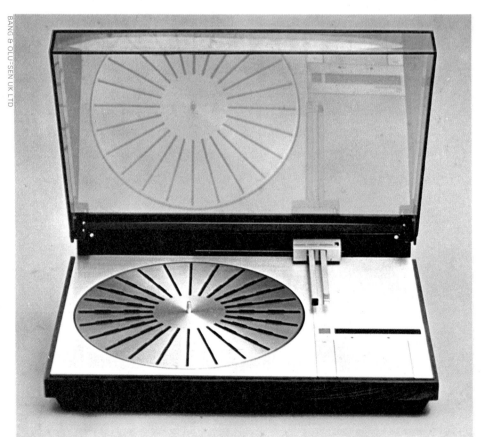

BANG & OLUFSEN UK LTD

Left: a turntable which has no tracking error, because the pick-up is driven across the record in a straight line by a servomotor rather than describing an arc from a tone-arm pivot. It duplicates the path of the cutting stylus which cut the master record. There is no extraneous lateral pressure of the stylus against the groove wall, since the stylus is not dragged by the groove. Contact of the record against the turntable is also kept to a minimum.

Right: two reasons why a record player does not reproduce the original signal faithfully.

Tracking error is caused by the fact that the cutting stylus moves straight across the record, but the pickup moves in a shallow arc, so that it is at an angle to the groove except at one point.

Tracing distortion: the cutter is shallow from front to back, and cuts a path that a round stylus cannot trace. Using an elliptical stylus reduces the distortion.

point of contact between the stylus and groove. This angle must be kept as small as possible so that the stylus tip closely follows the path of the cutting stylus used to cut the master disc (see RECORD MANUFACTURE, RECORD PLAYER).

Tracing distortion is a form of harmonic distortion, caused by the inability of the stylus to trace the groove modulations exactly because its tip radius is greater than that of the cutting stylus.

Cartridge specifications often quote a 15° *vertical tracking angle*. This means that when the stylus is deflected upwards it moves at an effective angle of 15° forward to the vertical, which is the angle at which the cutting stylus moves.

Noise Noise is due to the random electrical signals generated within a system, and is to some extent unavoidable because even when an amplifier is not carrying a signal there is a small amount of current flowing in the circuit (*quiescent* current), which produces a signal that covers basically the whole of the frequency spectrum and is often called 'white noise' (by analogy with white light, which covers the whole of the visible spectrum). Noise levels are frequently quoted as 'hum and noise' to include the level of 'hum' in the system. Hum is an unwanted low frequency noise produced by the mains current powering the system, and consists of a basic mains frequency tone (50 or 60 Hz) together with associated harmonics. The hum and noise current of the output of an amplifier, for example, is expressed in terms of the ratio between the level of the wanted signal and that of the hum and noise content. This *signal-to-noise* (S/N) *ratio* is measured in decibels, for instance '—66 dB at 50 watts' (which means that the noise power is less than 50 microwatts at 50 W output power).

Power outputs There is more than one way of measuring the power output or handling capacity of a piece of equipment, but the most meaningful is the *continuous RMS power* available without exceeding the stated harmonic distortion levels. RMS (root mean square) is the amplitude of an AC voltage waveform equal to the DC voltage which would dissipate the same power in a given load. This gives an indication of the amount of power that the equipment can handle continuously over a sustained period, as opposed to the unreliable figures for 'music power' or 'peak power' which indicate the *instantaneous peak power* available. These figures may be much higher than the continuous power figures, maybe as much as twice as high, and so are often used to make a piece of equipment appear more powerful than it really is.

Although very high power output levels are not needed for normal domestic purposes, it is better to have an amplifier capable of delivering more power than is usually required. The amplifier will then be running at less than its maximum output under most circumstances, with a reserve of power to cope with loud musical peaks and less risk of clipping distortion, or of overheating the output TRANSISTORS during prolonged periods of use.

Wow, flutter and rumble *Wow* and *flutter* are two forms of distortion caused by speed variations in the drive mechanism of a record deck (*transcription unit*) or a tape, cassette or cartridge player. Wow causes a slow variation in the pitch of the sound and is caused by speed variations at rates of 10 Hz or less. Flutter gives a quivering effect to the sound, and is caused by speed variations at rates of more than 10 Hz. Wow and flutter figures are usually quoted as percentages, the lower

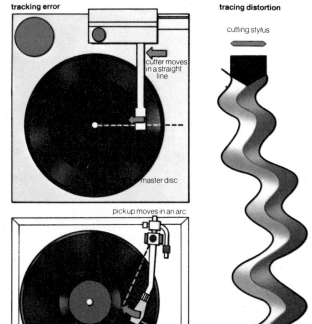

tracking error

cutter moves in a straight line

master disc

pickup moves in an arc

record

tracing distortion

cutting stylus

round stylus

elliptical stylus

OSBORNE / MARKS

the percentage the better.

Rumble is a form of noise produced by a record deck and transmitted through the turntable to the pickup, and thence to the amplifier to be reproduced by the speakers. It sounds rather like distant thunder and can be very obtrusive during quiet passages of music. High quality decks produce little or virtually no rumble, and a good hi fi turntable will produce rumble levels at least 45 dB below the required signal level.

Top: a turntable with platter removed to show the belt drive system, the simplest way to isolate motor noise, lowering rumble.

Above: a loudspeaker on test in an anechoic (sound absorbing) chamber, which allows its performance to be accurately measured.

Below: this amplifier has five extra tone controls spread over the frequency range for compensating older or unbalanced recordings.

Impedance and sensitivity For the most efficient transfer of power from one part of a system to the next, with minimum distortion, their respective output and input *impedances* should correspond as closely as possible. In general, matching is satisfactory when the input impedance is anything up to five or six times the source impedance, but not vice versa. Impedance is a circuit's effective opposition to current flow, and is made up of its RESISTANCE plus any inductive or capacitive *reactance* (see CIRCUIT, electrical). Impedance varies with frequency, so impedance figures are usually specified at a given frequency, generally 1 kHz. The impedance of a component is often very much greater than its resistance (also called DC resistance); for example a pickup cartridge with a DC resistance of 630 ohms may have a recommended load impedance of 47,000 ohms. Impedance matching is an important factor in hi fi system design, as any significant mismatching will seriously degrade the sound quality.

The *sensitivity* of an amplifier is the input voltage necessary for it to be able to develop its rated maximum output power, and the lower this input voltage is the higher the sensitivity of the amplifier. The input signal to an amplifier may generally be anything up to four or five times its stated sensitivity without trouble due to overloading.

Specifications Several organizations have drawn up minimum standards for the construction and performance of hi fi equipment. Discs and recorded tapes are made with the low frequencies attenuated (reduced in amplitude) and the high frequencies boosted, and the replay equipment must compensate for this by boosting the low frequencies in relation to the high ones. The internationally agreed standard for disc recording and replay *equalization* characteristics is the RIAA (Record Industry Association of America) standard (the same as British Standard 1928/61).

Tape equalization standards are either the CCIR (International Radio Consultative Committee) standard or that determined by the NARTB (also called NAB; the National Association of Radio and Television Broadcasters in the USA).

Other equipment specifications and test standards have been set by the IHF (the Institute of High Fidelity) and by the DIN (Deutsche Industrie-Norm, the German industrial standards organization) whose DIN 45 500 specifications lay down minimum standards for the performance of hi fi equipment.

HIGH SPEED PHOTOGRAPHY

High speed photography is used to study events which last for a very short period of time or to 'freeze' very rapid motion. For example, the technique can be used to study the behaviour of a bullet as it penetrates a target.

In high speed photography, light from the subject being photographed will fall on the film for only a very short period of time and must therefore be of high intensity to achieve a proper exposure. For this reason the subject is normally illuminated with flash apparatus unless it is highly self-luminous, such as a flame or spark. The equipment used will depend on the results required; if only a single picture is needed the equipment must be capable of producing a single high intensity flash of short duration and must include a triggering arrangement so that the picture is taken at precisely the right moment. If it is required to study motion, then a series of pictures must be taken in very rapid succession. Each picture will require a separate high intensity flash and each successive image must fall on a different section of the film.

Flash equipment The FLASHGUNS employed in normal photography use flashbulbs or cubes which produce a flash lasting for from about 1/80th to 1/100th second, or an electronic DISCHARGE TUBE, which produces a flash lasting for 1/75oth to 1/1000th second. While these flash times are suitable for most normal applications, they are too long if the event itself lasts for only a few microseconds, or if the motion to be photographed is very fast. For example, a bullet travelling at three times the speed of sound will travel approximately three feet (1.1 m) in 1/1000th second.

The most common flash lamp for high speed photography

SCIENCE MUSEUM

Above: a sequence of high speed photographs running from top left to bottom right showing a dragonfly taking flight.

Below: a photograph showing the passage of a bullet through a playing card. Because of the extremely short duration of the exposure, the image of the bullet is only very slightly blurred.

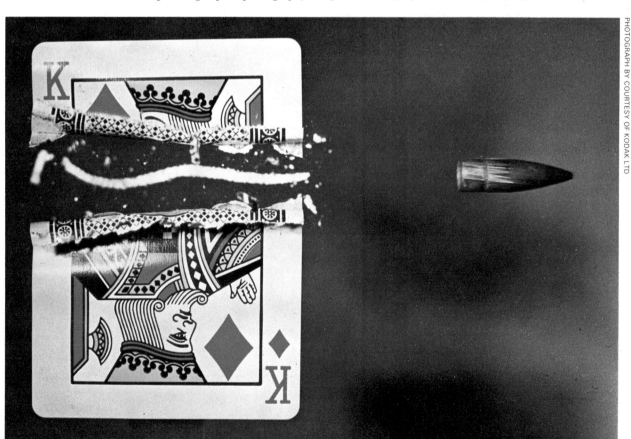

PHOTOGRAPH BY COURTESY OF KODAK LTD

is the xenon filled discharge tube. The flashes from such tubes are similar to daylight in their colour content except that they emit rather more light at the blue and ultraviolet end of the spectrum. This is useful because photographic emulsions are more sensitive to light at that end of the spectrum. The discharge tube is connected to a specially designed control circuit which ensures that the duration of the flash is very short, typically 0.5 microsecond (half a millionth of a second). For studying rapid motion the flash tube must deliver a large number of flashes per second. A flash rate of 4000 flashes per second is quite common. Devices such as *thyratrons* and *mercury arc* RECTIFIERS are used in the control circuit to ensure that each flash is distinct from the next. Multiple flash apparatus of this sort is called a STROBOSCOPE.

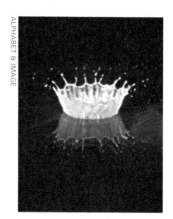

Left: a high speed photograph showing the crown-shaped splash produced by a drop striking the surface of a pool of liquid.

Below: cutaway of a high speed camera. The image from the photocathode is converted into an electron beam in the image converter and then focused on to a phosphor screen in two rows of images. Between each frame, the electron beam is deflected on to the aperture plate itself and therefore blocked.

Cameras If a series of pictures is to be taken the camera must arrange for each successive picture to fall on a fresh part of the film. This can be done with a normal 'still' picture camera by moving the camera or by deflecting the light entering the camera from the subject by using a rotating mirror. With this method a series of pictures can be taken using the same piece of film, but of course only a small number of pictures can be taken before the film is used up. Often it will be necessary to take a large number of pictures, for example if a cine film is to be made. Conventional cine cameras cannot be used in high speed photography because the number of pictures they can take per second is limited by the mechanical film advancing mechanism, which momentarily stops the film while each frame is exposed. In high speed cameras, the film passes continuously through the camera and its motion relative to the image is compensated for optically, using rotating mirrors or prisms. In this way the film and the image can effectively be made stationary relative to each other, although the film may be moving through the camera at speeds of up to 200 mile/h (322 km/h). High speed rotating prism cameras of this type can operate at picture frequencies of up to about 10,000 per second using a full 16 mm picture size, or up to 40,000 per second using 16 mm film with a picture height of 2 mm.

In high speed cameras the speed of the film is never absolutely constant and it is therefore important to record a *time base* on the film if the time intervals between the various events recorded are to be determined. This can be done by recording flashes whose precise frequency is known on to the edge of the film.

HOLLERITH TABULATOR (see card handling)

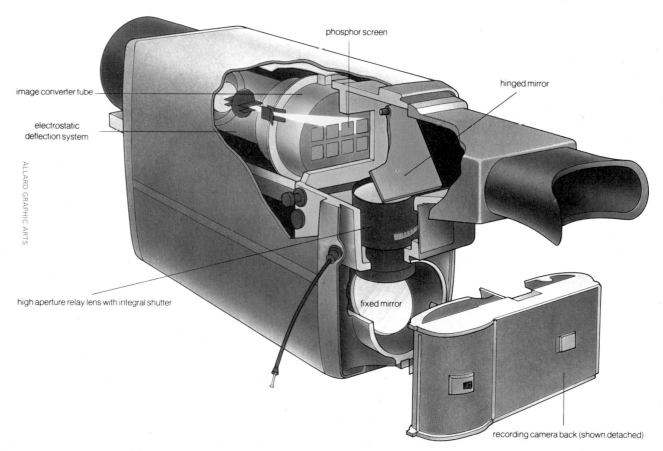

image converter tube

electrostatic deflection system

high aperture relay lens with integral shutter

phosphor screen

hinged mirror

fixed mirror

recording camera back (shown detached)

HOLOGRAPHY

Holography is, like photography, a technique for recording on film information about a scene or an object. The basic mechanisms by which the two techniques achieve their purpose, however, differ greatly, as do the nature of the images produced.

A conventional photograph yields a two dimensional representation of the subject in which the scenic depth that the eye perceives is collapsed into one plane—the plane of the print. The end product of holography, the *hologram*, captures the three dimensional information about the scene—that is, it includes information in depth.

A pseudo three dimensional effect can be produced by conventional photography by viewing two photographs of the subject simultaneously in a STEREOSCOPE, but only one view of the subject is presented in this technique—from one particular angle. Using holography, the reconstructed scene can be viewed from a range of angles and an observer moving his head from side to side will witness *parallax effects*—that is, the relative movement of two objects in the recorded scene because of the observer's motion.

Holography was conceived and predicted in 1947 by the British scientist, Dennis Gabor, but the practical demonstration of the technique had to await the invention of a particular type of light source—the LASER—in the early 1960s.

Lasers and coherent light

A hologram can be produced by recording on sensitized film, as in photography, but to understand the difference between the two processes it is important first to consider the nature of LIGHT.

Visible light is a form of ELECTROMAGNETIC RADIATION and as such travels through space as 'waves' of electrical and magnetic disturbances at a velocity of 186,000 mile/s (300,000 km/s). The distance between successive maxima, or crests, of these waves is termed the wavelength and the number of crests that pass a given point in one second is termed the frequency of the WAVE MOTION. The frequency of the wave multiplied by the wavelength equals the velocity of propagation and, because this is constant, higher frequencies mean shorter wavelengths.

Light sources used in conventional photography, for example sunlight or electric lighting, emit radiation over a wide frequency range (ultra-violet to infra-red)—white light contains a jumble of different frequencies (colours). Because of the disordered nature of white light it is not possible to record information about the depth of a scene. To record depth information the light source must be of a single frequency, that is, *monochromatic*; and with each wave in phase with every other wave—a property called coherence. With coherent light the crests of each wave travel together—that is, in phase. Such a beam of light is emitted by laser devices.

Holographic recording

Because a laser beam is highly ordered, that is, monochromatic and coherent, details of the depth of a scene illuminated by such a beam are contained in the phase relationships of the waves arriving at the holographic recording plate. A wave arriving from a more distant part of the scene will 'lag' behind waves from closer points and it is this information about lagging and leading waves which is recorded in a hologram.

To record this information a *reference beam* is required with which to compare the phase relationships of the *object beam*. This is achieved by splitting the laser beam into two parts: one is directed at the scene from which the reflected (object) beam is derived and the other part is aimed directly at the recording plate (this is the reference beam). Where the object and reference beams meet at the plate they will interact or *interfere*. Interference is a phenomenon associated with coherent light.

When the crests of two waves coincide an enhancement of light intensity or amplitude occurs through the wave energies adding together. This process is called *constructive interference*.

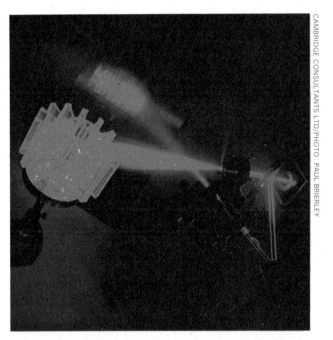

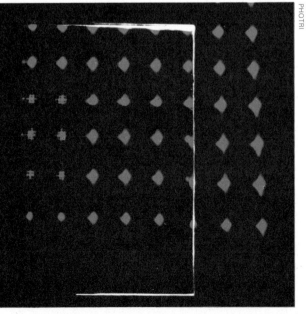

Top right: the acrylic object in the left foreground is being 'photographed' using a holographic technique. The laser beam is split in two—one is aimed at the object (the object beam) and the other (reference beam) directly on to the holographic recording plate.

Right: a hologram as a storage device. The laser beam is diffracted by the hologram, producing a pattern of stored information.

When the crest of one wave coincides with a minimum position, or trough, of a second wave a reduced intensity is obtained—*destructive interference*. Constructive interference occurs when the two waves arrive at a point *in phase* with each other. Destructive interference occurs when the waves arrive *out of phase*—that is, when one crest coincides with a trough—a phase difference of half a wavelength.

The resulting amplitudes at the holographic plate do not change with time, although the impinging waves are time varying. This means that *standing wave patterns* are established and it is these standing waves which are recorded on the light sensitive film or plate. Furthermore, this recorded pattern contains both amplitude and phase information about the object beam. A conventional photograph records only the amplitudes of the light arriving at the film.

The hologram
The developed holographic film, or hologram, looks nothing like the recorded scene. If the object being recorded is a simple flat reflecting surface the resulting interference pattern shows a series of light and dark bands, whereas the pattern produced by light reflected from a single point on an object consists of a series of concentric rings. A practical hologram of an object or scene is a highly complex pattern of superimposed circles from the many points on the object that reflect light.

Reconstructing the original scene
Normally, the hologram is developed as a transparency, although there are other ways of recording a holographic scene. To construct an image of the original scene this transparency must be illuminated with a beam of coherent light similar to that used as the reference beam in recording. Viewed from the other side, a complete reconstruction of the original object is obtained.

In detail, the reconstructing laser beam is modulated

Above: the object that can be seen in the bluish screen (foreground) is a truly three dimensional image produced by the interaction of a blue laser beam with the hologram (the screen). The image is seen behind the hologram, which appears to be a simple glass screen.

Below: five superimposed views of the same image from one hologram.

Right: a hologram records complete three dimensional information about an object. A laser beam—which is monochromatic (single colour) and coherent (all light waves travelling in phase)—is split into two beams. One is aimed at the object from which the 'object beam' is reflected, the other is aimed directly at the photographic plate (hologram). When the original reference beam is aimed at the processed plate, a reconstructed image is produced.

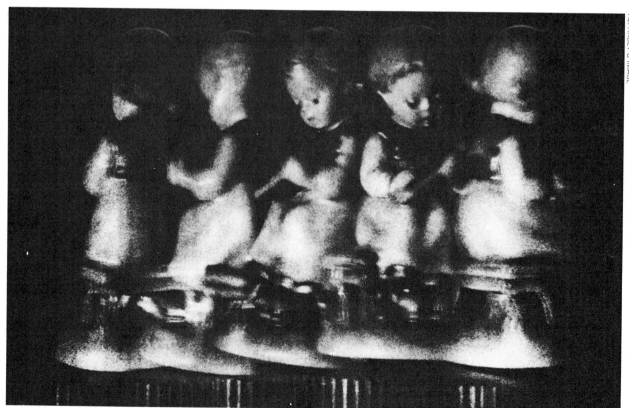

(changed) in amplitude and phase as it passes through the hologram transparency in such a way that it resembles the original object beam. This produces a *virtual image* of the object which, to the observer, appears to be behind the hologram. It is this image which can be seen by the eye. There is also a *real image* formed on the same side as the observer. This cannot be seen as it is a *focused* image, but with a screen placed in the focal area the image can be viewed on the screen. Shifting the screen backwards and forwards will bring different parts of the real image into focus.

Since colour is dependent on frequency, any hologram produced using a single laser beam will give a monochrome (single colour) reconstruction of the object. It is possible, however, by chosing three laser beams giving three different frequency beams (corresponding to the three primary colours—red, green and blue) to record and reconstruct a scene in full colour.

Applications of holography

Several properties of holograms render them of great importance for technological and engineering applications. One such feature is that many holograms may be stored in a single photographic plate. This is possible provided the direction of the reference beam relative to the plate is changed between exposures so that the superimposed interference patterns are not confused. Reconstructions are formed only when the developed plate is illuminated by a reconstructing beam in the appropriate direction. Thus if a hologram containing many patterns is rotated in the path of a fixed beam, the observer sees the many reconstructions appearing sequentially. In this way a large amount of information can be stored on a single plate and retrieved simply by illuminating at an appropriate angle. This technique is applicable to many fields of information and DATA STORAGE.

Another application uses holography to reveal small differences between the dimensions of a master object and a manufactured copy. The reflected object beam from the copy is directed at the hologram of the master. When viewed from the other side, interference patterns (fringes) will exist whenever there are differences between master and copy. Each fringe from a given reference point indicates a size difference of one half wavelength between the test object and the master. Use of a typical laser light source enables size differences of 0.000012 inch (0.0003 mm) to be readily detected.

Holography is a relatively recent discovery and new applications are continually being developed. The technique has been applied to the problem of producing sharp images of objects travelling at very high velocities and also to CHARACTER RECOGNITION. Furthermore, there are prospects of the future development of truly three dimensional images in the field of TELEVISION and cinema.

Limitations

The highly coherent light sources used in holography lead to odd DIFFRACTION patterns in the reconstructed image. These superimposed patterns are caused by dust particles in the air and on glass surfaces involved, bubbles or striations in the glass and reflections from air-glass interfaces. These 'impurities' in the image can be reduced by extreme care in removing dust and using highly polished pure glass but some impurities will always remain. One technique for further reduction of these diffraction patterns is to effectively spread them out over the whole image. This gives the image a 'speckle' appearance but this is subjectively less offensive than a multitude of diffraction rings.

Another important limitation in holography is the size of the scene that can be recorded. Larger scenes require larger and more powerful lasers to illuminate them.

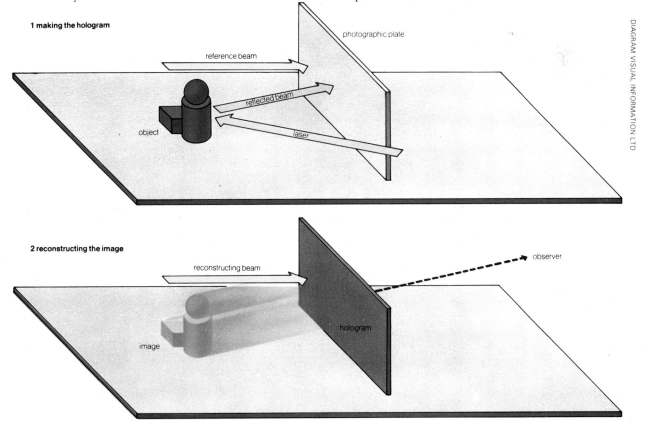

1 making the hologram

reference beam

photographic plate

reflected beam

object

laser

2 reconstructing the image

reconstructing beam

observer

hologram

image

HONNECOURT, Villard de (c1180–c1250)

Little is known about the life of Villard de Honnecourt, a Cistercian monk and architect born at Honnecourt, a small village on the River Scheldt near Cambrai, in about 1180 AD. As an architect he might have passed almost unnoticed, although he was responsible for the design of Cambrai cathedral, had he not left a remarkable notebook which luckily has survived, although a few pages are known to be missing. This book contained personal jottings and sketches on matters concerning his work. It is of interest primarily because of descriptions of mechanical devices which were in use in the thirteenth century and of which we would otherwise be totally ignorant.

The larger part of Villard's notebook is taken up with architectural studies (see CATHEDRAL BUILDING). Other sections deal with the construction of automata, such as a model of an angel which could be made to rotate or of an eagle which could be made to turn its head. Devices of this kind were quite a common feature of ecclesiastic buildings of this period. An interest in them may be seen as an extension of the architect's function, although by then they already had a long history rooted in the works of the Greek scientists at Alexandria in the first century AD. Villard's sketch of the pivot for the angel, however, shows that he had come very close to solving the problem of designing an escapement for a mechanical CLOCK.

Two sketches in the notebook deal with equipment for handling building materials, one being a screw jack, the other a hydraulic saw. The first is described by Villard quite simply as being useful for lifting heavy burdens. It is depicted as little more than a nut and screw operated by a cross-handle and contained within a stout wooden frame. It was evidently designed for lifting heavy pieces of wood or stone during building operations. No similar screw jack is known until about 1480, when jacks came into common use for training cannon and lifting wagons.

The hydraulic saw described by Villard has two functional elements. The saw blade is suspended vertically between a sapling branch at the top, which acted as a spring, and a hinged bar at the bottom. This bar could be forced downwards by a series of cams projecting from the main shaft of a water-wheel. After each such downward movement the saw blade was returned by the sapling spring. A wheel with projecting spikes was attached to the main shaft in such a way that it forced the log being sawn against the blade. Similar saws are unknown until the Renaissance, when one finds them described by such engineers as Leonardo da VINCI.

A further device sketched by Villard is a system of gimbal rings designed for carrying a small fire-basket. It shows six concentric rings with the fire-basket in the centre, while the carrying handle would have been attached to the outer ring. The rings are pivoted so that, no matter at what angle the handle is held, the fire-basket would have remained upright. Probably Villard had in mind the carrying of censers, then greatly used in churches, when he drew this design. However, gimbals were not in general use until the Renaissance, when they were applied to magnetic COMPASSES to keep them steady at sea.

While Villard's primary interest lay in ecclesiastical building, he was equally obliged to consider questions of military defence, since no distinction was then made between architects and engineers. In his notebook there is a series of sketches of a stone-throwing machine or trebuchet (see BALLISTA).

In his day Villard's notebook was certainly not unique, for other architects are known to have kept their own records, but

these have since been lost or destroyed. Furthermore, Villard's book does not suggest that he was a great innovator, but rather that he was in the habit of making notes of things he had seen and which he felt might prove useful. The book thus assumes an importance far beyond that intended by its author. For the historian of technology it serves as a reminder that the understanding of the Middle Ages is very imperfect, and that some machines, which we might otherwise believe to be inventions of the Renaissance, were in fact known and used at least two centuries earlier.

Below: Villard's drawing of a screw jack, the first known.

Bottom: this saw, driven by a water wheel, is seen in a slightly confusing top view to show all the working parts.

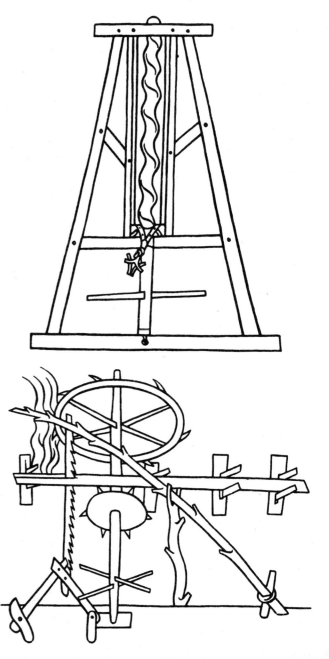

HOOKE, Robert (1635–1703)

Robert Hooke was one of the most versatile scientists of his time; he is best remembered for his work in physics, mechanics and microscopy.

Born on the Isle of Wight, the son of a minister, he was apprenticed to a painter before entering Westminster School. Later, at Oxford, he met a group of scientists, becoming Robert BOYLE's assistant. Here he made an improved air pump and began work on designing watches regulated by springs instead of pendulums, an important step towards the chronometer, a rugged but highly accurate CLOCK for finding a ship's longitude at sea. Hooke had a great capacity for making instruments and apparatus and conducting successful experiments.

After some of his Oxford friends had joined in forming the Royal Society of London, Hooke was appointed Curator of Experiments in 1662. His duties were to provide several experiments for each of the weekly meetings. In 1665 he became Professor of Geometry at Gresham College in London, and here he spent the remainder of his life.

His most successful publication was the *Micrographia* of 1665, a book of microscopical observations, famous for its magnificent illustrations. Here Hooke's contemporaries could, for the first time, see the detailed structure of a bluebottle or a flea, or observe the compound eye of a fly. Many were intrigued by this sight of a new and unknown world; many more thought Hooke was absurd in studying such trivia—especially fleas and lice.

His interests ranged from astronomy to geology and included theories of light and combustion. The fundamental law of ELASTICITY still bears his name. He made an important contribution towards explaining the motion of planets by saying that their orbits resulted from combining an inertial motion in a straight line with the attractive force of the Sun, and that this attractive force varied inversely as the distance squared. Though Hooke could not demonstrate mathematically that this was the case, he passed his insight on to the far superior mathematician, Sir Isaac NEWTON, and later complained when Newton would not publicly acknowledge his contribution.

Hooke's abilities were not confined to what we could call science. After the Great Fire of London in 1666, the City appointed him as surveyor and he worked for many years under his friend Sir Christopher Wren. Not only did he survey sites and foundations, but as an architect in his own right, he designed a number of important buildings.

Hooke was hardly a very happy man. He was touchy, especially when he thought someone was stealing his ideas. He was often ill, and continually subjected to indigestion, headaches and insomnia. There is no surviving portrait, but he was certainly ugly—thin and crooked, with a sharp chin and large eyes and forehead. His hair was long and untidy. But appearances were indeed deceptive. Beneath this forbidding exterior was a man of humanity and great scientific intuition. The perceptive Samuel Pepys wrote after their first meeting that Hooke 'is the most, and promises the least, of any man in the world that ever I saw'.

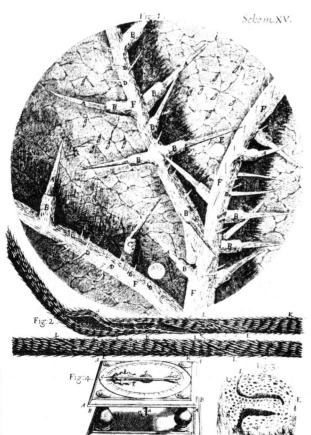

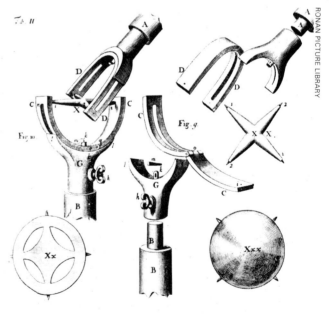

Left : Robert Hooke was one of the first to make detailed study of the microscopic world. In his book 'Micrographia' published in London in 1665 were drawings of the underside of a stinging nettle leaf (Fig 1). Below this is a drawing of the beard of a wild oat (Fig 2) with a cross-sectional view in Fig 3. Hooke used the wild oat beard in his hygrometer (Fig 4) used for measuring atmospheric humidity. The beard expands in a damp environment.

Above : Hooke was an extremely versatile scientist. Amongst his many inventions was the Hooke's universal joint.

HORN and KLAXON

As the speed of motor vehicles increased around the end of the 19th century, some means of audible warning became necessary. The first type of horn to gain general acceptance was the bulb horn, a trumpet-like instrument operated by squeezing a rubber bulb. When the bulb was squeezed, the blast of air produced caused a reed to vibrate, as in some WOODWIND INSTRUMENTS, and the sound waves this produced were amplified by the shape of the horn.

Klaxons A more efficient warning device was the mechanical klaxon, which used a vibrating diaphragm (similar in principle to a LOUDSPEAKER cone) to produce the sound. The klaxon was operated by a spring loaded plunger, which had a corrugated surface within the body of the klaxon that ran down the back of the diaphragm causing it to vibrate rapidly. The sound produced was amplified by a horn in front of the diaphragm.

The plunger-operated klaxon continued in use up to the 1920s despite the introduction of the electric klaxon in 1912. This had a DC electric motor which drove a corrugated disc that vibrated the diaphragm, producing a higher, stronger note than the manual klaxon. Another form of manual klaxon also had a corrugated disc, which was turned by a handle.

Electric horns A typical modern electric horn consists of an electric coil and a metal diaphragm, with a set of contacts between them. When the horn button is pressed, current flows in the coil, setting up a magnetic field which attracts the diaphragm towards the coil. As the diaphragm moves it opens the contacts, cutting off the supply of current to the coil, in a similar manner to the contact arrangement on an electric

ZEFA/PICTOR

Above: an old, brass, trumpet-type car horn.

Above right: a modern electric horn.

Below: an old advertisement for a combined bulb horn and electric klaxon. Working at either 8 or 12 volts, the klaxon's motor drove a ten-toothed wheel that vibrated a steel alloy diaphragm.

NATIONAL MOTOR MUSEUM

COMBINATION
KLAXON ELECTRIC and HAND HORN.

	Brass	N.P. or Black Enamel	Black Nickel
XH144 8 Volts.	£16 16 0	£18 0 0	£18 8 0
XH145 12 Volts.	17 4 0	18 8 0	18 16 0

Is a Type L instrument with the addition of an unusually powerful and effective hand horn. Each is operated separately.

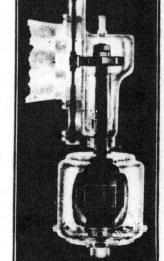

The ghost outline here produced shows the beautifully assembled parts of the **KLAXON** Horn. Each is a specimen of the best class material and workmanship.

BELL. When the current stops flowing in the coil, the magnetic field collapses and the diaphragm springs forward away from the coil. This allows the contacts to close again, completing the circuit to the coil, and the cycle is repeated as long as the horn button remains depressed. The vibrations of the diaphragm are amplified by a small horn, and there is often an adjusting screw provided, which alters the amount of movement of the diaphragm by altering the opening and closing positions of the contacts, thus altering the pitch of the sound.

Air horns The latest types of horn are driven by compressed air and produce powerful high single or multiple notes. The compressed air is supplied by a COMPRESSOR driven by a DC electric motor, and there are usually two, three or five horns, which are of different sizes and so produce notes of different frequencies (see BRASS INSTRUMENTS).

The compressor is basically of the rotary vane type, and in some horns there is a gear mechanism which drives a disc valve that distributes the air to each horn in turn, giving an alternating note. The disc valve may be controlled by an electromagnet so that the horns can either be operated in sequence (*consecutive operation*) or all together (*concurrent operation*), the mode of operation being selected by means of a switch.

To prevent arcing across the horn button contacts caused by the heavy current needed to drive the compressor motor, the horn button operates a RELAY which has heavy duty contacts that complete the circuit to the motor.

HORN, FRENCH (see brass instruments)

Below left: an electric klaxon. The motor drives a corrugated disc which vibrates a diaphragm, producing a loud strong note.

Below right: a modern electric horn. Current passes through the coil and the diaphragm, attracted by the magnetic field set up, opens the contacts. The current ceases, the diaphragm returns and the cycle is repeated, producing vibration.

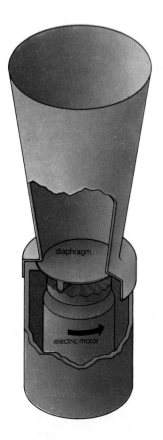

diaphragm

electric motor

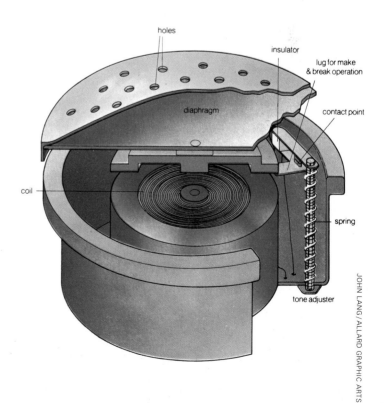

holes

insulator

lug for make & break operation

diaphragm

contact point

coil

spring

tone adjuster

HOUSE TRANSPORT METHODS

Houses have been moved for centuries. Henry VIII did it when he put together two smaller colleges at Cambridge to make Trinity College. Formerly, however, houses were nearly always moved by dismantling them and reconstructing them on the new site. Today it is often cheaper to jack up the house and move it without taking it apart.

Houses are moved because of road construction, new building projects, the clearance of areas that are to be flooded for new reservoirs, and other reasons. Moving houses is far more common in North America, where most houses are of wood frame construction, which is inherently strong and very light, and where roads are wider and straighter. In Britain, with comparatively narrow, winding roads, bridges, round-abouts and other obstructions, it is much more difficult to move a house any distance without considerable inconvenience. Even so, it is sometimes cheaper to move a house a short distance than to build a new one. If the house is of considerable historical or architectural interest, it may be moved to save it from demolition.

Each house moving job must be studied carefully and the method of operation chosen depending on the structure of the house, the route over which the move will take place, and the nature of the new site. Thus the engineer must start at both ends of the problem. The construction of the house must be studied to determine how the different parts of the building are supported, and to calculate the weight supported by each part of the foundation. Then the route and the new site must be studied to determine whether a gradient exists, and if so how much; whether the ground is soft or firm and what obstructions are in the way; and whether the house can be moved in a straight line or must be turned through an angle.

The moving method will be either to install tracks on the route or to use a large wheeled or tracked transporter. Large buildings are rarely moved long distances and tracks will always be used; for smaller buildings the transporter may be a heavy lorry [truck] or purpose-built *bogies* made up of large numbers of closely spaced wheels.

Once the transport system has been decided attention can be turned to the building and the design of the chassis. A method of constructing beams of reinforced concrete beneath existing walls was developed in England in the 1940s; this method is best for brick or masonry buildings. If tracks are to be used to move the building, brackets are bolted directly to the beams; specially constructed hydraulic jacks are fixed to the brackets. The building is then jacked up between 18 inches and three feet (about 0.5 to 1 m) to allow for tracks to be run underneath the foundation at ground level. This is accomplished by thrusting off timbers or concrete pads placed beneath the beams during the construction. The jacks are extended to lift the building and temporary packings are placed under the beams on each side of the jacking positions; the jacks are retracted, packings placed beneath them and the process repeated until the house is high enough. This must be carefully planned so that support under the building is always equal at each point. When the house is high enough, the tracks are laid and wheels to run in them are fitted to the jacks.

If the building is to be moved on groups of wheels without tracks, the concrete beams can be smaller and lighter and supported themselves at more closely spaced intervals by a second frame of steel beams. This may be a BAILEY BRIDGE type of construction erected around the building, which can be quickly assembled and quickly removed when the move is

completed. In the case of timber framed buildings, the whole building can be supported by a steel chassis, dispensing with the concrete beams. This may take the form of steel trusses carrying the load to Bailey bridging, or of a network of main steel beams resting on the wheels with smaller beams carrying the wall loads to the main beams. Smaller lighter buildings can be supported entirely by heavy timber. The advantage of timber is that it can be easily cut and fitted to the job and is lighter to handle.

The condition as well as the construction of the building must be taken into account. If the building is of brick or masonry and in good condition, the support must be absolutely rigid to avoid cracking. If it is an old timber building in poor condition which is to be restored after moving, a considerable amount of flexibility is allowed and the supports can be much lighter. If the building is to be moved on tracks, it is very expensive and time consuming to pack the ground to an absolute level to prevent movement of the track as the weight passes over; a thick layer of well packed ground is needed underneath. A method which can be used to compensate for some local movement of the track is to support the building on jacks over each wheel, and join the jacks together in three groups, providing approximately equal pressure so that they act as a single three point support.

In Suffolk in 1972 an Elizabethan manor house 90 feet long and 40 feet wide (about 27×12 m) was moved $\frac{5}{8}$ mile (1 km). Planning permission had been given for a housing and commercial estate provided the house, scheduled for preservation, was moved bodily to a new site over the brow of a hill so that the new housing estate would not be in view. At one point the house was hauled up a hill which inclined the building ten feet (about 3 m) out of level. A steel frame was installed inside the house to strengthen it and the load was carried to a Bailey bridging framework around the outside. The house was jacked up nine feet (2.7 m) to allow for a chassis and transporter system made up of a line of fourteen wheels at the rear, grouped to balance the load, and separately steerable groups of six wheels each on the front corners, with smaller steering bogies in front. The structure was winched over unprepared ground using pulley blocks anchored into the ground, and lowered into place on the other side of the hill, 60 ft (about 18 m) higher than the original site.

A brick house was moved in Staffordshire recently, using reinforced concrete chassis beams with brackets, jacks and wheels running in tracks. The jacks were linked in three groups and the building was moved three hundred yards (274 m) including a right-angled turn, without any cracks appearing in the brickwork.

HOVERCRAFT (see aircushion vehicles)

Above far left: a wood frame house is like a large, strong wooden box, and is comparatively easy to move. This one, in New Jersey, USA, was sawn in half by carpenters before moving.

Above left: this brick house in Staffordshire was moved on tracks. The reinforced concrete chassis beams can be seen, as well as the support under the tracks. The creepers on the house were moved along with it by digging the roots up and putting them in bags.

Left: Ballingdon Hall in Suffolk was moved after 380 years on its original site. A steel framework constructed around the house distributed the load evenly. There were so many spectators that a fee was charged for watching, which went to a local church fund.

HUYGENS, Christiaan (1629–1695)

Christiaan Huygens was born in The Hague on 14 April 1629. His grandfather, his father, and later his older brother were in the service of the House of Orange, and Christiaan grew up in a very cultured environment. His father, Constantijn Huygens, an accomplished man of science and letters and a brilliant poet, carefully planned Christiaan's private education in languages, literature, mathematics and music. The French philosopher René Descartes was a frequent visitor to the Huygens household and the precocious Christiaan was heavily influenced by Descartes' 'mechanistic' philosophy of nature, according to which the universe is entirely filled with 'vortices' of particles of various sizes, and all natural phenomena had to be explained in terms of particles pushing or hitting other particles. Huygens remained a 'Cartesian' until his death.

After two years at the University of Leiden and two years at the College of Orange in Breda, Huygens returned to his father's house where, supported by his father, he devoted himself to the study of nature. Except for several trips abroad, he stayed in The Hague until 1666, and during this very fruitful period he made important contributions to mathematics, astronomy, optics, and mechanics, quickly establishing himself as one of Europe's foremost scientists, and when he accepted the prestigious appointment to the newly founded Académie Royale des Sciences of Paris in 1666, he was regarded as its most distinguished member. He lived in Paris, except for several trips home, until 1681, when for reasons of health and religion he returned to The Hague.

In 1656 Huygens was able to adapt the principle of the pendulum to the regulation of the CLOCK, an idea which increased the accuracy of clocks enormously. His *Horologium* of 1658, in which he described the pendulum clock, however, was only a beginning. Huygens went on to investigate the pendulum, showing that only a pendulum bob describing a cycloidal arc was truly isochronous (having regular periodicity), and establishing the fundamental relationship between length and period of a pendulum. His *Horologium Oscillatorium*, published in 1673, presented these researches, as well as his calculation of *centrifugal force* and the value he had found for the acceleration of a falling body due to gravity ('g') by means of the pendulum.

Having taught himself how to grind lenses, Huygens set out to improve the TELESCOPE. By 1655 his telescopes were good enough to allow him to discover a satellite of Saturn (later called Titan). Shortly afterwards he also solved the problem posed by the strange appearance of the planet itself, and in his *Systema Saturnium* (1659) he published his results: Saturn is surrounded by an unattached ring. Among his other contributions to astronomy is the first determination of the rotation period of Mars. He continued his efforts to improve the telescope, and as telescopes became longer in order to minimize the optical problems posed by the primitive lenses, Huygens introduced the *aerial telescope* in which the objective lens and the eyepiece (now over 100 feet apart) were no longer connected by a tube.

Theoretical investigations of optical systems and the nature of light were not neglected. In the early 1660s he invented a compound eyepiece which minimized the colour fringes caused by the non-ACHROMATIC LENSES then in use; this 'Huygenian eyepiece' is still used in telescopes. In the late 1670s, in response to NEWTON's theory of the compound nature of white light—a theory which supposed light consisted of particles travelling through a vacuum—Huygens developed his wave theory in defence of Cartesian philosophy. He postulated that light is an irregular series of shock waves travelling with a finite speed through the 'aether' (ETHER) made up of elastic Cartesian particles. Light then was not an actual transfer of particles, as it was according to Newton's theory, but rather a tendency towards motion, transmitted by the continuous but irregularly spaced particles. Each particle transmitted the pressure (or impact) to all particles touching it in the direction of the pressure, and therefore each particle can be considered as the originating point of a new hemispherical wavefront of this pressure. Only in the overall direction of the light's path is the cumulative effect of these individual wavefronts perceptible. He published this principle in his *Traité de la Lumière* in (1690).

Although Huygens was certainly Europe's foremost scientist between 1655 and 1687 (the year of Newton's *Principia*) he fell into oblivion in the eighteenth century. His brilliantly elegant mathematical solutions, in the classical manner of the Greeks, were superseded by the calculus of Newton and Leibniz, and his wave theory was forgotten with the general acceptance of Newtonian science and the corresponding decline of Cartesian science. Only in the nineteenth century was his wave theory of light resurrected through the work of YOUNG and FRESNEL.

Left: a reconstruction of Huygens' pendulum, the most important development in clocks until the twentieth century. He also studied the physics of pendulums and calculated centrifugal force, as well as improving telescopes and postulating a wave theory of light. He published his work in a series of papers beginning in 1658.

Below: Christiaan Huygens, from a contemporary print.

HYDRAULIC MECHANISMS

Mechanisms which are operated by liquid under pressure are called hydraulic mechanisms. In order to understand the working of hydraulic mechanisms it is necessary to consider two basic principles. The first is that liquids are virtually incompressible, even when subjected to very high pressures, and the second, which was discovered by the 17th century scientist PASCAL, is that pressure applied to an enclosed liquid is transmitted with undiminished force in every direction. For example if a cylinder containing a piston of 1 sq inch (6.45 sq cm) area is connected by a pipe to a cylinder containing a piston of 10 sq inch (64.5 sq cm) area and a 10 lb (4.5 kg) weight is placed on the smaller piston, then a 100 lb (45 kg) weight will need to be placed on the larger piston to balance the smaller one. It follows that the bigger the larger piston is made, the greater the weight, proportionately, that the 10 lb on the smaller piston will support. However, it must be noted that in order to lift the 100 lb weight 1 inch (2.54 cm) the smaller piston would have to be depressed 10 inch (25.4 cm) to displace the required volume of liquid.

Although some research into the principles of hydraulics was carried out by Archimedes as early as 250 BC, it was not until the late 18th century that Joseph Bramah constructed the earliest known hydraulic mechanism. This was a hydraulic press, and consisted of a large cylinder containing a piston with a ramrod which was applied to the material to be pressed; pressure was built up by a hand PUMP with a small piston and water was the liquid used. Since that time the use of hydraulic machinery has expanded rapidly to every branch of engineering, chiefly because of the simplicity of the components required, and also the fact that the liquid can be carried through small bore piping to operate mechanisms far removed from the source of pressure; aircraft and ships, especially tankers, use hydraulics extensively.

Hand pumps have now been superseded by power driven pumps as a source of pressure, although they are still used on aircraft for servicing the system and in case of emergency. They are also used on simple mechanisms such as lifting jacks, where they form part of the unit. The lower part of the jack is used as a reservoir for the liquid; the pump is usually at the side and transfers the liquid into the jack cylinder to extend the piston which performs the lifting. A needle valve with a threaded spindle is unscrewed to open a passage for the liquid to escape to the reservoir from the cylinder when the jack is required to be lowered.

Present day hydraulic systems use a light mineral, or castor based, oil as the liquid because it has a low freezing point and also serves as a lubricant. Maximum system pressures vary between 1000 and 5000 psi (68–340 bar) but are usually about 2500 psi (170 bar). The section of the hydraulic system which is concerned with the pressurizing and supply of the liquid is termed the power system and is sometimes supplied by manufacturers as a separate unit called a power pack, which can be made in various sizes to suit the pressure and volume of liquid required to operate the mechanisms.

The requirements of a power system or pack are that in addition to supplying sufficient liquid at the correct pressure it should not be subjected to undue shock caused by sudden increases in pressure which may occur when an actuator reaches the end of its operation. Also the delivery from the pumps should be off-loaded when not required to operate the mechanism, in order to prevent overheating.

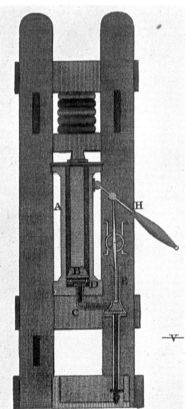

Left: a picture of Joseph Bramah's press from a publication of 1816. The operating lever is on the right of the press.

Below: the rotating drum of a truck for delivering premixed concrete is driven by a hydraulic motor (lower centre).

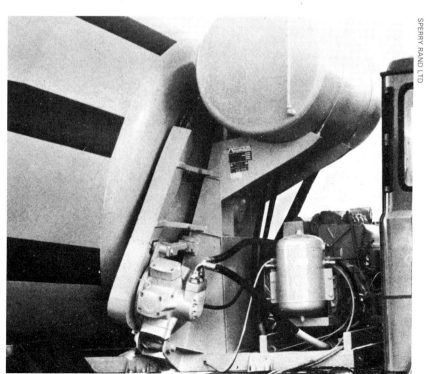

A typical power system consists of a reservoir, a power driven pump (several may be used), a filter, a relief valve, an accumulator, a cut-out valve (pressure regulator) or a pressure switch, and a non-return valve (check valve). The reservoir contains a supply of liquid for the pumps and accommodates the returning liquid from the system; the pumps build up the pressure; the filter ensures that the liquid is free from foreign matter and the accumulator smooths out any fluctuations in pressure and ensures a steady build up in addition to storing liquid, under pressure, for emergency or supplementary use. The cut-out valve automatically by-passes the liquid from the pumps back to the reservoir when the maximum pressure is reached; the non-return valve prevents the pressurized liquid leaking back when the cut-out valve has operated, and the relief valve is incorporated as an additional safeguard should the cut-out valve fail.

From the power system the liquid is piped to a selector valve (there may be several) which is usually manually controlled, and then to a jack, actuator or hydraulic motor which operates the particular mechanism. A return line is taken from the selector valve to the reservoir.

System components Reservoirs are metal tanks with the pump feed lines taken from the bottom and the system

Below: the chief components of a hydraulic power pack. Hydraulic fluid is pumped from the reservoir to the delivery line through a non-return valve. Normally the cut-out valve remains closed, but if the pressure exceeds a certain value, the piston will move to the left (lower diagram), unseating the valve and opening the by-pass line to the reservoir. A relief valve (upper diagram) prevents build-up of pressure if the cut-out valve fails.

return line entering the top through a filter. A filler cap is incorporated at the top and a *sight glass* is fitted vertically alongside the tank to indicate the liquid level. On military aircraft, which are subjected to rolling and various other aerobatics, the reservoir is a sealed cylinder containing a piston which exerts a slight pressure on the liquid to ensure that the pump is kept primed irrespective of the position of the aircraft.

The pumps are driven by the engines on aircraft and vehicles but on stationary equipment they are normally driven by electric motors. The two most common types are the *gear pump* and the *radial cylinder pump*. The gear type is very simple and comprises two meshed gears, one of which is driven. The gears are enclosed in a casing with very small clearances between the gears and case to ensure the minimum of internal leakage. The inlet port enters the case at a point where the gear teeth separate and the outlet port is taken from the opposite side where they mesh. Liquid is carried around the case from the inlet to be expelled at the outlet.

The radial cylinder type has an odd number of cylinders (usually 5 to 11) disposed in a block around a driving shaft bore. The pistons are attached to a *bearing ring*, which fits on to an *eccentric* on the driving shaft. As the shaft revolves, the pistons reciprocate in the cylinders because of its eccentricity. Each cylinder has a small delivery valve situated in a passage between the top of the cylinder and a channel leading to the delivery port. The inlet ports are drilled into the cylinder walls in such a position that they are uncovered by the pistons on the retraction stroke to allow the liquid to fill the cylinders. On the outward stroke the pistons cover the inlet ports and the liquid trapped is forced past the delivery valves to the delivery port.

Accumulators invariably comprise a cylinder containing a

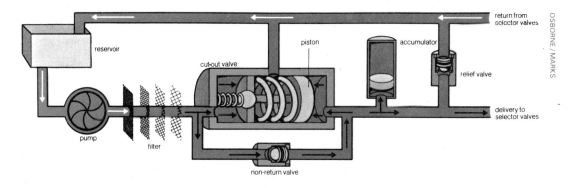

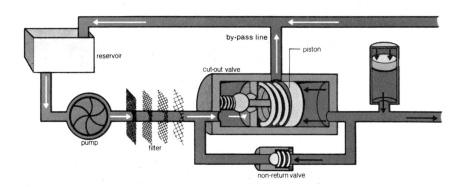

floating piston. One end of the cylinder is charged with air or nitrogen to a pressure of one third to half the maximum system pressure, forcing the piston towards the end of the cylinder; the opposite end is connected to the system pressure line. As the system pressure builds up it is applied against the piston in the accumulator until it is equal to the air pressure. The increasing pressure then forces the piston into the cylinder, the air pressure rising with the liquid pressure.

When the liquid pressure reaches its maximum and the pumps are off-loaded, the pressure is maintained in the system by the air in the accumulator. This reserve of liquid can be used to operate the units until the liquid pressure drops to a level at which the pumps cut in. On aircraft, additional accumulators are used to maintain a liquid supply to operate the systems used in landing, that is brakes, undercarriage and flaps (or air brakes), in case of failure of the main supply.

Cut-out valves vary in design but the principle of operation is similar. They consist of a cylinder which houses a spring loaded piston at one end and has a chamber containing a *non-return valve* at the other. Non-return valves are small loaded valves, inserted in the pipe lines to allow liquid to pass in one direction only. Liquid from the pumps is introduced into the valve chamber and also passes through an external non-return valve

Right: a remotely controlled mechanical arm is operated by means of hydraulic rams. The feed pipes are at the top left corner.

Below: the selector valve and actuator of a hydraulic system. The position of the selector valve piston determines whether the actuator will move to the right (upper diagram) or left (lower diagram). The arrows represent the flow of hydraulic fluid.

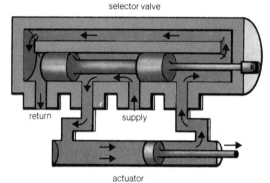

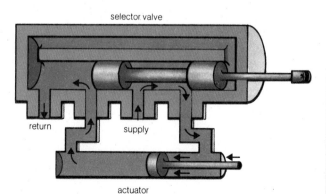

into the piston end of the cylinder and into the accumulator and the pressure lines. An additional port between the piston and the internal valve is connected to the reservoir return line.

As pressure builds up it is exerted against the piston, which moves in the cylinder against the spring until an extension on it contacts the non-return valve and unseats (opens) it. The liquid from the pumps now passes beneath the valve and leaves the cylinder at the return line port, completing an idling circuit. The system liquid pressure is maintained by the external non-return valve, which is now seated (shut). When the system pressure falls below a certain level the piston is forced back by the spring, the valve becomes seated and the liquid from the pumps is again delivered into the system.

Where pumps are driven by electric motors, a pressure operated switch may be used to stop the motors when the maximum pressure is reached instead of running the motors continuously and by-passing the liquid. The switch cuts the motors in when the pressure has dropped to a certain figure.

Relief valves are more heavily spring loaded than non-return valves, and are inserted between the pressure line and the return line and are set usually by an adjusting screw, to open at a pressure slightly higher than the cut-out pressure. They protect the system if the cut-out valve or pressure switch fails.

Selector valves are the means by which the operator controls the actuator or jack which functions the mechanism. Their function is to transfer the pressure to one side or other of the actuator cylinder and by-pass the opposite side to the return. The most common type is one which has a waisted plunger sliding in a ported bore. Four ports are usually employed, one each for pressure and return liquid and one for each side of the actuator. In one position of the plunger one of the waists forms

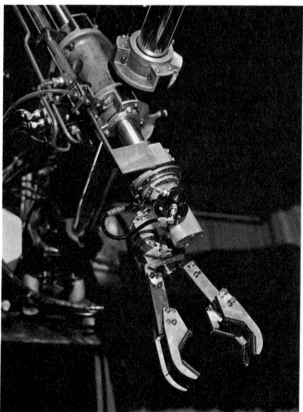

SPERRY RAND LTD

LANSING BAGNALL/PHOTO: PAUL BRIERLEY

PICTUREPOINT

a passage between the pressure port and an actuator port, the other waist joining the return and the other actuator port, causing the actuator to move in a particular direction. Moving the selector plunger to its other position changes the pairing of the ports and reverses the movement of the actuator. Where the hydraulic mechanism is some distance from the control point, the selector valves may be operated electrically by a solenoid, thus saving lengthy pipe runs.

Actuators are sometimes called jacks and consist of a cylinder containing a ramrod and piston. The cylinder is fixed to the structure and movement of the ramrod operates the mechanism, usually in a reciprocal movement. They can also be used to operate semirotary mechanisms such as butterfly valves, which are used extensively on oil tankers.

Where a hydraulic system is required to provide continuous rotary power, it is connected to a *hydraulic motor* rather than a jack or actuator. Hydraulic motors are similar in construction to rotary pumps, two common types being *gear motors* and *vane motors*. A gear motor, like a gear pump, consists of two inter-meshing gearwheels in a closely fitting housing having an inlet and an outlet port. Hydraulic liquid under pressure is fed to the inlet port and passes between the gear teeth and the motor housing to the outlet, thus driving the gearwheels which are coupled to the mechanism to be driven. A vane motor has a rotor fitted with a number of movable, radially extending vanes which are spring loaded to press against the motor housing. The rotor is eccentrically mounted in the housing. Hydraulic liquid under pressure is introduced through an inlet on one side of the rotor, passes between the rotor and the housing, thus driving the rotor around, and then leaves the motor through an outlet on the other side of the rotor.

To give some indication of the extent to which hydraulic components are used, a modern oil tanker of 250,000 tons employs some 22 miles (35 km) of piping and over 100 actuators. The selector valves are mounted on a huge console and each valve has an indicator which shows whether it is open or closed; this enables the cargo to be discharged with a minimum of personnel.

Modern airliners use hydraulic equipment to retract and lower the undercarriage and steer the nose wheel in addition to operating the flaps or air brakes, wheel brakes and flying controls (ailerons, elevators and rudder).

Power presses are almost solely operated by hydraulics, as is much of the equipment on bulldozers and trench diggers. Most vehicle BRAKES are operated hydraulically.

Top left: the tracks of a tracked vehicle are driven by means of hydraulic motors. The motor shown in the picture is of the multi-cylinder type; it is similar in construction to a radial cylinder pump. The use of hydraulic motors allows each track to be independently driven and eliminates the need for complex drive shafts and gearing. Each motor is connected to the power unit by means of small bore piping, which can be seen in the picture.

Centre left: the fork of a fork lift truck is raised and lowered by means of a hydraulic ram and a chain linkage. The ram has a smooth, polished surface to provide a fluid-tight fit with the end seal of the actuator cylinder.

Left: a hydraulically operated platform used for servicing street lights. One of the hydraulic rams can be seen at the pivoted joint between the two main lifting arms, and the hydraulic mechanism is controlled by levers mounted on the platform itself.

HYDRO- & AERODYNAMICS

Hydrodynamics and aerodynamics are both branches of fluid dynamics, which is the study of fluids in motion. The fundamental laws governing the movements of gases, such as air, and liquids, such as water, are identical. The equations representing these 'natural laws' are, however, so complex that, although formulated over a hundred years ago, they cannot be easily solved to account for all situations and conditions.

The equations which describe in a general fashion the motion of fluids were first developed by C L M H Navier in 1820 and subsequently perfected by G G Stokes in 1845. These equations, now called the Navier-Stokes equations, relate velocity, density, pressure, compressibility, viscosity and the spatial dimensions of the fluid. Because of the number of variables involved, the subject of fluid dynamics has been broken down into a number of subdivisions where certain conditions predominate and others can be ignored. This results in a whole series of solutions —each applying in a limited range of circumstances.

Historically, hydrodynamics came first and consequently includes the greater number of assumptions. Water is, however, almost incompressible, which means that the density of water does not change with the pressure applied to it. This property of water allows the original Navier-Stokes equations of fluid dynamics to be greatly simplified.

Laminar and turbulent flow
Two kinds of fluid flow are possible—*laminar* and *turbulent*. In laminar flow, the fluid moves as series of 'sheets' or *laminae*, sliding one over the next where there is a difference of speed between them (that is, a *velocity gradient*). In turbulent flow, particles of fluid can move in any direction—only the mean velocity and direction being defined. Osbourne Reynolds (1842–1912) showed the difference between these two types and demonstrated that the VISCOSITY of the fluid was one of the important parameters determining which type of flow occurred.

Viscosity is a measure of the internal resistance or FRICTION of a fluid to relative motion and is akin to shear modulus, mentioned in ELASTICITY. High viscosity is a characteristic of a 'thick' fluid (such as engine oil) and is normally a condition for laminar flow. Low viscosity fluids are more likely to be turbulent, but ultimately this depends on the magnitude of viscous forces to other forces (such as pressure and inertial forces) present in the system. 'Reynolds number' is a non-DIMENSIONAL quantity giving the ratio of inertial forces to viscous force and combines the viscosity of the fluid with other important properties of the fluid and body or duct around or through which the fluid is flowing.

Because inertial forces usually predominate, most natural phenomena have turbulent flow conditions. The equations of turbulent flow involving viscosity were, however, found impossible to manipulate, so the assumption of *inviscid* (non-viscous) flow was made. Solutions to these much simplified equations refer to *potential flow*, which is the name given to flows where only potential or pressure forces are present and viscous or shear forces are neglected. This is equivalent to flow with an infinitely large value of Reynolds number, which is at the extreme end of the turbulent flow range.

Aerodynamics
At the beginning of the present century, aerodynamics was introduced with the possibility of flight in air. Because of the concentration of effort, aerodynamics—building upon the theories of hydrodynamics—soon outstripped its parent. It started with the same assumptions as hydrodynamics (for example inviscid flow) with the added assumption of incompressibility replacing what was a fact for

Top: laminar flow in a rectangular duct. The velocity of the fluid is least at the sides of the duct and increases towards the centre in a gradual and non-turbulent way.

Above: turbulent flow. The thin cylinder is producing a classical pattern of contra-rotating vortices in the wake of the passing water. Such turbulence can also be seen in the motion of a flag.

water. Prandtl showed that the effect of viscosity for flow around streamlined (smooth) bodies was confined to a thin layer immediately adjacent to the body. This region is called the *boundary layer*. Outside the boundary layer, viscous forces are negligible and consequently *potential flow* theories apply. The analysis of streamline bodies enabled AEROFOIL design to advance rapidly.

Whereas smooth, streamlined bodies have an unbroken and stable boundary layer, 'bluff' (unstreamlined) bodies do not. The flow starts to separate because of misbehaviour of the boundary layer and potential flow solutions, even away from the body, become inaccurate. Even today, no complete theory for low speed flow around bluff bodies exists, but an understanding of what happens physically has been built up over the years.

Below : moving fluids are difficult to predict because of the number of variables involved—such as density, velocity, pressure, compressibility and viscosity. Consequently, a number of general solutions have been formulated to cater for certain situations. Laminar flow (top left) occurs in a smooth pipe where viscous (fluid friction) forces are larger than inertial forces. An obstacle in the flow (top right) alters fluid directions, speeds and pressures and inertial forces predominate over inertial forces, causing turbulence.

Below right : this photograph, taken with an exposure time less than one millionth of a second, shows the shock wave produced from a model of an aircraft wing undergoing tests in a wind tunnel.

Bottom right : the motorboat is travelling faster than the surface waves it produces—giving them their characteristic shape.

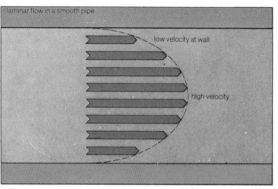
laminar flow in a smooth pipe

low velocity at wall

high velocity

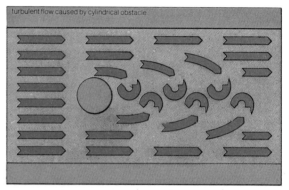
turbulent flow caused by cylindrical obstacle

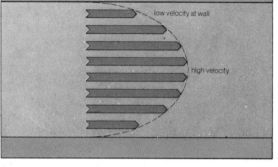
boundary layer around a streamlined body

potential flow

viscous flow (laminar)

boundary layer

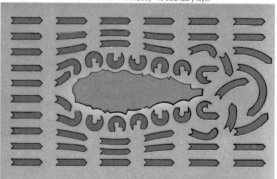
flow separation around bluff (unstreamlined) body–no boundary layer

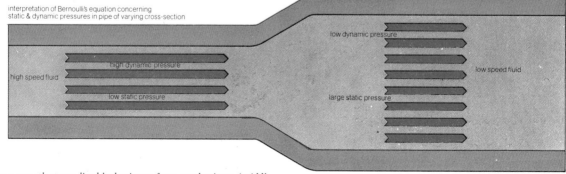
interpretation of Bernoulli's equation concerning
static & dynamic pressures in pipe of varying cross-section

high speed fluid

high dynamic pressure

low static pressure

low dynamic pressure

low speed fluid

large static pressure

Near a smooth streamlined body viscous forces predominate (middle left) —flow is laminar within boundary layer. Bluff bodies (middle right) produce turbulence (flow separation). Bernoulli's equation relates static and dynamic pressure by energy conservation (below).

Bernoulli's equation and high speeds

As aircraft speeds increased, it was found that the assumption of incompressibility introduced errors. The reason for this can be explained by *Bernoulli's equation*.

Bernoulli's equation is a statement of energy CONSERVATION in a fluid. A fluid, like any moving body, has kinetic ENERGY through its motion and potential energy because of its 'potential' to move under the influence of the earth's gravitation (see DYNAMICS). At all points in a fluid there is a *static* PRESSURE proportional to the height of fluid above that point—this is a measure of the potential energy of the fluid at that point. The kinetic energy of the fluid is proportional to the square of the velocity and gives rise to a *dynamic* pressure. If no energy is added to or taken away from the fluid stream then total energy will be conserved even if there is an interchange between kinetic energy (dynamic pressure) and potential energy (static pressure)—this is the principle behind Bernoulli's equation.

Because dynamic pressure is proportional to the square of the fluid velocity, the rate at which pressure changes with increasing velocity will depend on the absolute velocity as well as its rate of change. Consequently, the higher the speeds involved, the larger will be the pressure changes and the greater the density changes because of compressibility. Below 130 mile/h (209 km/h) the density changes can be ignored and air can be treated as incompressible, but above this airspeed the assumption becomes increasingly inaccurate.

Mach numbers and the speed of sound

SOUND is a pressure wave of *small* magnitude and its speed of propagation in the fluid is called the speed of sound. The airflow around a body creates higher air pressures in the vicinity which

UKAEA

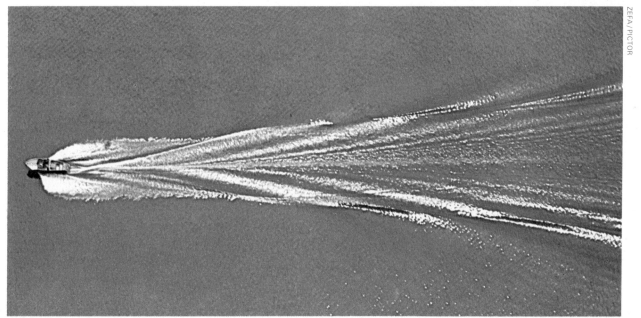

ZEFA / PICTOR

travel upstream, giving advance warning of the presence of the body. Because of this pressure wave the air moves in a curved path ahead of the body, passing around it with the minimum of disturbance.

If the air speed is greater than the speed of sound, these warning signals cannot propagate upstream at all and no warning is given—this is called SUPERSONIC *flow*. In this situation the air must change direction suddenly when it encounters the body. If the deviation asked of it is small it does so, producing a small amplitude shock wave attached to the body. If the deviation is large, a large amplitude shock wave can move ahead of the body (large amplitude waves travel faster) and behind this the air is slowed to subsonic speed. These shock waves are commonly called sonic BOOMS.

With such different flow systems on either side of the speed of sound, it becomes imperative to know whether the air-speed is above or below this value. Unfortunately, the speed of sound does not have a unique value, but varies with TEMPERATURE. In this situation it becomes convenient to divide the airspeed by the speed of sound—this ratio is called the *Mach number* after Ernst Mach, an Austrian scientist who studied the flight of bullets.

Hypersonic flow
When airspeeds increase still further, the rise in temperature and pressure behind shock waves becomes so large that the air *dissociates*, that is, some of the molecules of nitrogen and oxygen which constitute air break down into atoms. Behind the body, temperatures and pressures decrease and the molecules re-form.

Considerable quantities of energy are absorbed and given out in these processes so that the flow in this region is affected. This subject is called *hypersonic flow*.

Slip flow
Atmospheric pressure at sea level is caused by the weight of air above the point of measurement (see BAROMETER). Consequently, at higher altitudes, pressure and density decrease. There comes a height (above 50 miles, 80 km, above

sea level) where the density is so low that the mean free path (the average distance between collisions of the molecules) is of the same order of magnitude as the body under consideration. Air no longer behaves as an entity (usually called a *continuum*) and pressure and forces become the result of individual molecular collisions with the body surface. This part of the subject is called *free molecular* or *Newtonian flow*. There is no sharp division between continuum and molecular flow, rather a progressive change, and this part of the subject is called *slip flow*.

Below : a peculiar characteristic of the TSR 2 was the intensity of the vortices generated by the wingtips, which caused a helical vapour trail to form when flying slowly through damp air.

Bottom : hydrodynamic tunnel demonstration of wing vortices. Turbulence occurs in a fluid when inertial pressure forces become significant in comparison with viscous forces.

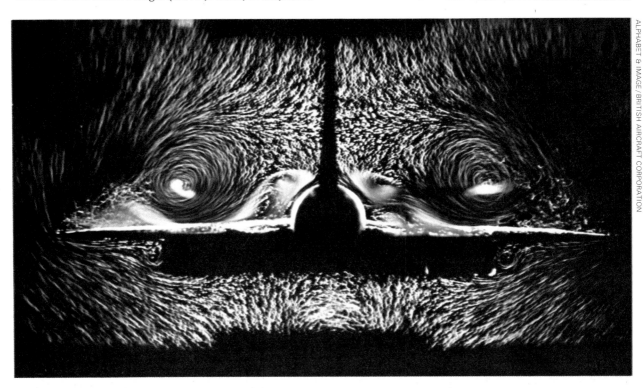

HYDROCARBON

Hydrocarbons are organic compounds which contain only carbon and hydrogen atoms. They can be divided broadly into two groups, *saturated* and *unsaturated* hydrocarbons. Saturated hydrocarbons contain only single BONDS whereas unsaturated hydrocarbons contain one or more double or triple bonds. Unsaturated hydrocarbons are generally more reactive than saturated hydrocarbons, for example they can readily be *hydrogenated* (adding hydrogen atoms to a molecule) to give their saturated counterparts. The diagram shows the hydrogenation of acetylene through to ethane.

Acetylene, containing a single triple bond, is the most reactive of the three compounds; ethylene, having a double bond, comes next; and ethane with only single bonds is the least reactive. Because carbon has a VALENCY of four and hydrogen has a valency of one, each carbon atom has four bonds to it and each hydrogen atom only one. Hydrocarbons such as acetylene which contain triple bonds are called *alkynes*, those containing double bonds like ethylene are called *alkenes* or *olefins*, and those which contain only single bonds, in other words saturated hydrocarbons such as ethane, are called *alkanes* or *paraffins*. The following compounds are simple examples of alkynes, alkenes and alkanes:

Alkynes: $CH{\equiv}CH$ $CH_3-C{\equiv}CH$
         acetylene   methyl acetylene
Alkenes: $CH_2{=}CH_2$ $CH_3-CH{=}CH_2$ $CH_3-CH{=}CH-CH_3$
         ethylene   propylene   butene-2
Alkanes: CH_4 CH_3-CH_3 $CH_3-CH_2-CH_3$
         methane   ethane   propane

In some alkanes and alkenes the carbon atoms are linked together to form rings rather than open chains, and these are called *cycloalkanes* and *cycloalkenes*. *Cyclohexane* and *cyclohexene*, shown in the diagram, are examples of these.

Benzene, C_6H_6, is a special type of hydrocarbon and can be represented by the formula shown in the diagram; it is not normally regarded as an alkene. Although the formula does show the atomic constitution of benzene, it is not a very satisfactory representation because the double bonds are not localized between particular pairs of carbon atoms, but the electrons forming the bonds 'flow' around the ring giving each bond a partly single and partly double bond character. The result of this is that benzene is much less reactive than might be expected. Compounds, including hydrocarbons, which contain benzene rings are called AROMATIC COMPOUNDS. Other hydrocarbons which can be considered to be benzene derivatives include diphenyl, $C_6H_5.C_6H_5$, and triphenylmethane, $(C_6H_5)_3CH$, used for dyestuffs, and the condensed ring compounds naphthalene, $C_{10}H_8$, and anthracene, $C_{14}H_{10}$, which are both used for dyes.

Products illustrating the use of hydrocarbons and their derivatives: 1 an acetylene lamp, 2 calcium carbide used to generate acetylene, 3 asphalt, 4 polyethylene film, 5 nylon, 6 white spirit (a petroleum distillate), 7 a paraffin lamp, 8 phenol, 9 ethyl alcohol, 10 trinitrotoluene (TNT), 11 mothballs which contain naphthalene, 12 a bowl made of polypropylene, 13 coal tar, 14 a candle made of paraffin wax and 15 liquefied butane fuel for cigarette lighters.

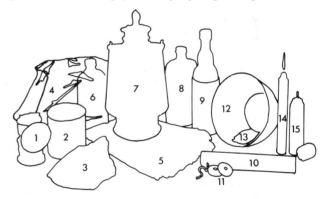

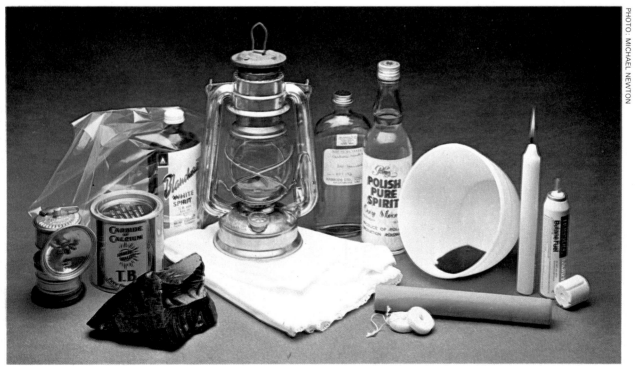

Production of hydrocarbons Most hydrocarbons are derived from oil or COAL TAR. In OIL REFINING, crude oil is first distilled to separate it into fractions having different boiling points. These fractions are then further processed by DISTILLATION, *thermal cracking, catalytic cracking, hydrocracking* and sometimes *catalytic reforming* to give the desired hydrocarbons. Natural gas, which is used for domestic heating, is composed largely of methane.

Alkanes The lower alkanes, those having from one to four carbon atoms, are gases at room temperature although propane, C_3H_8, and butane, C_4H_{10}, are often stored in liquid form under pressure. In this state they are often referred to as LPG (liquefied petroleum gases) and are used as fuels for heating and cooking, particularly in areas where electricity and town gas are not available. Portable burners, for example camping stoves and cigarette lighters, often use liquefied butane as a fuel. The lower alkanes are also used as starting materials in the manufacture of other industrially useful chemicals. Butane, for instance, can be dehydrogenated to give the alkene *butadiene*, $CH_2=CH-CH=CH_2$, used in the manufacture of synthetic rubbers, and methane may be chlorinated to give such products as *dichloromethane*, CH_2Cl_2, an industrial solvent, and *carbon tetrachloride*, CCl_4, an intermediate in the manufacture of aerosol propellants. The chlorination of ethane yields *ethyl chloride*, CH_3-CH_2Cl, which is used in the production of *tetraethyl lead*, $Pb(C_2H_5)_4$, an antiknock additive for petrol [gasoline]. The cycloalkane *cyclopropane*, C_3H_6, is sometimes used as an anaesthetic gas although great care must be taken since it forms explosive mixtures with air.

Petrol [gasoline] is composed of a large number of different hydrocarbons mostly containing from 4 to 12 carbon atoms per molecule. For use in internal combustion engines it is important that petrol should have good antiknock qualities, in other words the fuel-air mixture must not ignite prematurely in the cylinder, and this is measured by the fuel's *octane number*.

The alkane *iso-octane*, $CH_3C(CH_3)_2CH_2CH(CH_3)_2$, has very good antiknock properties and is the standard against which other fuels are rated; it is arbitrarily given an octane number of 100. Fuels having octane numbers lower than 100 have inferior antiknock properties to iso-octane, while fuels with octane numbers greater than 100 have better antiknock properties. The octane number of a low grade petrol can be increased by incorporating additives such as tetraethyl lead.

Paraffin [kerosene] is a mixture of hydrocarbons having from 10 to 16 carbon atoms per molecule. It is used as a jet engine fuel and for domestic heating. Lubricating oils, waxes and bitumen are also complex mixtures of hydrocarbons with other organic compounds.

Alkenes The most important alkene is ethylene, C_2H_4, used in the manufacture of a large number of industrial chemicals: for example *ethylene oxide, C_2H_4O,* an intermediate in the production of *ethylene glycol,* which is used as an antifreeze; *styrene, $C_6H_5CHCH_2$,* used in the manufacture of the PLASTIC *polystyrene; ethyl alcohol, CH_3CH_2OH,* a widely used industrial solvent; and *ethylene dichloride, CH_2ClCH_2Cl,* which can be converted into vinyl chloride, $CH_2=CHCl$, the starting material for the plastic PVC (polyvinyl chloride). Ethylene can be polymerized under high pressure and temperature to give the plastic polyethylene (polythene) which has a large number of applications, for example making plastic films, mouldings, pipes, cable coverings and netting.

Propylene, like ethylene, is a starting material in the manufacture of many important industrial chemicals such as the KETONE *acetone,* and it may be polymerized to give the plastic polypropylene.

Alkynes Acetylene, a gas at room temperature, is by far the most important of the alkynes. It is prepared either by the action of water on *calcium carbide, CaC_2,* made by heating together lime and coal, or from petroleum feedstocks under severe cracking conditions. The preparation from calcium carbide can be written as follows.

Hydrogenation of acetylene

$$H-C\equiv C-H \xrightarrow{H_2} \underset{H}{\overset{H}{C}}=\underset{H}{\overset{H}{C}} \xrightarrow{H_2} H-\underset{H}{\overset{H}{C}}-\underset{H}{\overset{H}{C}}-H$$

acetylene   ethylene   ethane

Cyclic hydrocarbons

cyclohexane   cyclohexene   benzene

napthalene   diphenyl

$$CaC_2 + H_2O \rightarrow CH{\equiv}CH + CaO$$
calcium carbide · · · water · · · · · acetylene · · lime

Because of its high reactivity, acetylene is a useful starting material for making other organic compounds. For example, it reacts with hydrogen chloride, HCl, to give vinyl chloride, the starting material for PVC:

$$CH{\equiv}CH + HCl \rightarrow CH_2{=}CHCl$$
acetylene · · · · hydrogen chloride · · · · · vinyl chloride

Acetylene is also widely used in oxy-acetylene WELDING.

Aromatics The principal aromatic hydrocarbons are benzene, *toluene*, $C_6H_5CH_3$, which is a benzene ring with one hydrogen replaced by a —CH_3 group, and *xylene*, $C_6H_4(CH_3)_2$, which is a benzene ring with two hydrogen atoms replaced by —CH_3 groups. There are three different types of xylene depending on the relative positions of the two —CH_3 groups on the benzene ring. Benzene, toluene and xylene are flammable liquids at room temperature.

Benzene is used in the manufacture of styrene, the starting material for polystyrene, cyclohexane, used in the production of nylon-6, *dodecyl benzene*, used in detergents, *aniline*, used in the manufacture of dyestuffs, and *phenol* ('carbolic acid'), the starting material for a number of plastics.

Toluene can be nitrated using a mixture of nitric and sulphuric acids to give the explosive TNT (trinitrotoluene). It is also used to make *toluene diisocyanate* (TDI), a starting material for plastic foams.

The xylenes are used as solvents in paints, lacquers and insecticides. *Terephthalic acid*, which is used to make polyester fibres such as Terylene, is derived from one of the xylenes.

HYDRO-ELECTRIC POWER (see power station)

Below left: the diagrams referred to in the text.

Below: spherical tanks for storing liquefied petroleum gases (LPG). The tanks are silvered to prevent them from overheating in the sun.

HYDROFOIL

A hydrofoil boat is analogous in principle to an aircraft. It comprises a boat-shaped hull to which are attached 'wings' or hydrofoils which generate lift as they travel through the water, in the same way that the AEROFOIL design of the aircraft wing provides lift in the air. When the hydrofoil boat attains speed, the lift provided by the flow of water over the hydrofoil is sufficient to lift the hull entirely clear of the water. Once out of the water, the hull no longer suffers resistance from friction with the water, or from waves in rough water, so that higher speeds and a more stable ride can be attained.

The hydrofoil is not a new idea; a patent was issued to the Frenchman Farcot in 1869. Around 1900 the Italian Forlanini was building successful hydrofoil boats. The WRIGHT brothers experimented with them before their successful aircraft was flown at Kitty Hawk in 1903; Alexander Graham BELL designed one; and the Russian designer Alexeyev and the German Hans von Schertel have been among the most important hydrofoil engineers since World War 1.

Since water is several hundred times as dense as air, the hydrofoil can be much smaller than the wing of an aircraft. There are two principal types of hydrofoil boat design: the *fully submerged* hydrofoil and the *surface piercing* hydrofoil.

Surface piercing hydrofoil This design is by far the most popular for civilian use because of its simplicity. If lift is lost due to the hydrofoil breaking through waves, the craft sinks deeper into the water, thereby immersing more of the foil or foils which generates more lift. Large numbers of passenger ferries built under licence to designs of the Swiss Supramar company are now in service, and all except the largest of these are of this type.

Below: a Soviet hydrofoil of the Kometa type. The Soviet Union is the largest operator of hydrofoils in the world. The Russians operate the surface-piercing type, mainly as passenger ferries on inland waterways. The foils can be seen in this picture.

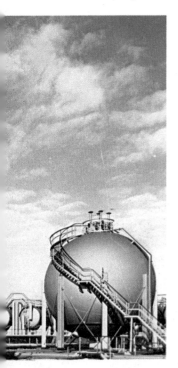

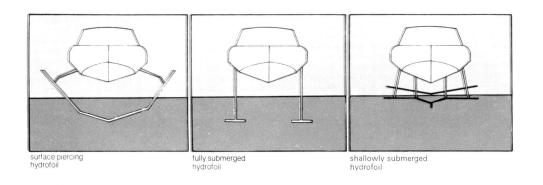

surface piercing
hydrofoil

fully submerged
hydrofoil

shallowly submerged
hydrofoil

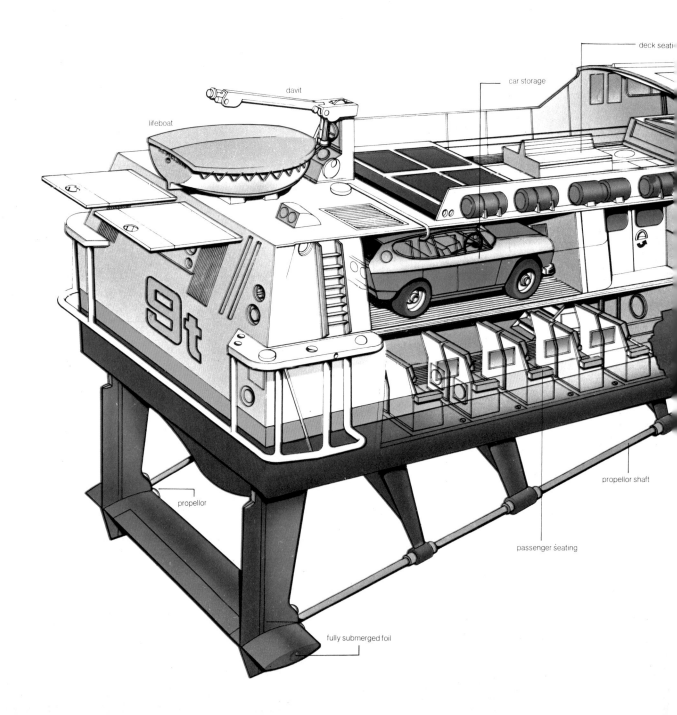

deck seati

car storage

davit

lifeboat

9t

propellor

fully submerged foil

propellor shaft

passenger seating

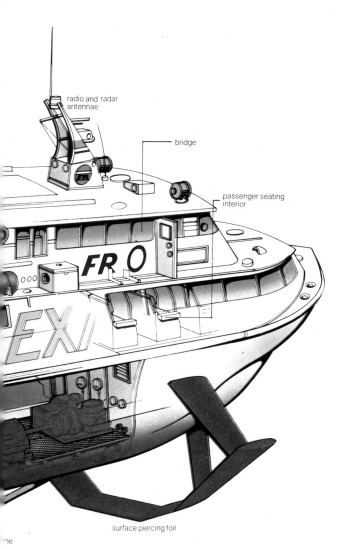

radio and radar
antennae

bridge

passenger seating
interior

surface piercing foil

A 200 ton naval hydrofoil, *Bras D'Or*, built in Canada, has demonstrated that the surface piercing design is suitable for operation on the open sea, where rough water can be expected. Foilborne speeds in excess of sixty knots have been achieved. The Russians, who are by far the biggest operators of hydrofoils, mostly on lakes and rivers, build several types of shallowly submerged hydrofoil craft, closely related to the surface piercing type. Examples are the *Kometa*, *Meteor* and *Raketa* types.

Fully submerged hydrofoils In this type of design only vertical struts pierce the water surface, and changes in lift are effected by changing the angle of attack of the foil to the water. This is achieved by hydraulic or pneumatic cylinders activated by electrical signals from a sonar device pointing ahead of the craft, which reads the oncoming wave height and selects a suitable hydrofoil angle to give the necessary lift.

The principal user of this type of craft is the United States, which has built large naval craft, some having retractable hydrofoils which can swing up out of the water to allow the boat to operate in the conventional way in shallow channels. One of the most successful designs of this type is the *Tucumcari*, built by Boeing. Another system of stabilization, used on smaller craft, uses mechanical sensor-floats on arms ahead of the craft, mechanically linked to the fully submerged foils.

An early variation of the hydrofoil configuration was the 'ladder' type, the more 'rungs' being immersed the greater the lift generated. An early hydrofoil boat of this type was the Bell-Baldwin HD4 which in 1919 attained a speed of sixty knots on the Bras D'Or lakes in Canada.

In some designs the large part of the hull weight, usually between 80 and 90%, is supported by a large foil or foils located forward on the hull; in others the large foils are located aft. The remaining hull weight is supported by a smaller foil which can be turned to provide a steering function while the craft is foilborne.

Propulsion Power units for commercial craft usually consist of marine DIESEL engines which drive propellers at the end of long inclined shafts. In military craft, sometimes designed for anti-submarine duties towing sonar equipment, and where light weight and high speed are considerations but cost is not, GAS TURBINES are used. Often an entirely separate propulsion system is also fitted for when the craft is operated at low speeds in the hullborne way. Water jets have also been used.

Limitations Above about fifty knots, hydrofoils have to be specially designed to cope with increased turbulence, in the same way that wings of supersonic aircraft have to be designed to cope with breaking the sound barrier. Hydrofoils will not replace the largest ocean-going vessels for the same reason that limits the practical size of aircraft: the cube-square law. As the size of a hydrofoil (or an aerofoil) increases, its weight increases in cubic increments, while the area available to support the weight only increases in square increments.

A large commercial hydrofoil designed to carry passengers and automobiles. These are highly manoeuvrable and can slow down and stop in a distance three times their own length. The craft skims over the surface of the water, creating very little disturbance and therefore causing minimum damage to harbours and river banks. Also it is affected far less by wind and turbulence than most ships and hovercraft. The three small diagrams show basic types of hydrofoil: the surface piercing foil, the fully submerged type and a shallowly submerged type.

HYDROGEN

In 1766 CAVENDISH published a paper on the existence of a distinct substance which he called 'inflammable air', but it was left to LAVOISIER, who in 1783 explained the composition of water, to name it hydrogenium.

Hydrogen is the lightest element, one litre weighing only 0.0898 gramme at 0°C and one atmosphere pressure, and forms diatomic molecules (with two atoms): H_2. This colourless, odourless gas is highly flammable, burning vigorously, and often explosively, in air or oxygen when ignited by a flame or even a single spark, and forming water. Because it is highly reactive, hydrogen is found combined with other elements in the Earth's crust. It occurs widely in compounds such as water, rocks and petroleum (crude oil), as well as in many other organic compounds, which form the basis of all vegetable and animal life. Hydrogen, however, exists as a pure element in small amounts in air (0.00005% by volume) and occurs in vast quantities in all stars including the Sun.

There are two other ISOTOPES of hydrogen: *deuterium*, D, has one neutron and one proton in its nucleus (ordinary hydrogen has only a proton in its nucleus) and is known as heavy hydrogen because it is twice as heavy as ordinary hydrogen; *tritium*, symbol T, is three times as heavy as ordinary hydrogen and radioactive, having a half-life of $12\frac{1}{2}$ years. Being radioactive, it can be used for labelling hydrogen containing compounds and is used in radiobiology. Deuterium is used to produce lithium deuteride, which is an essential part of the H-BOMB.

Manufacture In the USA about 75% of all hydrogen is manufactured from natural gas, which is mainly methane, CH_4. Refinery gas, which is produced during OIL REFINING and is a mixture of methane, propane, C_3H_8, and butane, C_4H_{10}, can also be used for hydrogen production. The natural or refinery gases are treated with steam at about 700 to 800°C (1292 to 1472°F) in the presence of a nickel CATALYST. The gases react with the water, forming carbon monoxide and hydrogen:

$$CH_4 + H_2O \rightarrow CO + 3H_2$$
methane   water   carbon monoxide   hydrogen

Separation of hydrogen and carbon monoxide is achieved by treating the gas mixture with steam in the presence of a catalyst at elevated temperatures, giving carbon dioxide and hydrogen. The carbon dioxide is then removed by absorption in a suitable chemical solution, such as a carbonate.

The other main method uses ELECTROLYSIS, which offers the advantage of providing pure hydrogen. In the electrolytic decomposition of brine during the manufacture of caustic soda, one of the by-products is hydrogen. Where electricity is cheap, it is economic to obtain hydrogen from the electrolysis of water. The plant consists of a series of cells, each cell containing water in which some sodium hydroxide is dissolved to make it conductive. Two electrodes in plate form, one of iron and the other of nickel-plated iron, are immersed in the water. The electrodes are separated by an asbestos diaphragm or metal mesh, which keeps the gases produced separated. When a current is passed, the water decomposes, hydrogen going to the cathode and oxygen to the anode, where they are collected respectively.

Other methods of obtaining hydrogen commercially include from water gas, which is produced by passing steam over red hot coke, as a by-product, in coal and coke oven gas production, and by the partial combustion of carbonaceous material such as fuel oil or coal, which is burned under carefully

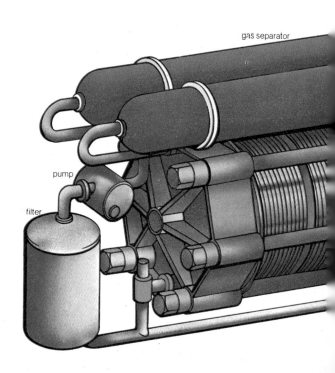

gas separator

pump

filter

Left : balloons, the earliest form of aerial reconnaissance, were used by both the Confederate and Union armies during the American Civil War (1861–65). Here a balloon unit is inflating a varnished silk balloon with hydrogen. In spite of the small amount of leakage they retained enough gas to make ascents 2 weeks after initial inflation.

Below left : a hydrogen plant, based on the reforming of naphtha, having a capacity of 47 million cu ft (1.3 million m³) per day. Naphtha is the cut that comes off the petroleum distillation column between the raw gasoline and kerosene cuts. Catalytic reforming strips hydrogen from the various hydrocarbons in the naphtha, and they are changed to aromatic compounds such as toluene.

Below : hydrogen production by pressure electrolysis of water. Cell voltage drops with high pressure and saves power consumption.

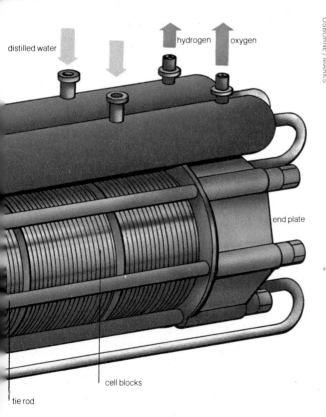

distilled water   hydrogen   oxygen

end plate

cell blocks

tie rod

controlled conditions with limited oxygen in the presence of steam. All these methods, however, result in gas mixtures of hydrogen, carbon monoxide, carbon dioxide, nitrogen and traces of impurities, so the hydrogen must be separated as described above.

Applications of hydrogen

The main uses of hydrogen include AMMONIA MANUFACTURE, hydrofining and hydrocracking in the oil industry, methanol production from hydrogen and carbon monoxide, the hydrogenation of vegetable oils and fats and the manufacture of hydrochloric acid, HCl. Hydrofining is used to remove sulphur from petroleum fractions, which is undesirable, for example, in diesel oil, while hydrocracking is used to introduce more hydrogen during the cracking of wax distillates to make the lighter hydrocarbons found in petrol [gasoline].

Because of its great heat of combustion, hydrogen is also used for cutting and WELDING, and the oxyhydrogen flame can reach temperatures above 2000°C (3632°F). In electric arc welding atomic hydrogen (H rather than H_2) is formed, resulting in exceptionally high temperatures of the order of 4000°C (7232°F). Hydrogen is a strong reducing agent and will reduce metal oxide ores to the pure metal. Compressed hydrogen is used for cooling dynamos because of its low density, high heat conductivity and the fact that coronas (electrical discharges) cannot produce ozone, which destroys the insulating material. Hydrogen lowers the winding temperature more than air cooling, thus reducing winding resistance and losses, and improving output power.

Hydrogen compounds

Water, H_2O, is undoubtably the best known hydrogen compound but the common ACIDS such as hydrochloric, HCl, sulphuric, H_2SO_4, nitric, HNO_3, and acetic, CH_3COOH, and the common alkalis, sodium hydroxide, NaOH, potassium hydroxide, KOH, and ammonium hydroxide, NH_4OH, are also familiar. *Hydrogen peroxide*, H_2O_2, is a thick syrupy liquid with strong oxidizing properties usually sold as a solution in water (3%) and is used for bleaching and as a disinfectant. Stronger 30% solutions are used commercially. Pure hydrogen peroxide is very unstable, readily decomposing to water and oxygen. Strong 90% hydrogen peroxide is used for military and technical applications, especially as an oxidant in rocket fuels.

Hydrogen sulphide, H_2S, is a poisonous gas with a smell of rotten eggs. Readily decomposed, it is a by-product in various industrial processes such as hydrofining and is also formed by the decomposition of organic matter containing sulphur compounds; it occurs naturally in some mineral springs, especially in volcanic regions. Another poisonous gas having a nasty smell is *hydrogen phosphide* (phosphine), PH_3; both are flammable.

The pungent colourless gas *hydrogen chloride*, HCl, dissolves readily in water to form the corrosive acid, hydrochloric with the same formula, HCl. *Hydrogen bromide*, HBr, is also a gas and closely resembles hydrogen chloride but gives a weaker acid when dissolved in water. *Hydrogen iodide*, HI, is a heavier gas which dissolves in water to give hydriodic acid, the basis

A hydrogen electrolytor consists of 100 to 556 narrow pressure cells, each of which is formed by two electrodes and divided into anode and cathode compartments by a diaphragm. Electrolyte (caustic potash) is pumped from below together with feed water. The generated gases form an emulsive mixture with the electrolyte and pass through separate ducts into two drums above, where they are separated from the electrolyte, which is recycled.

LURGI

OSBORNE / MARKS

of many iodide salts; while *hydrogen fluoride*, HF, is a liquid which dissolves in water to give an acid. It is used as a catalyst in organic reactions and as a reagent in the preparation of fluorides, hydrofluoric acid, and uranium. The highly poisonous liquid, *hydrogen cyanide*, HCN, dissolves in water to form hydrocyanic acid (prussic acid) with a faint smell of bitter almonds. It is used as a fumigant, in electroplating and the synthesis of organic compounds.

Most of the above compounds can be termed *hydrides*, that is, compounds formed by combining hydrogen with other elements. Those formed with non-metallic elements are usually gases or liquids, for example ammonia, NH_3. ALKALI and ALKALINE EARTH METALS form crystalline compounds with hydrogen, which adopts the role of an electronegative element, for example, *lithium hydride*, LiH, sometimes used as a hydrogen carrier. Lithium aluminium hydride, $LiAlH_4$, is widely used as a reducing agent in organic chemistry for adding hydrogen atoms to molecules, such as when a carboxylic group $-COOH$ is turned into an alcohol group $-CH_2OH$.

The number of organic compounds containing hydrogen is too vast to be dealt with here and is covered elsewhere in this publication (see ALDEHYDE, ALCOHOL, AMINE, AMINO ACID, AROMATIC COMPOUND, CARBOHYDRATE, CARBOXYLIC ACID, HYDROCARBON, KETONE).

HYDROGEN BOMB (see H - BOMB)

HYDROGEN BOND (see hydrogen compounds)

HYDROGEN ION (see proton transfer reactions)

HYDROLOGY

Hydrology is the study of the physical laws and natural phenomena that govern the distribution of water resources. Water is man's most valuable natural resource; he could manage without oil or diamonds, but water is essential to life. Although it is the most plentiful substance on Earth, all but 3% of the world's water supplies are in the oceans and seas, where the salt content makes it unfit to drink without first putting it through an expensive DESALINATION process.

Even the fresh water supplies found within the land masses are mostly unobtainable. The majority is in the form of polar ice, and half of the remaining liquid water is so deep below the Earth's surface that it is too difficult to extract. The result is that a mere 0.34% of the world's total water resources is actually usable—the portion making up rivers, lakes, or stored in the top half-mile (0.8 km) of the Earth's crust.

Hydrological cycle The natural fresh water supply is governed by physical laws dictating the rates of evaporation, *precipitation* (rain, hail or snow), *drainage* through the soil, and *runoff* into streams and rivers. It is this hydrological cycle, the process of circulation of fresh water, that forms the basis of hydrology because although the cycle is unending, it can be influenced by man's activities.

The cycle begins and ends in the sea. The Sun's heat evaporates fresh water from the surface of the sea, and the warm, moist air rises and is replaced by cold, dry air. The warm air cools as it rises, and expands as the atmospheric pressure falls at higher altitudes, causing the moisture to either condense into droplets or freeze into ice crystals. This forms clouds, which later fall as rain, hail, sleet or snow.

Most of this precipitation goes back into the sea, but some falls over the land surface. Not all the water falling on the land surface enters the fresh water system, however, for over half

Left: hydrologists sinking a stainless steel tube which will carry a neutronic probe to measure ground moisture. The probe emits 'fast' neutrons which collide with the hydrogen atoms of the water molecules and are converted into 'slow' neutrons. The rate at which slow neutrons are created gives an indication of the amount of moisture in the ground.

of it is evaporated again before it can drain into the soil. From this soil store plants absorb the water they need to maintain life; the rest flows back to the sea by way of rivers, lakes, and underground channels, and it is from these sources that man extracts the water he needs.

Early civilizations settled and flourished by the banks of rivers and lakes, because these provided a plentiful supply of fresh water. Although the average person drinks only about two pints (1.1 litres) of water (in various forms) per day, since about 3000 BC water has been increasingly used for many other purposes, including baths, toilets, irrigation, swimming pools, and laundries, and as a result the average daily consumption per head in industrial countries is about 50 gallons (227 litres).

In addition, approximately 40% of the water supplied by water purification works is needed for industrial purposes. Nearly two thirds of industrial water is used for cooling and condensing, for example between 10,000 and 50,000 gallons (45,460 to 22,730 litres) are needed during the manufacture of one ton of steel.

Measurements One of the difficulties encountered in providing adequate water supplies is that there is a wide seasonal variation in the flow of most rivers and in the amount of precipitation falling over a given area, but the demand for water is fairly constant throughout the year. Engineers try to control this situation by finding ways of storing the excess produced in wet seasons for use during dry periods. The task facing the hydrologist is to understand the relationship between rainfall and the volume of water available in rivers and elsewhere, and from this understanding to draw up formulae for predicting water behaviour under different weather conditions and in response to different rates of use.

Careful measurements, taken over many years, of rainfall and streamflow in river basins give the research worker the information necessary to solve the basic equation: runoff = precipitation—evaporation—change in soil storage.

Right: an explosion set off during a seismic survey for water.

The shock waves are detected by twelve geophones placed around the area, and their signals are fed into an oscillograph (below left) whose trace is photographed with a Polaroid camera (below). The trace patterns indicate the amount of underground water in the area.

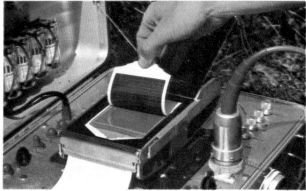

Rainfall is mostly monitored by raingauges, measuring vessels fitted with simple funnels to collect the rain, which have been in use since the early seventeenth century (see METEOROLOGY). Streamflow variations can be estimated by keeping a record of the levels in the water channel, the oldest example being the calibrated posts along the River Nile in Egypt, for which records are available for as far back as AD 622.

More precise measurements must take into account the variations in flow velocity which occur from bank to bank, and from bed to surface, so the entire flow may often be diverted through a weir with a uniform cross-section where accurate measurements of level can be made. This method is possible in research experiments, but for the majority of cases the stream has to be divided arbitrarily into cross-sectional areas and FLOWMETERS used to measure the current. Unfortunately it is not yet possible to measure evaporation directly, but from measurements of the climatic factors which control evaporation (such as temperature, wind speed, humidity and solar radiation) it is possible to calculate the potential rate with reasonable accuracy.

Applications
One of the many uses of hydrology is in helping to decide on the best locations for water storage reservoirs. Sites for reservoirs are often unavailable in densely populated areas, which are usually where they are most needed, and as a result many reservoirs have to be sited far from the main points of consumption. The volume of runoff water supplying the reservoir can be affected by many factors, including the type of vegetation cover in the area and the building for towns and roads, all of which alter the surface of the land and the rate at which water may be lost by evaporation or prevented from draining into the soil.

As well as being concerned with WATER SUPPLY, hydrology is also involved in FLOOD CONTROL and EROSION CONTROL, two areas in which the ability to predict the amount of runoff and soil storage under various conditions is very important.

HYDROLYSIS

Hydrolysis is the term applied to chemical reactions where water is one of the active participants in the reaction. In INORGANIC CHEMISTRY the term is normally used to describe the partial decomposition of a salt dissolved in water into an acid and an alkali. An example of this is to be found in solutions of potassium cyanide, KCN, where some prussic acid, hydrogen cyanide—HCN, and potassium hydroxide, KOH, are formed by hydrolysis, as follows:

$$\text{KCN} + \text{H}_2\text{O} \rightarrow \text{HCN} + \text{KOH}$$

potassium   water   hydrogen   potassium
cyanide   cyanide   hydroxide

It is the formation of prussic acid, a volatile liquid at room temperature, which gives potassium cyanide solutions their characteristic 'bitter almonds' smell. In ORGANIC CHEMISTRY the term hydrolysis is used more broadly to include reactions where organic compounds are decomposed by solutions of acids or alkalis in water.

Organic hydrolysis reactions are common in industry. For example, ethyl alcohol, an important industrial raw material, may be obtained by the hydrolysis of ethylene in the presence of a phosphoric acid CATALYST. Also, *esters* (a class of related organic compounds) are readily hydrolyzed by alkalis to give an ALCOHOL and an organic SALT of the alkali concerned. The hydrolysis of esters is called *saponification*. In SOAP MANUFACTURE fats, which contain a mixture of triglycerides (esters formed from the trihydric alcohol glycerol and fatty acids such as stearic, oleic and palmitic), are saponified using sodium hydroxide to give a mixture of sodium salts of fatty acids and glycerol. Glycerol is used in the manufacture of CELLOPHANE and also as an additive to tobacco to prevent it from drying out.

A hydrolysis reaction is employed in the manufacture of the industrial chemical *phenol*, C_6H_5OH, by the Raschig process. Phenol is an AROMATIC COMPOUND in which one of the hydrogen atoms on a benzene, C_6H_6, ring has been replaced by a *hydroxyl group* (a grouping of one oxygen atom linked to one hydrogen atom). Phenol is important because it is the starting material for a wide range of useful materials including

Below: dextrose, a type of glucose, is manufactured by hydrolysis of starch. One of the final steps in the process is centrifugation, and the picture shows dextrose 'cake' being cut in a centrifuge.

PLASTICS (such as nylon and polyurethane), DETERGENTS, drugs (such as ASPIRIN), DYES and EXPLOSIVES. In the Raschig process, which is a continuous rather than a batch process, benzene is first reacted with hydrogen chloride (hydrochloric acid is a solution of hydrogen chloride in water) and air to give *chlorobenzene*, C_6H_5Cl, and water. The chlorobenzene is then hydrolyzed using a phosphoric acid catalyst to give phenol and hydrogen chloride, HCl, which is re-used in the first reaction.

The reaction sequence may be written as follows:

$$C_6H_6 + HCl + \tfrac{1}{2}O_2 \rightarrow C_6H_5Cl + H_2O \rightarrow C_6H_5OH + HCl$$

benzene hydrogen chloride oxygen chlorobenzene water phenol hydrogen chloride

A further application of hydrolysis is in the manufacture of glucose from corn starch. Starch molecules are composed of glucose units joined together by *glycoside* linkages. Hydrolysis with hydrochloric acid breaks these linkages to release glucose. The raw glucose so produced is then subjected to various purification steps including treatment with bone charcoal to decolorize it and crystallization. Glucose is widely used by the medical profession and in the food industry.

HYDROMETER (see specific gravity)

HYDROPHONE

A hydrophone is a device for detecting sound waves travelling in water; it is the underwater equivalent of a MICROPHONE. Sound waves both in air and underwater consist of small fluctuations in the pressure caused by the rapid motion of some object. These sound waves travel through water with a speed of about 4800 feet per second (1460 metres per second), 4.5 times faster than through air.

Underwater sounds are generated by such things as the motion of waves on the sea surface, ship's engines as well as a variety of biological sounds. The 'singing' of whales and porpoises can be heard many miles away, some fish can make noises and even a type of shrimp can make a loud clicking sound. These sounds range in frequency, or pitch, from those too low for the human ear to detect, through the audio range of human hearing to the ultrasonic, too high to hear. One of the more important sources of sound in the sea are the sonars, or ASDIC's, fitted to many ships. These sonars generate a pulse of sound which travels away from the ship until it is reflected back from some underwater object and is received back at the ship. This echo enables the range and bearing of the reflecting object to be determined.

The devices used to generate and listen to the underwater sounds are called *transducers*. Those which convert electrical energy into sound energy and are used to generate sound are called *transmitting* transducers. Hydrophones are transducers which convert the sound energy into electrical energy and are used in conjunction with *electronic* AMPLIFIERS to listen to sound. Normally one of two methods is used to convert sound into electricity, or vice versa: either PIEZOELECTRIC MATERIALS or *magnetostrictive metals*.

Construction Piezoelectric crystals are naturally occurring materials, such as quartz, that generate a voltage when subjected to a pressure and can thus be used as hydrophones. They will also change shape, thus generating sound, when a voltage is applied to them, so they can also be used as transmitting transducers. These naturally piezoelectric crystals have been mainly replaced by *ferroelectric ceramics*, like barium titanate, which do not naturally possess piezoelectric properties but can be given them by heating the ceramics above a critical temperature, the *Curie temperature*, and allowing them to cool, while in a strong electric field.

A typical hydrophone has a piezoelectric crystal mounted in a waterproof container, such as a rubber bag filled with castor oil, which will let the sound waves reach the crystal but will also insulate it electrically. On opposite faces of the crystal are fixed two thin silver contacts, each connected to a wire which leads out of the hydrophone container. If the hydrophone is being used in a sonar system, these wires will be connected to electronic amplifiers and display equipment located inside the ship. Hydrophones have a high resonance frequency and give an undistorted response to the sound over a wide range of frequency. Transmitting transducers often have metal pieces fixed to the ceramic to change the acoustic properties and thus generate very loud sounds at a chosen frequency.

The other common type of transducer uses the principle of *magnetostriction*. Some metals, such as nickel, when they change shape in the presence of a magnetic field cause a change in this field that can be used to generate an electric current. Sound waves will slightly change the shape of materials they strike, so magnetostructive metals can be used in hydrophones. These metals can also be used as transmitting transducers by applying a varying magnetic field which causes the metals to change shape, thus generating sound. In use, these transducers commonly take the form of tubes or laminates of the magneto-strictive metals wound with electric coils that generate the magnetic fields, all enclosed in a waterproof container.

HYDROSTATICS (see statics)

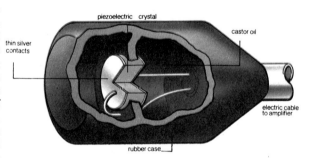

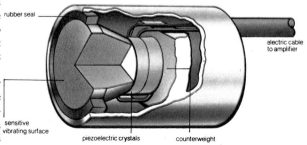

OSBORNE / MARKS

HYGROMETER

A hygrometer is a device for measuring the humidity, that is, the amount of water vapour in the air. The word comes from Greek words meaning 'wet measure'. The first hygrometer was built by Leonardo da VINCI and measured the weight of a ball of wool which absorbed moisture according to the humidity. Since then several types of instrument have been developed.

The *evaporation* method calculates the humidity from the difference in the readings of two thermometers; the bulb of one is kept wet by means of a wick in water. The *condensation* or *dew point* device also utilizes two thermometers, one of which has its bulb submerged in ether. Air is bubbled through the ether to cool it by evaporation and the temperature at which condensation forms on the outside of the container is compared with the temperature of the other thermometer.

The most common designs are based on the same principle as da Vinci's hygrometer: certain organic substances absorb moisture readily. Such substances are called *hygroscopic*; human hair is the most commonly used. The length of a hair changes as it absorbs moisture and the change can be easily magnified and recorded on a chart or a graph.

Several more elaborate designs are used for certain purposes. An instrument used for observing the upper atmosphere measures the changes in electrical resistance of certain substances, such as lithium chloride, as they absorb moisture. At

Below: a GLCC hygrometer used for obtaining the dew point of gases. The gas enters through the tap and passes over the wet and dry bulbs of the thermometers in tubes A and B. The increase in pressure in tube C raises the liquid level in tube D, which can be read against the scale.

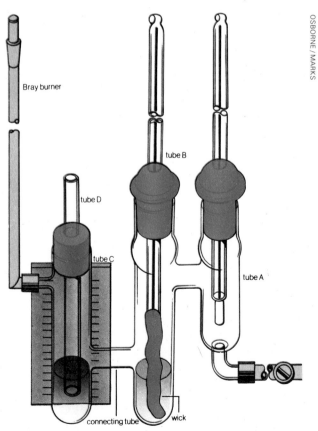

Left: a typical piezoelectric hydrophone. The crystal is electrically insulated by the castor oil within the rubber casing. It can convert any change in the surrounding pressure transmitted by the water into a voltage difference which is picked up by the amplifier. The crystal also changes shape under pressure, producing a sound and can therefore be used as a transmitting transducer.

Top: a naval trials ship equipped with hydrophone booms (centre and right) for tracking underwater vehicles.

Centre: a cable used for seismic surveys contains hydrophones along its length. When in use the cable is trailed behind a ship.

Bottom: a portion of the cable shown in the centre picture with the outer covering removed to show one of the hydrophones.

temperatures below freezing, where condensation or evaporation methods cannot be used, a SPECTROGRAPHIC instrument can be used which measures the absorption of radiation by water vapour at different places in the ELECTROMAGNETIC spectrum. Devices are under development for measuring the low humidity thought to exist at other places in the solar system by means of an ELECTROLYTIC moisture cell; the conductivity rather than the resistance of the medium is measured. The most accurate method is weighing a chemical which extracts moisture from air.

Other methods measure the varying thermal conductivity of a gas; varying impedance of a CAPACITOR, or the change of frequency of a PIEZOELECTRIC crystal.

Hygrometers are used to regulate, by means of FEEDBACK control, the humidity in air-conditioned atmospheres and industrial control processes, as well as in meteorology and the study of outer space.

Humidity measurements The humidity of the atmosphere is usually defined in terms of *relative humidity*, which is the ratio of the pressure of water vapour actually present in the atmosphere at a given time to that of the *saturated* (maximum possible) water vapour pressure at the same temperature, expressed as a percentage. Alternatively the weight of water vapour in unit volume of saturated air at the same temperature may be used. The dew point (temperature at which water condenses out of the atmosphere at a given atmospheric pressure) may also be used to calculate relative humidity because the saturated vapour pressure at the dew point is equal to the aqueous vapour pressure at the temperature of the experiment. By using tables which give the saturated vapour pressure at various temperatures it is possible to obtain the relative humidity.

HYPERSONIC FLIGHT (see supersonic flight)

HYPO (FIXER) (see photochemistry)

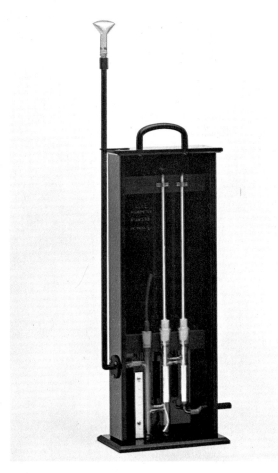

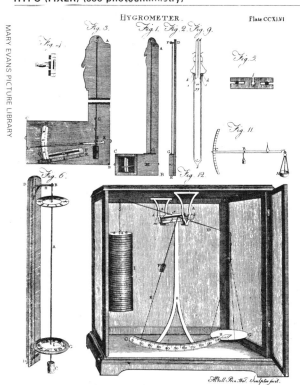

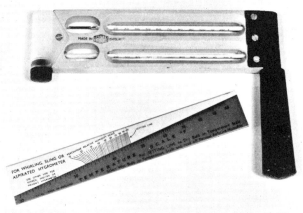

Left : illustrations of hygroscopic hygrometers from the 1797 edition of the Encyclopedia Britannica.

Above top : a wet and dry bulb hygrometer developed for the old Gas, Light and Coke Company (GLCC) for measuring the water vapour content of town gas. The dew point of the gas is determined by passing gas over one bulb and comparing the two thermometers.

Above : a whirling hygrometer. Whirling it ensures a fast, equal air flow over both wet and dry bulbs.

HYPOCAUST

The hypocaust, originally invented in the first century BC for heating sweat baths, was developed by the Romans into the first central heating system. Remains of hypocausts can be seen on sites throughout the Roman Empire, and the system is still operating in the *hammams*, or Turkish baths, of the Near East.

'Hypocaust' is a word of Greek origin and means a place where there is 'fire underneath'. The hot gases from furnaces burning wood, charcoal, or even in some cases coal, are passed under the floors of the rooms, either through covered channels, or in the spaces formed by supporting the floors on short pillars, called *pilae*, made of stone or tiles. The floors were usually concrete, and often were decorated in mosaic patterns.

To provide a draught, chimneys were necessary. These could be single channels or pipes set into the walls. Often the gases rose through a cavity made by fastening tiles, usually specially shaped for the purpose, against the inner faces of the walls, before decoration. The latest, and most frequently found, tiles for this purpose were the *tubuli*, or box flue tiles. The faces of these rectangular pipes were often combed or rolled with a pattern which 'keyed' the tile to the plaster, and which makes even a small fragment easily recognized.

Lining the walls had two effects. It prevented condensation in steam baths, and increased the heat entering the room by

Right: under this ancient steam bath in Salamis is a hypocaust.

Below: hypocaust system built into a Roman dwelling. These provided one of the earliest forms of central heating and were also used to heat sweat baths. A wood or coal fire burns beneath the flooring and the hot gases and air circulate freely under the main floors which are supported by brick pillars. A lead boiler is built immediately above the fire and the water in the bath is kept hot by a heat exchanger or testudo.

C M DIXON

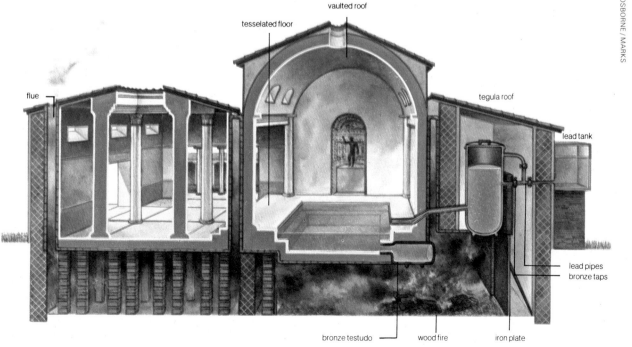

OSBORNE / MARKS

vaulted roof

tesselated floor

tegula roof

flue

lead tank

lead pipes
bronze taps

bronze testudo   wood fire   iron plate

PHOTO: PETER CLAYTON

Above: the floors of the bathing rooms, over the hypocaust, were usually made of concrete and often decorated in mosaic patterns.

radiation. Lining was most important in improving the warmth of the rooms, and made possible the development of the very large sunbathing lounges with wide windows which were characteristic of the large imperial baths or *thermae*.

The ingenuity of the Roman heating engineer can be seen to the best advantage in small domestic baths. In a typical installation the furnace heated first a hot sweating chamber (*caldarium*) and then a warm acclimatizing room (*tepidarium*). The furnace heated a boiler which provided the baths with running water at temperatures which could be controlled by mixer taps. It also heated the static water in the bath tub, which was often provided with a metal heat exchanger called a *testudo* meaning 'tortoise' over the furnace.

HYSTERESIS (see magnetic materials)
ICE-MAKING (see refrigeration)

IGNITION

In order for combustion of a fuel to take place, it is necessary that a source of oxygen is present and that the *fuel-oxidant* mixture has a composition which lies within the *limits of flammability* (see FLAME and FLASHPOINT). If such a mixture is heated slowly in a closed container, then any heat released by the *chemical reaction* will be lost through the walls of the vessel. If the rate of heat release is equal to the rate of loss of heat, then a *steady state* is achieved and the reaction is known as *slow combustion*. If, however, the rate of heat evolution produced by the reaction is greater than the rate of heat loss, the temperature will rise above a critical value depending on both the reactants and the container, and the rate of energy release will increase even further. The stage at which this *self acceleration* occurs is known as *ignition* and the corresponding temperature is the *ignition temperature*. In this case, it is said that the reaction has become *autocatalytic* and its rate will accelerate until an *explosion* occurs.

Ignition temperature and energy In the above example, the temperature at which the gas-air mixture is ignited is the *self-ignition* or *auto-ignition temperature*. This phenomenon is exhibited by all gaseous and finely divided liquid and solid fuels. In practice, it is not feasible to heat the

C.E.G.B.

entire fuel-air mixture to the ignition temperature and it is usually necessary to heat only a small volume of the fuel to a temperature (not always the same as the self-ignition temperature) at which a *combustion wave* passes through the system and total ignition is achieved.

When speaking of a small volume achieving a given temperature, what really matters is that enough ENERGY be added to the system in order that it can become self-accelerating. This minimum amount of energy is known as the *ignition energy*. In other words, the *activation energy* of each reaction must be supplied in order to initiate the reaction. This is akin to rolling a ball over a hill, where, if the ball can be rolled, say, 10 m to the top of the hill, it will then fall, say, 100 m to the valley below. In this example, the energy of reaction is represented by the *potential energy* equivalent to 90 m and this is obtained by investing the equivalent of 10 m of activation energy.

A further feature of ignition is that of *ignition delay* or the *induction period*, which is the delay between the application of initiation and the onset of combustion. This induction period and the ignition energy depend on many factors including the type of fuel, whether it is flowing or stationary, the type of ignition device, whether this is continuous or intermittent, and the rate of energy transfer from the ignition device.

Ignition devices There are many ways in which the ignition energy can be supplied, ranging from hot wires to sparks and pilot flames, and the choice really depends on the fuel to be burned and the combustion device.

In general, gas flames are the easiest to ignite and domestic appliances provide simple examples of the way in which this is achieved. In using a match, the ignition energy of the chemicals on the match is provided by the heat of FRICTION and the *heat of combustion* of the wood or cardboard is then sufficient to ignite the gas. This may also be provided by the energy of a hot wire, as in a battery lighter, or an electric spark produced by a CAPACITOR or PIEZOELECTRIC crystals.

With *atomized* liquid fuels (dispersed into droplets), ignition is more difficult and although a large *spark generator* or lighted oily rag often suffices in industry, one common technique is to ignite a small volume of gas with a spark and allow this ball of flame to pass into and ignite the oil spray. Indeed, the ignition of difficult fuels by first initiating gaseous combustion is fairly common. *Pulverized fuel* flames are usually ignited by introducing coal into a gas flame, which is then slowly turned off.

Liquid and solid fuels which are not finely dispersed are more difficult to ignite and ignition of vapours is usually achieved first. With a domestic coal fire, paper and then wood are used in this way, though it may be noted that the ignition of a single piece of coal is very difficult as any heat released is lost immediately by RADIATION instead of being reflected by other pieces, thus promoting the necessary rise in temperature.

In internal combustion engines, there are two main types of ignition. Petrol [gasoline] engines use a *spark ignition* system (see IGNITION SYSTEMS, CAR), and DIESEL ENGINES achieve ignition by compressing air to raise the temperature.

IGNITION SYSTEM, car

Unlike the DIESEL ENGINE, in which the fuel in the cylinders is ignited by the high temperature of the air compressed by the pistons, the petrol [gasoline] engine uses a high voltage electric spark to ignite the fuel-air mixture. In applications where complete independence from other electrical systems is required, such as some MOTORCYCLES, stationary power units and AIRCRAFT, the power for the spark is usually provided by a MAGNETO. In a car, however, a BATTERY is necessary to provide a satisfactory power supply for its other electrical

Below: some of the main components of a vehicle ignition system. The picture shows a distributor cap, a coil, high tension leads, a capacitor, a rotor, a contact breaker, and a tube of lubricant.

Above: a light distillate oil burner unit. The oil is forced under pressure through a jet and the mist produced ignited by a spark.

Left: flames inside a power station boiler. The heavy oil used is initially heated to about 120°C and atomized into a fine mist by forcing it under a pressure of about 600 psi through a fine nozzle. A propane gas flame ignites the oil, itself electrically ignited.

equipment, and so a battery powered ignition system is used.

Many early engines used 'hot tube' ignition, in which a tube of metal (usually platinum) screwed into the cylinder was heated to red heat by an external flame. The outer end of the tube was sealed, and on the compression stroke of the piston some of the fuel-air mixture was forced into the glowing tube where it ignited, the flame then spreading through the combustion chamber to ignite the remaining fuel.

Reliable electric ignition systems were first developed in the 1890s by several car makers, including BENZ and de Dion-Bouton. These early systems worked on essentially the same principles as modern coil ignition systems, and comprised a battery, contact breaker, INDUCTION COIL and SPARK PLUGS. The development of TRANSISTORS and THYRISTORS during the 1950s led to the introduction of semiconductor ignition systems, which use electronic switching systems to control the ignition coil.

Conventional systems The distributor, containing the contact breaker, capacitor, rotor arm, distributor head and timing mechanisms, is driven at half engine speed through a 2 to 1 reduction gearing from the engine crankshaft. The distributor is set so that the contact breaker is just opening as one of the pistons nears the top of its compression stroke, and at this point the rotor arm carried on top of the distributor shaft is opposite one of the electrodes in the distributor head. A heavily insulated cable connects this electrode to the spark plug in the cylinder about to fire.

The low tension (low voltage) circuit of the ignition system is supplied with current from the battery through the ignition switch. When the contact breaker points are closed, a current of 3 or 4 A flows through the primary winding of the ignition

coil, which consists of a few hundred turns of heavy gauge insulated copper wire, and sets up a magnetic field in the laminated iron core of the coil.

As the distributor shaft turns, a cam mounted on it opens the contact breaker points, interrupting the primary winding current. The magnetic field then 'collapses', causing a high voltage (up to 30,000 V) to be *induced* (see INDUCTANCE) in the secondary winding, which is made up of 15,000 to 30,000 turns of very fine insulated copper wire wound around the iron core (the primary winding is wound over the secondary winding).

The magnetic field associated with the induced secondary voltage will, in its turn, induce a voltage (the *back emf*) in the primary winding, and this can be as high as 500 V. This voltage can arc across the opening contacts, dissipating some of the stored energy in the coil and burning the points, and to prevent this arcing a CAPACITOR is connected across the points.

The induced high voltage pulse flows along a lead to the central contact of the distributor, through the rotor arm, and from there to the appropriate spark plug. When the voltage at the spark plug is sufficiently high, the fuel-air mixture in the gap between the plug electrodes ionizes, and the energy stored in the ignition coil discharges across the gap in the form of a spark which ignites the mixture in the combustion chamber (see CONDUCTION).

Electronic ignition The functions of the circuit breaker and distributor cam may be performed electronically, giving more accurate timing, higher spark energy, higher operating speeds and longer life. The circuit breaker has two functions: to interrupt the coil primary current and to time the spark at the correct firing intervals (for instance at 90° intervals for a four cylinder engine).

OSBORNE / MARKS

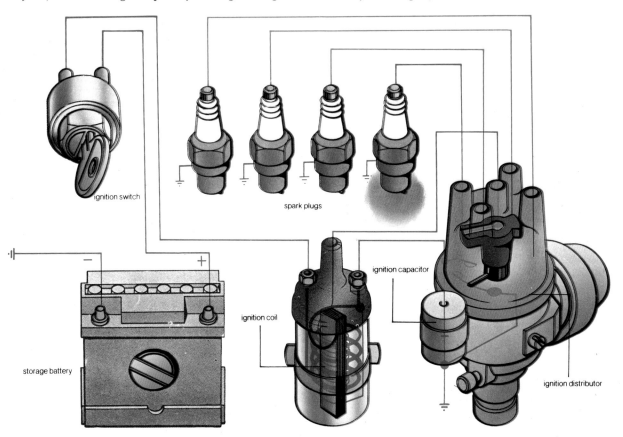

ignition switch

spark plugs

storage battery

ignition coil

ignition capacitor

ignition distributor

Two separate electronic circuits are required to accomplish these two functions. Circuit breaking is achieved by means of a high voltage power transistor and timing by a shaft position sensor. The signal from the position sensor is used, after suitable modification and amplification, to switch the power transistor on and off.

There is a wide variety of shaft position sensors (TRANS-DUCERS) available for use in ignition systems, including opto-electrical units (in which a beam of light focused on a PHOTOELECTRIC CELL is interrupted by a shutter) and various forms of magnetic pulse generator. In a typical magnetic unit the distributor cam is replaced by a soft iron *reluctor*, a device similar in shape to the cam but having much sharper and more pronounced projections, one for each cylinder. The reluctor operates in conjunction with a fixed stator pole carrying a detector coil and the whole assembly is energized by a permanent magnet. As the reluctor revolves its projections pass within 0.02 inch (0.51 mm) of the tip of the stator pole, causing the magnetic field in the detector coil to rise and fall, producing a small signal voltage across its terminals.

The signal voltage amplitude varies in almost direct proportion to the engine speed and its waveform may also change in shape. The most consistent point in the signal waveform for timing purposes is the point at which it crosses the zero point from positive to negative. The input circuit of the electronic unit therefore contains a considerable degree of amplification and a means of detecting the crossover point. When the crossover point is detected, the unit generates a second waveform, usually a square wave, which after some current amplification can be used to switch the power transistor controlling the primary circuit of the coil.

The power transistor operates in a similar manner to a contact breaker. When it is switched on by the position transducer it allows current to flow from the battery through the ignition coil primary winding, and when a projection on the reluctor passes the stator pole the power transistor is switched off, interrupting the primary current and so causing a voltage to be induced in the secondary winding. The high voltage induced is then switched to the spark plug in exactly the same way as with a circuit breaker distributor. Electronic ignition has been in general use on Formula 1 and Formula 2 racing cars since 1960, and since 1970 has been used on a number of makes of standard production automobiles.

Right: a distributor with a magnetic transducer instead of a contact breaker. As this unit is for use on a four cylinder engine, the soft iron reluctor has four projections.

Left: a coil ignition system for a four cylinder engine. The primary current flows from the battery to the coil via the ignition switch, and from the coil through the contact breaker to earth [ground]. The secondary current flows from the coil through the rotor and HT leads and returns to earth through one of the plugs after sparking across the gap.

IMAGE INTENSIFIER

An image intensifier is a direct viewing device which amplifies an optical image by electronic means. Among many applications, image intensifiers are used for amplifying X-ray images in medical diagnoses, in astronomy for the recording of very faint images at the focus of a telescope, and for observing scenes at night which appear dark to the naked eye—particularly useful in military applications.

Amplifying light Light energy from a scene comes in the form of *photons*—'packets' of energy. Their energy, while sufficient to affect the retina of the eye, is quite low in electronic terms, and furthermore they cannot be amplified or accelerated in any direct way. To amplify light, therefore, the photons must be converted into a form which enables the energy to be increased.

The normal way to do this is to make the photons hit a material which will readily give off ELECTRONS. This is done by using an element such as caesium, which has large ATOMS with single electrons in their outermost shells. These can easily be dislodged, the energy of a photon being quite sufficient.

Electrons form the working basis of all electronic apparatus, as they have a negative charge and can easily be accelerated to higher energies under the influence of an electric field. Their direction can be controlled by using electric or magnetic fields, so they can be focused.

In a PHOTOMULTIPLIER TUBE, which amplifies small light signals, the electrons are accelerated by a series of electrodes at different electrical potentials along the tube. This, however, does not preserve an image and the tube is used simply to detect light.

Intensifiers In its simplest form an image intensifier consists of a sealed glass cylindrical tube several centimetres in diameter and in length, evacuated of air, with the light-sensitive layer (*photoemitter*) deposited on the inside surface of one of its flat transparent end windows (the *faceplate*), and a fluorescent screen thinly coated with aluminium on the other.

Light from a faint scene to be viewed is first focused into an optical image by a lens system, such as that in a photographic camera, through the faceplate on to the photoemitter. A substantial fraction of the photons in the incident image eject electrons from the photoemitter into the vacuum space in direct proportion to the intensity at each point of the optical image, producing a corresponding electron image. This electron image then is accelerated down the axis of the tube to the fluorescent screen by a potential difference of 10 to 15 thousand volts, being focused by means of a system of *electron optics* (see below). At the screen, the high energy acquired by the electrons enables them to penetrate the thin aluminium film and then to excite the fluorescent material to glow in the same manner as the display screen of a CATHODE RAY TUBE. The aluminium film serves as a reflector, causing all of the fluorescent light to leave through the output window. A commonly used fluorescent material, known as P-20 phosphor, has a glow colour closely matching the response of the human eye. Thus the electron image is converted again to an optical image to be viewed by an observer. The important feature of this device is that the output image is brighter than the incident image; typically, a light amplification of 50 is achieved.

By attaching such intensifier stages properly in series (*cascaded*), arranging for the output of one stage to feed the input of the next, it is possible to provide very high overall amplification. For example, a cascaded set of four image intensifier stages can achieve a light amplification of 10,000,000.

Another means of achieving amplification in image intensifiers is by use of an array of microscopic *channel electron multipliers*. A channel electron multiplier is made from a minute glass tube, about 50 times longer than its diameter. The inner surface is coated with a semi-insulating layer, and a potential difference is applied between the ends, producing an electric field increasing along its length. When an electron enters the low-potential end of the tube several *secondary electrons* are emitted from the inner wall. These are accelerated by the electric field until they strike another point on the wall and in turn release still more electrons. This collision process is repeated several times as new generations of electrons rapidly cascade down the length of the tube, swelling in numbers at each impact. The electron gain of the device, that is, the number of electrons leaving the far end of the tube for each electron entering it, is at least 10,000. For use in image intensifiers, as many as a million channel electron multipliers can be stacked in a disc-like array resembling a minute honeycomb about 2 centimetres in diameter and 1 millimetre thick. Such an array, known as *microchannel plate*, is then used to intercept the electron image leaving the photoemitter in an image intensifier and to pass a corresponding highly amplified electron image to the fluorescent layer for viewing. A single intensifying stage of this kind can equal the combined amplification of a stack of several simple intensifier stages of the kind described above.

Photoemitters

Interest in image intensifiers was first stimulated in the 1930s by the concern for increasing the sensitivity of TELEVISION camera tubes. The best photoemitter then available was a compound of silver, oxygen and caesium, which, however, had insufficient sensitivity for intensification to be achieved. During World War 2 imaging devices employing this photoemitter were put to use for night-viewing purposes by taking advantage of this compound's infra-red sensitivity. Modern image intensifiers mostly use a photo-emitting compound of sodium, potassium, caesium and antimony, highly sensitive throughout the visible light range.

Electron optics

Focusing of the electron image can be done in several ways. The simplest is *proximity focusing*; this depends merely on locating the photoemitter and fluorescent screen so closely together that the electron image has little chance to spread while it is being accelerated to the screen.

A more effective technique is *electrostatic focusing*, achieved by passing the electrons between charged electrodes. In order to reduce distortions in this type of imaging, the photoemitting surface must be made concave. A FIBRE OPTIC faceplate then is used to match the incident flat optical image to the concave photoemitting surface inside the tube. Fibre optic plates are made up of an array of transparent, microscopically narrow, glass fibres fused together but each acting as a separate 'light pipe'. High definition images can be transmitted through such a fibre optic plate, each element of the image being carried by a different fibre. In simple intensifying stages not employing microchannel plates, the fluorescent output surface also is deposited on such a fibre optic plate. This enables several stages to be efficiently coupled together simply by placing the flat outside faces of the fibre optic plates in contact.

Such intensifier systems, consisting of three coupled stages having a light amplification of 40,000, are used in the *starlight telescope*: a small, lightweight image intensifier system for viewing scenes at night even under moonless conditions.

Magnetic focusing is carried out by means of a cylindrical electromagnet or permanent magnet placed around the intensifier tube. The chief advantage of this is that excellent images are obtained with a flat photocathode. Because of this, several stages of intensification can be cascaded inside one glass envelope by depositing the fluorescent screen of one stage on to a very thin transparent mica coupling membrane, on the other side of which is the photoemitter of the next stage. The high image quality achieved with such multi-stage intensifiers makes them the preferred devices for demanding applications such as astronomy.

Applications

The most widespread use of image intensifiers is for night surveillance, either for security or military purposes. In many cases high image quality is not needed, and cheap, lightweight devices can be used. Similar tubes may be used for wildlife photography.

X-rays can be intensified as well as light, and by using an image intensifier in place of the screen normally used for FLUOROSCOPY it is possible to use much lower X-ray doses than previously. In astronomy, image intensifiers have made it possible to record images of faint objects with either greater sensitivity or a reduced exposure time, by building up an image on a photographic plate behind the intensifier. Alternatively, in the *electronographic* tube, the electrons in the tube are made to strike a photographic plate directly.

Astronomers use a variety of other image tubes based on television camera principles. These scan a charged image with an electron beam, and by storing the charge for a length of time before scanning, it is possible to record very faint objects. Such image tubes can be used on the finder telescope attached to the main telescope to help in locating the correct field of view.

IMPEDANCE (see circuit, electrical)
INCENDIARY BOMB (see bomb)

Top right: simple magnetically focused image intensifier stage. The solenoid, which is a coil extending right round the tube, provides the magnetic field while the high voltage supply is stepped, using resistors, to give each annulus a progressively higher potential. Several stages can be coupled to give greater amplification still.

Below: cosmic rays striking a sapphire plate produce minute flashes of light which may be viewed with an image intensifier. A commoner intensifier application is the military rifle sight shown at right.

Above right: a simple magnetically focused image intensifier stage, which uses electromagnets to focus and accelerate the electrons. Several stages can be coupled together for very high amplification.

Below right: Stonehenge viewed at night through an intensifier.

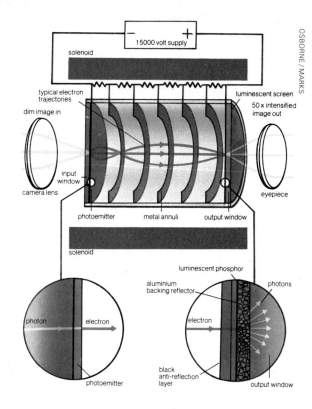

15000 volt supply

solenoid

typical electron
trajectories

dim image in

input
window

camera lens

photoemitter   metal annuli   output window

solenoid

luminescent screen

50 x intensified
image out

eyepiece

luminescent phosphor

aluminium
backing reflector

photon   electron

photoemitter

black
anti-reflection
layer

photons

electron

output window

OSBORNE / MARKS

CATHODEAN LTD / PHOTO : PAUL BRIERLEY

INDUCTANCE

The word *inductance* comes from *induce*, meaning 'to bring about' or 'to give rise to'. In ELECTROMAGNETISM it refers to the ability of a current 'to give rise to' a voltage.

Basic principles In our normal understanding of *electricity* we consider current (or flow of electrical charges) to be the result of a voltage difference (that is, an electrical pressure difference). This is, however, a purely *electrical* phenomenon concerning the force (voltage difference or voltage gradient) that sets electrical charges into motion.

Moving charges (current) set up a magnetic field; when the current flows along a wire the magnetic field surrounds the wire and the strength of this is proportional to the magnitude of the current. Conversely, a wire *moving* through a magnetic field or a stationary wire situated in a *changing* magnetic field has a voltage induced in it. The size of this induced voltage depends on the *rate of change* of magnetic field. These are ELECTROMAGNETIC phenomena and form the basis of induction.

Inductance and changing current Voltage differences give rise to currents which in turn create magnetic fields. Therefore, because the induced voltage is proportional to the rate of change of magnetic field (or magnetic flux as it is usually called) it is also proportional to the rate of change of the current.

A changing magnetic flux will induce a voltage in any wire in the vicinity—this is known as *mutual inductance*. Furthermore, this same field will invariably interact with the very wire along which the current was flowing—this is *self inductance*. In this situation the induced voltage is always in opposition to the voltage trying to create the change in current in the first place. Self inductance is therefore a 'damping' factor to any change in current.

Self inductance Because the magnitude of induced voltage is proportional to the rate of change of current, high frequency (fast changing) current signals will produce larger induced voltages than low frequency (slow changing) signals. Furthermore, as these induced voltages always try to 'impede' the very current that produced them, they will impede higher frequencies more than lower frequencies. Direct (DC) currents are not affected by inductance at all.

In many situations self inductance can be a nuisance. For example, when transmitting a signal along a wire, the self inductance of the wire will impede the higher frequencies more than the lower ones. *Inductors*, on the other hand, are devices which are designed to have a specific self inductance and are useful for their frequency dependent properties. An inductor will allow DC currents to flow through unhindered but will progressively restrict higher and higher frequencies.

When combined with CAPACITORS they form 'tuned circuits' which are of fundamental importance in OSCILLATORS. Capacitors have reverse frequency characteristics to inductors—that is, they impede low frequency and DC currents more than high frequencies. Together they impede both the low and high frequencies alike, but at a particular frequency in between show practically no impedance at all—depending on the values of CAPACITANCE and inductance. A tuned circuit is one example of a frequency FILTER and inductors are generally used in such applications.

Mutual inductance Mutual inductance—the ability of a changing current in one conductor to induce a voltage in a second (and separate) conductor—forms the basis of the TRANSFORMER.

Here, two coils of wire are mounted on a common magnetic circuit (usually a solid iron ring or *core*). An alternating (AC) voltage across the terminals of the first (primary) coil causes a current to flow in that coil, which in turn sets up an alternating magnetic flux in the magnetic circuit. This alternating flux expands and contracts around the secondary coil and induces a voltage in it. The size of this secondary voltage in relation to the primary voltage depends on the ratio of turns of the two coils.

Apart from this particular application, mutual inductance is usually a hindrance. It means, for example, that a signal in one wire will affect the voltage-current relationships in a second and totally separate wire where no such effect was required. Again, this becomes a more important problem at higher frequencies where the effect is greater.

In electrical CIRCUITS care must be taken in the design to minimize 'stray' self and mutual inductance because these will be important factors in determining the highest frequencies that can be handled by the circuit. Also, it will affect the speed with which the device can operate.

Unit of inductance The unit of inductance is the *henry* (symbol H), named after Joseph Henry (1797–1878), who first discovered the phenomenon of self induction. When a rate of change of current of one ampere per second induces a voltage of one volt then the inductance is one henry. Inductance therefore has the units of volts per amp per second or volt-seconds per amp. One henry is an extremely large inductance, and normally inductors are measured in millihenrys (one thousandth of a henry).

Left: this unit creates a high temperature plasma through induction heating and is used for producing borax compounds. Plasma is a very good conductor of electricity, because the gas atoms are ionized, and currents are easily induced in it.

Below: cooking with an induction cooker. The ice-cream remains cold while the saucepan heats up from the eddy currents induced in the metal.

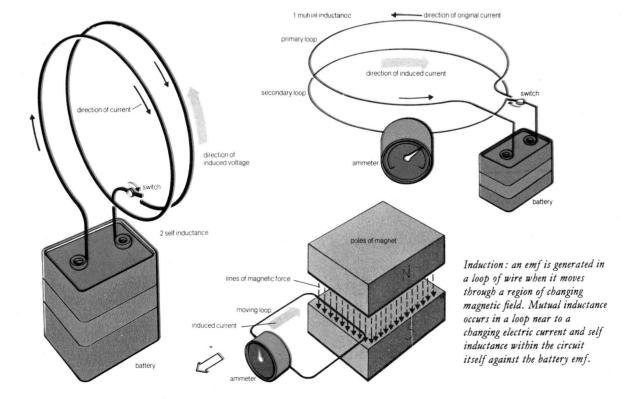

1 mutual inductance

direction of original current

primary loop

direction of current

direction of induced current

secondary loop

switch

ammeter

battery

direction of induced voltage

switch

2 self inductance

battery

poles of magnet

lines of magnetic force

moving loop

induced current

ammeter

Induction: an emf is generated in a loop of wire when it moves through a region of changing magnetic field. Mutual inductance occurs in a loop near to a changing electric current and self inductance within the circuit itself against the battery emf.